Bibliography on Deafness

the	american
volta	annals
review	of the deaf
1899—1976	1847— 1976

edited by
George W. Fellendorf, Ed.D.

Copyright © 1966, 1973, 1977 by
The Alexander Graham Bell Association for the Deaf, Inc.

Revised Edition

All rights reserved. No part of this book may be reprinted, or reproduced, or utilized in any form or by any electronic, mechanical, or other means now known or hereafter invented, including any information storage and retrieval system, without permission in writing from the publisher.

Printed in the U.S.A.

The Alexander Graham Bell Association for the Deaf, Inc.
3417 Volta Place, N.W., Washington, D.C. 20007, U.S.A.

Library of Congress Catalogue Card Number 77-86323
ISBN 0-88200-111-6

Foreword to the Revised Edition

The educational, vocational, and personal opportunities for hearing-impaired individuals have undergone considerable growth over the past 130 years. Since 1847, the American Annals of the Deaf has chronicled this growth, The Volta Review making its debut in 1899. Together, these two journals offer a broad overview of the past and present history in the field of education of the deaf.

Until recently, the readership of these two journals consisted primarily of teachers, school administrators, and a select group of professionals deemed responsible for the education and medical treatment of hearing-impaired children. Deafness was considered a mystery to all but those specially trained to meet its challenge. Today, however, the challenge of preparing handicapped children for adulthood in as near normal an educational and family situation as possible is being met by laymen and experts alike. Parents, teachers, audiologists, speech pathologists, psychologists, friends, and relatives of hearing-impaired individuals are discovering and using the wealth of information contained in the many articles, personal stories, and research reports of The Volta Review and the Annals.

In response to this increasing demand for information on deafness the first Bibliography on Deafness was published in 1966 covering articles printed in these two journals through 1965. A supplement, printed in 1973, included works from 1966 through 1972. This new, revised edition combines the two previous ones and updates the listings through 1976.

The revised edition of the Bibliography on Deafness has been reorganized to emphasize the progression of attention, or lack of same, to topical interests over the years. Whereas the earlier edition and its supplement listed entries under each category alphabetically by author, regardless of the year of publication, the new edition lists entries by year of publication, with the oldest entry appearing first. Hopefully, this format will facilitate quick identification of the latest or earliest contributions to either journal within the category headings, and allow researchers to scan the historical development within each category.

Another significant improvement is the increased number of categories. The first edition had 28 categories in its Table of Contents; this edition has 44. Many old categories have been broken down and thus expanded into smaller, more specific headings and subheadings. Many other categories, omitted from the first edition and supplement, have been added to the new version. "Education," for example, has been subdivided to recognize curricula in different subject areas, and "Health Care" and "Psychoeducational Testing," omitted in the original versions, have been added to the revised edition.

Perhaps this Bibliography will stimulate students and researchers to reflect on the progress, or lack of progress, which has characterized the field for 13 decades. Hopefully, it will stimulate some young educational innovator or scientist to develop a technique or device which will open up new opportunities for hearing-impaired children and adults in the future.

The editor is indebted to a large number of persons who have, over the years and more recently, contributed to this publication. In addition to the late Josephine Carr, Desmond Phillips, and others referred to in the Forewords to the earlier edition and supplement, I would like to acknowledge Kenneth and Wanda Lane and Bettie Loux Donley for their contributions to the organization, layout, and content of this revised edition.

George W. Fellendorf
September 1, 1977

Guide To Using the Bibliography

A. SUBJECT INDEX

1. Articles are listed chronologically according to date of publication, with the earliest entry appearing first. The format used for citing entries is as follows: name of author, title, year of publication, volume number, pages. Unsigned articles are listed chronologically, with lines indicating absentee authors.

    Northcott, Winifred N. Preparing your child for his first year away from home. 1967, 69, 391-393.

    _____. Analysis of the Annals statistics (pupils and teachers in American schools for the deaf, 1893-1910). 1911, 12, 719-720.

2. Each article is listed only once; there are no cross-references.

3. Research findings and reports are listed under the category related to the subject of the research.

4. Under the Education category are general articles which do not specifically fit into any of the other categories.

5. Of historical interest to students, teachers, and researchers in education of the deaf are numerous Volta Review articles by or about Alexander Graham Bell, his father Alexander Melville Bell, his wife Mabel, and other members of the famous family. If primarily historical in content, the articles are listed under the category, Bell Family. Topical articles by members of the Bell family will be listed under the corresponding subject headings if applicable to those categories.

6. Articles on the subject of television are indexed under Media and Visual Aids.

7. The American Annals of the Deaf publishes annually a listing of American and Canadian schools and classes for the deaf and a membership directory of the Convention of American Instructors of the Deaf (CAID). Although not indexed here, this statistical presentation gives tabulated information on the following:

schools and classes in the U.S. and Canada; post-secondary facilities for deaf students; centers for deaf-blind children; teacher-training programs; university programs for professional specialists in deafness; federal offices providing services for the education of deaf children and youth; rehabilitation personnel serving the deaf in the U.S.; rehabilitation centers, community services, and mental health facilities for the deaf; social and recreational groups and programs; civic services; clinical and evaluative programs and services; speech and hearing agencies in the U.S. and Canada; professional organizations and national centers of information on deafness; selected research on deafness; state programs for the hearing impaired; instructional materials centers for handicapped children, and professional committee memberships.

8. In general, articles of less than two pages in length are not included in this bibliography.

B. AUTHOR INDEX

1. The numbers following the authors' names indicate the pages where their writings are listed in the Subject Index.

2. In the case of multiple or joint authors, all authors shown in the Subject Index appear in the Author's Index.

Note: Both the American Annals and The Volta Review publish an annual subject and author index in their December issues.

Table of Contents

Aphasia..1
Audiology......................................2
Auditory Training..............................7
Bell Family...................................16
Careers/Vocational Education..................18
Communication (Aural/Oral, Manual,
    Simultaneous, Comparisons).................28
Curriculum (Art, Mathematics, Music and
    Rhythm, Hygiene and Physical Education,
    Reading, Science, Social Studies)..........38
Deaf-Blind....................................65
Deaf Youth and Adults.........................68
Early Detection/Diagnosis.....................70
Education.....................................72
Foreign Programs/International Trends.........91
Hard of Hearing...............................96
Health Care/Medical...........................99
Hearing Aids/Group Systems...................101
Heredity/Etiology............................108
Higher Education.............................110
Infant/Preschool.............................112
Language Acquisition.........................119
Mainstreaming/Integration....................142
Media/Visual Aids............................145
Multiply Handicapped.........................155
Parent-Child.................................159
Psychoeducational Testing....................168
Psychology...................................172
Religion.....................................185

Schools (Day, Histories and Reports
   on Specific Schools, Residential).........187
Social Development..........................192
Speech......................................195
Speechreading...............................216
Teacher Preparation/Certification...........235
Technological Devices/Sensory Aids..........238
Author Index................................241

Editors, The Volta Review

Frank W. Booth........................1899-1910
F. K. Noyes...........................1910-1912
Ernest Gregory........................1912-1914
Fred DeLand...........................1914-1920
Josephine Timberlake..................1920-1953
Alice Dunlap..........................1953-1957
Jeanette Johnson......................1957-1963
George W. Fellendorf..................1963-1976
Wilbert L. Pronovost..................1976-

Editors, American Annals of the Deaf

Luzerne Rae...........................1847-1854
Samuel Porter.........................1855-1868
Lewellyn Pratt........................1868-1870
Edward A. Fay.........................1870-1920
Irving S. Fusfeld.....................1920-1943
Ignatius Bjorlee......................1943-1944
Leonard M. Elstad.....................1945-1948
Powrie V. Doctor......................1948-1968
McCay Vernon..........................1968-

Audiology (Contd.)

THE VOLTA REVIEW (Contd.)

SMALLEY, Lillian D. Some angles of the acoustic method. 1932, 34, 248-251; 280-281.

UPHAM, Louise. Experiments with bone conduction at Mount Airy. 1932, 34, 252-253.

DAVIES, Gladys B. Testing for the hard of hearing child. 1932, 34, 399-400; 423-424.

MASON, Marie K. A laboratory method of measuring visual hearing ability. 1932, 34, 510-516.

COLLINS, Helen M. The 4-A audiometer and the C.W.A. in Florida. 1934, 36, 294-295; 310-311.

GARDNER, W. Morton. Getting results in hearing tests. 1934, 36, 359-361; 374.

GUILDER, Ruth P., and HOPKINS, Louise A. The importance of auditory function studies in the educational program for the auditorially handicapped child. 1936, 38, 69-74; 116-117; 149-155; 180-181.

ELLIOTT, Sarah L. Auricular possibilities in classes with varying hearing percentages. 1936, 38, 389-390; 428.

GARDNER, Warren H. Audiometer testing in Iowa schools. 1936, 38, 727; 749-750.

BODYCOMB, Margaret. The auricular program at Mt. Airy. 1937, 39, 202-204; 246.

GARDNER, Warren H. Testing kindergarten children with the 4-A audiometer. 1937, 39, 229-231; 247.

GARDNER, Warren H. Hearing tests in 37 Iowa school systems. 1937, 39, 699-701; 722.

COTTON, Jack C., and HALL, Jayne. Administration of 6-A audiometer tests to kindergarten and first grade children. 1939, 41, 291-292; 312-314.

_____. A panel discussion on acoustics. 1944, 46, 261-263; 318; 332-334; 380-382.

HUDGINS, Clarence V., and ROSS, D. A. The measurement of hearing. 1947, 49, 128-130; 146; 173-174; 196-198.

Audiology (Contd.)

THE VOLTA REVIEW (Contd.)

BERRY, Gordon. Auditory symptoms from dental bite, (a review). 1947, 49, 509-530.

FLETCHER, Harvey. The science of hearing. 1948, 50, 351-352; 386.

KEASTER, Jacqueline. Quantitative hearing tests for young children. 1948, 50, 465-468.

MORLEY, D. E. Rationalism in testing the hearing of children. 1948, 50, 468-478.

STEIN, Shirley P. Mobile clinics in the field of hearing. 1950, 52, 17-20; 50-52.

MCCONNELL, Freeman. The child with a high frequency hearing loss. 1951, 53, 295-297; 328.

SORTINI, Adam J. The efficacy of acoustic programs. 1952, 54, 201-203.

PAULS, Miriam, and HARDY, William G. Basic audiologic concepts. 1953, 55, 407-408.

EMPEY, Margaret. Pure tone audiometry with young children. 1953, 55, 439-442.

BEEBE, Helen H. The direct tone introduction test and the chewing method. 1954, 56, 19-23.

HARDY, William G. Modern audiology: version of 1862. 1955, 57, 98-100.

YENRICK, D. E. Audiology and the deaf child. 1955, 57, 353-356.

KOCH, Albert. Industrial audiology. 1956, 58, 28-31.

ROSEN, Jack. The place of GSR audiometry in work with young children. 1956, 58, 387-391.

LABENZ, Paul J. Potentialities of auditory perception for various levels of hearing loss. 1956, 58, 397-402.

PALVA, Tauno. Self-recording audiometry in hearing evaluation. 1958, 60, 156-163; 190.

STRIZVER, Gerald L. Frequency discrimination. 1958, 60, 304-306.

COSTELLO, Mary Rose. Changing concepts in audiology. 1958, 60, 395-398.

Audiology (Contd.)

THE VOLTA REVIEW (Contd.)

ROACH, Robert E. Preparation of the audiologist and his responsibilities in the residential school for the deaf. 1958, 60, 398-403.

FRUEH, Frank. The audiologist in the residential school. 1958, 60, 405-408.

TITSWORTH, Elizabeth. Aims and goals of an auditory program in a school for the deaf. 1958, 60, 408-411.

MERKLEIN, Richard A., and BRISKEY, Robert J. Audiometric findings in children referred to a program for language disorders. 1962, 64, 294-298.

NOBER, E. Harris. The role of an audiologist at a school for the deaf. 1962, 64, 428-429.

MCGEE, T. Manford. Research in hearing. 1962, 64, 460-464.

NOBER, E. Harris. Pure tone air conduction thresholds of deaf children. 1963, 65, 229-233; 241.

SHEPHERD, David C., et al. Audiologic assessment of children. 1963, 65, 486-495.

KENDALL, David C. The audiological examination of young children. 1964, 66, 734-740; 795.

DOYLE, John B., et al. Electrical stimulation in eighth nerve deafness. 1965, 67, 82-84.

MILLER, Alfred L. Light--an unconditioned stimulus in EDR audiometry. 1965, 67, 494-499.

BRODERICK, Thomas G., and KRANZ, Fred W. The new ISO audiometric standard zero reference. 1965, 67, 570-571.

EMERICK, Lon, and SHIMOTA, James. Clinical audiometry: man as a point of reference. 1967, 69, 510-512.

HODGSON, William R. Auditory characteristics of post-rubella impairment. 1969, 71, 97-103.

GERBER, Sanford E. Auditory behavioral responses of some hearing infants. 1969, 71, 340-346.

ROSS, Mark, et al. Visual, auditory, and combined mode presentations of the WIPI test to hearing impaired children. 1972, 74, 90-96.

Audiology (Contd.)

THE VOLTA REVIEW (Contd.)

LOWELL, Marilyn O., and LOWELL, Edgar L. Evoked response audiometry. 1973, 75, 109-113.

_____. Regional conference on the auditory approach. 1973, 75, 344-358.

JONES, Barbara L. The audiologist in the educational environment. 1973, 75, 545-550.

BOVE, Celeste F., and FLUGARTH, James M. Frequency components of noisemakers for use in pediatric audiological evaluations. 1973, 75, 551-556.

MCCROSKEY, Robert L., and DEINES, Rick R. An annotated bibliography on testing the hearing of infants. 1974, 76, 436-444.

LING, Daniel, and NAISH, Sally Jo. Threshold variations in repeated audiograms. 1975, 77, 97-104.

ANNALS OF THE DEAF

SCHICK, Helen C., and MEYER, Max F. The use of the lectometer. 1932, 77, 292-304.

GOETZINGER, Cornelius. A consideration of audiometric curves in relation to intelligibility for speech. 1947, 92, 238-250.

ALBRIGHT, Arline. Audiometric testing methods and classification of original hearing acuity response curves. 1948, 93, 360-376.

FRUEH, Frank. Audiological services at a school for the deaf. 1962, 107, 229-231.

HENDERSON, Sara C., and FRANCIS, Doris H. (editors). The meaning of deafness: the report of a workshop for audiologists. 1962, 107, 464-596.

PICKETT, J. M., and MARTIN, E. S. Some comparative measurements of impaired discrimination for sound spectral differences. 1968, 113, 259-267.

Audiology (Contd.)

ANNALS OF THE DEAF (Contd.)

MAZEAS, Roger. Hearing capacity, its measurement and calculation. 1968, 113, 269-274.

LING, Daniel. Three experiments on frequency transposition. 1968, 113, 283-294.

GUTTMAN, Newman, and NELSON, John R. An instrument that creates some artificial speech spectra for the severely hard of hearing. 1968, 113, 295-302.

MATKIN, Noel D., and OLSEN, Wayne O. An investigation of radio frequency auditory training units. 1973, 118, 25-30.

PORTER, Thomas A. Otoadmittance measurements in a residential deaf population. 1974, 119, 47-52.

RUBIN, Martha, and VENTRY, Ira M. Speech detection thresholds and comfortable loudness levels for speech in children with limited hearing. 1975, 120, 564-567.

ROSS, Mark, and CALVERT, Donald R. Guidelines for audiology programs in educational settings for hearing impaired children. 1976, 121, 346-350.

Auditory Training

THE VOLTA REVIEW

MERKL, W. Employment of the partial hearing of pupils. 1903, 5, 101-111.

URBANTSCHITSCH, Victor. On the value of methodical exercises in hearing. 1904, 6, 48-52.

MARAGE, R. Measurement and development of hearing power in the deaf. 1904, 6, 127-129.

BARROWS, C. M. A method of teaching hearing to the deaf. 1905, 7, 332-342.

Auditory Training (Contd.)

THE VOLTA REVIEW (Contd.)

ANDERSON, J. Scott. Development of the hearing. 1910, 12, 175-176.

FERRERI, Giulio. Systematic acoustic exercises. 1911, 13, 5-8; 228-230; 1912, 13, 473-476.

WRIGHT, John D. Teaching a deaf child to hear language. 1918, 20, 7-9; 1923, 25, 171-173.

GOLDSTEIN, Max A. Demonstration: auricular training. 1919, 21, 157-160.

MCKENZIE, Lilla B. Stimulating the language centers through auditory channels. 1919, 21, 725-732.

BUCHANAN, Nancy. Not more learning but better hearing. 1920, 22, 2-4.

WRIGHT, John D. What do you mean by "auricular training"? 1920, 22, 6-8.

VAN INGEN, Elizabeth. Aural work with acousticons. 1920, 22, 68-73.

GOLDSTEIN, Max A. An acoustic method. 1920, 22, 716-719.

WRIGHT, John D. Teaching a hearing vocabulary. 1920, 22, 720-723.

LACROSSE, EDWIN L. The value of auricular training. 1921, 23, 356-357.

JONES, Miss Ogwen. Auricular or acoustic training. 1925, 27, 8-10.

PAXSON, Ruth. Acoustic work done at Central Institute. 1925, 27, 10-13.

VAN INGEN, Elizabeth. Eight years of auricular work at Rochester. 1925, 27, 13-16.

NEWHART, Horace. Efforts toward prevention of deafness in school children. 1926, 28, 440-449.

ELSTAD, Leonard M. The use of the audiophone no. 10-A in the Wright Oral School. 1926, 28, 675-677.

STEVENSON, Elwood A. Misconceptions and misinterpretations of auricular work with the deaf. 1926, 28, 677-683.

NILSON, Roy F. Acoustic education. 1927, 29, 296-297.

FORRESTER, T. C. The problems of training the remnants of auditory perception. 1928, 30, 136-140.

Auditory Training (Contd.)

THE VOLTA REVIEW (Contd.)

ELSTAD, Leonard M. Auricular training. 1928, 30, 276-278.

BERRY, Amelia E. Audiometer testing and auricular training with the audiophone. 1929, 31, 780-782.

CUDDY, Nelle M. Auricular training in our schools. 1930, 32, 173-174.

KELLY, J. B. Physical factors affecting the instrumental utilization of residual hearing in the education of the deaf. 1930, 32, 561-565.

WILCOX, Rachel M. Training residual hearing (The Clarke School). 1931, 33, 70; 341-344.

PHARIS, Dorothy M. Auricular training. 1931, 33, 163-164.

MONTAGUE, HARRIET A. A class for the conservation of hearing. 1931, 33, 197-199; 232-233.

MCKENZIE, Lilla B. Physiological and psychological factors to be considered when building a program of acoustic education. 1932, 34, 522-525.

WRIGHT, John D., and WINSTON, Matie E. Training little deaf children to use their small amounts of hearing. 1932, 34, 583-589 (January).

HAESELER, Charlotte. Auricular work with a group aid, building a hearing vocabulary. 1933, 35, 211-212.

SENSENIG, Anne. Speech and vocabulary development through auricular training. 1933, 35, 212-213.

MURPHY, Margaret. Unit of work in connection with hygiene. 1933, 35, 247-249.

GILL, Dorothy. Auricular work. 1933, 35, 420-422.

GUILDER, Ruth P., and HOPKINS, Louise A. Program for the testing and training of auditory function in the small deaf child during preschool years. 1935, 37, 5-11; 79-84.

LAMB, MARION H. Listening in (with the first auricular class at Mt. Airy). 1936, 38, 197-199; 250.

O'CONNOR, Clarence D. Acoustic training in the curriculum. 1936, 38, 263-269; 308-309.

Auditory Training (Contd.)

THE VOLTA REVIEW (Contd.)

NUMBERS, Mary E. Using the hearing of children so deaf that they entered school speechless. 1937, 39, 133-137.

O'CONNOR, Clarence D. Speech acoustic training and related problems. 1937, 39, 267-270.

TIMBERLAKE, Josephine B. The re-education of residual hearing. 1937, 39, 349-351; 372-373.

PROCTOR, Dorothy M. Giving my little boy a hearing vocabulary. 1937, 39, 494-496; 562-564; 595-598.

MOORE, Lucile M. Time--and the hearing ear. 1937, 39, 500-502; 533-534.

SMITH, Sherman K. Auditory training for the deaf. 1938, 40, 199-203; 252.

BRALY, Kenneth, et al. Some aspects of acoustic work. 1938, 40, 325-327.

BRALY, Kenneth. Hearing, discrimination and interpretation. 1939, 41, 69-70.

LYNNDELLE, Vivian. Hearing conservation in a school system. 1940, 42, 29-32; 59-61.

PROBYN, June Y. The training of residual hearing. 1941, 43, 5-8; 74; 90-92; 154-156.

DOYLE, F.W. Oakland's acoustic program. 1941, 43, 517-520; 566-567.

ELLIOTT, Sarah L. A questionnaire on acoustic training. 1942, 44, 73-75.

NUMBERS, Mary E. Learning to hear. 1941, 44, 557-558; 600-601.

HEIDER, Fritz. Acoustic training helps lip reading. 1943, 45, 135; 180.

KENNEDY, Mildred. Re-education of hearing: try taking it seriously. 1944, 46, 30; 54.

KLING, Gertrude N. Auricular work. 1946, 48, 83; 114-115.

WHITEHURST, Mary W. Auricular training at Hoff Hospital. 1946, 48, 277-278; 300-308.

HARRIS, Grace. An acoustic training program for severely deaf children. 1946, 48, 557-560; 606-612; 767-769; 790-796; 1947, 49, 29-31; 48-52.

Auditory Training (Contd.)

THE VOLTA REVIEW (Contd.)

KENNEDY, Mildred. Learn to listen. 1947, 49, 21; 52-54.

WHITEHURST, Mary W. Training the hearing of a young deaf child. 1947, 49, 215; 252-254.

SCOTT, Elizabeth. Auditory training cannot begin too early. 1948, 50, 423-425.

HUDGINS, Clarence V. A rationale for acoustic training. 1948, 50, 484-490.

DICARLO, Louis M. Auditory training for the adult. 1948, 50, 490-496.

ASALS, Frances B., and RUTHVEN, Henrietta C. Acoustic training for the primary grades. 1948, 50, 498-510.

BENDER, Ruth E. The discovery and training of hearing in young deaf children. 1948, 50, 572-574; 592-594.

RACHLIN, Carol. Auditory training remade my life. 1949, 51, 276-277.

LARSEN, Laila L. Recordings for auditory training. 1949, 51, 461-462; 472-474.

MADDEN, Anne M. A new world of sound. 1949, 51, 551-553; 578.

COAKLEY, Estelle L. Auditory training at Northwestern. 1950, 52, 23-25; 40.

POULOS, Thomas H. Acuity and perceptive accuracy of monaural and binaural hearing. 1950, 52, 314-316; 326.

TAUSSIG, E., and STONER, M. Phonograph records for the young child. 1950, 52, 355-358; 378.

HERRICK, Helen. An auditory training program for nursery schools. 1950, 52, 448-451; 482-484; 497-499; 528-530.

STEIN, Shirley P. Hearing conservation in rural areas. 1951, 53, 316; 324-326.

VAN DER VEER, Gladys. The class for the conservation of hearing and speech correction. 1953, 55, 355-356.

BANGS, Tina E. Methodology in auditory training. 1954, 56, 159-164.

HUDGINS, Clarence V. Auditory training--its possibilities and limitations. 1954, 56, 339-349.

DOERFLER, Leo G. (moderator, panel discussion). Auditory training. 1954, 56, 350-354; 368; 393-396; 417; 402-407.

Auditory Training (Contd.)

THE VOLTA REVIEW (Contd.)

UDEN, A.v. Sound perception and breath control. 1955, 57, 61-62.

YENRICK, D. E. The use of amplification in schools for the deaf. 1955, 57, 158-160.

FITZGERALD, Margaret H. Auditory training in schools for the deaf. 1955, 57, 167-170.

SISTER MARY FANCHEA. Auditory training at St. Joseph's Institute. 1955, 57, 260-262.

SCOTT, Elizabeth V. Auditory training. 1955, 57, 297-299.

SIMMONS, Audrey A. Some hints for auditory training for the young child. 1955, 57, 397-398.

FIELD, Lois G. All they need is a boost from you. 1956, 58, 197-199.

ASALS, Frances B., and RUTHVEN, Henrietta C. Auditory training for the primary grades. 1956, 58, 205-207.

HARDY, William G. Problems of audition, perception and understanding. 1956, 58, 289-300; 309.

FORT, Berneice. My experience with auditory training. 1957, 59, 214-215.

BOLLBACH, Betty L., and CRANE, Norman W. A meaningful approach to auditory training. 1957, 59, 243-247.

COX, Jerome R., SCHOENFELD, Sidney L., and TOTOKI, Akira. Evaluation of the acoustical environments for group hearing aids. 1957, 59, 383-385.

BRADDOCK, Mary J. Teaching the use of the telephone to the severely hard of hearing. 1957, 59, 442-444.

DICARLO, Louis M. The effect of hearing one's voice among children with impaired hearing. 1958, 60, 306-314.

QUIGLEY, Stephen P. The vocal effects of delayed auditory feedback and their implications for the teaching of speech to the deaf. 1958, 60, 314-316.

BOLLBACH, Betty L. Enriching deaf children's experience through auditory training. 1958, 60, 411-413.

SISTER MARIANNA. Let's help them listen. 1958, 60, 413-416.

Auditory Training (Contd.)

THE VOLTA REVIEW (Contd.)

HUTTON, Charles. Combined auditory and visual stimuli in aural rehabilitation. 1959, 61, 316-319.

ANSELMINI, Andrew A. Auditory training: design for growth, basic considerations. 1959, 61, 322-323; 342.

WALLIN, Margaret K. Auditory training: design for growth, guiding principles. 1959, 61, 374-376.

RESNICK, Libby, and WALSH, Margaret. Auditory training: design for growth, sources for auditory experiences and related activities. 1959, 61, 413-419.

ANSELMINI, Andrew A., and WALLIN, Margaret K. Auditory training: design for growth, instructional techniques. 1959, 61, 461-466; 486.

POULOS, Thomas H. A short term aural rehabilitation program. 1960, 62, 345-347.

MORGAN, Lucia C. Effect of temperature and humidity on hearing acuity. 1960, 62, 364-368.

STOCKDELL, Kenneth G. A hearing conservation program. 1960, 62, 376-377.

WATSON, T. J. The use of residual hearing in the education of deaf children. 1961, 63, 328-334; 385-392; 435-440; 487-492; 1962, 64, 31-38; 84-88.

WHITEHURST, Mary W. Testing the hearing of preschool children. 1961, 63, 430-432; 463.

GRIFFITHS, Ciwa. The auditory approach for preschool deaf children. 1964, 66, 387-397.

POLLACK, Doreen. Acoupedics: a uni-sensory approach to auditory training. 1964, 66, 400-409.

WHITEHURST, Mary W. Integration of auditory training and lipreading. 1964, 66, 730-733.

JEFFERS, Janet. Formants and the auditory training of deaf children. 1966, 68, 418-423.

HIRSH, Ira J. The ears of the deaf unstopped. 1966, 68, 623-633.

WEDENBERG, Erik. Experience from 30 years auditory training. 1967, 69, 588-594.

Auditory Training (Contd.)

THE VOLTA REVIEW (Contd.)

FELLENDORF, George W. The verbotonal method--questions and answers. 1969, <u>71</u>, 213-224.

ROSS, Mark. Loop auditory training systems for preschool hearing impaired children. 1969, <u>71</u>, 289-295.

_____. Comments concerning the verbotonal method. 1969, <u>71</u>, 289-295.

WHITEHURST, Mary Wood. Two pioneers in auditory training. 1970, <u>72</u>, 185-188.

CRAIG, William N., et al. Preschool verbotonal instruction for deaf children. 1972, <u>74</u>, 236-246.

POLLACK, Doreen, and ERNST, Marian. Learning to listen in an integrated preschool. 1973, <u>75</u>, 359-367.

WITHROW, Frank B. The fine art of auditory training, or is anyone listening? 1974, <u>76</u>, 415-419.

TWEEDIE, David. Videoaudiometry: a possible procedure for "difficult-to-test" populations. 1975, <u>77</u>, 129-134.

ROBINSON, Dale O., and GAETH, John H. A procedure for testing/training prelinguistic hearing impaired children. 1975, <u>77</u>, 249-254.

EISENBERG, Diane, and SANTORE, Frances. The verbotonal method of aural rehabilitation: a case study. 1976, <u>78</u>, 16-22.

ERBER, Norman P. The use of audio tape-cards in auditory training for hearing impaired children. 1976, <u>78</u>, 209-218.

ANNALS OF THE DEAF

CAMP, Anna R. Some lessons in auricular training. 1903, <u>48</u>, 217-237.

BELL, Alexander G. The process of audition. 1906, <u>51</u>, 280-286.

ANDERSON, Mrs. J. Scott. The development of hearing. 1910, <u>55</u>, 349-353.

GOLDSTEIN, Max A. An acoustic method. 1920, <u>65</u>, 472-481.

Auditory Training (Contd.)

ANNALS OF THE DEAF (Contd.)

GOLDSTEIN, Max A. The acoustic method. 1924, 69, 160-187.

BUNCH, C. C. Deafness and residual hearing. 1925, 70, 104-122.

LACROSSE, Edwin L. Auricular training in the Wright Oral School. 1925, 70, 302-310.

FORRESTER, T. C. The problems of training the remnants of auditory perception. 1928, 73, 145-155.

FORRESTER, T. C. Residual hearing and its bearing on oral training. 1929, 74, 193-199.

ELSTAD, Leonard M. Auricular training and oral instruction. 1929, 74, 199-205.

JOHNSON, Elizabeth H. Testing results of acoustic training. 1939, 84, 223-233.

VOELKER, Charles H. Tested auditory behavior rather than hearing acuity is a function of age. 1941, 86, 1-6.

NELSON, Boyd E. The essentials of acoustic programs. 1942, 87, 274-287.

JESSEMAN, Victoria C. The use of residual hearing. 1942, 87, 408-414.

JOHNSON, Clyde W. A survey of acoustic training programs and accomplishments in the public residential schools for the deaf. 1943, 88, 279-295.

FAUTH, La Verne, and WARREN, W. A study of the proceedings of the convention of the American Instructors of the Deaf. 1850-1949: auricular training. 1950, 95, 280-311.

HEDGECOCK, Leroy D. Audiologic aspects of rehabilitation of the deaf. 1958, 103, 210-214.

FRISINA, D. Robert. Basic considerations in auditory training. 1958, 103, 459-466.

LLOYD, Glenn T. A beginning experimental program in the use of the telephone for deaf and hard of hearing children. 1960, 105, 427-429.

FRISINA, Robert. The auditory channel in the education of deaf children. 1966, 111, 633-647.

Auditory Training (Contd.)

ANNALS OF THE DEAF (Contd.)

PIMONOW, Leoni. Technical and physiological problems in the application of synthetic speech to aural rehabilitation, 1968, 113, 275-281.

ROSS, Mark, and GIOLAS, Thomas G. Effect of three classroom listening conditions on speech intelligibility. 1971, 116, 580-584.

Bell Family

THE VOLTA REVIEW

BELL, Alexander G. Address of the president. 1899, 1, 67-82.

DELAND, Fred. World benefactions of Alexander Graham Bell. 1905, 7, 167-171.

HITZ, John. Alexander Melville Bell. 1905, 7, 421-439.

FULLER, Sarah. Alexander Melville Bell. 1907, 9, 269-272.

BELL, Mrs. Alexander G. What the Melville Bell symbols mean to me. 1908, 10, 308-311.

BELL, Alexander G. Notes of early life. 1910, 12, 155-160.

BELL, Alexander G. A census of the able-bodied. 1910, 12, 403-406.

_____ The Melville Bell symbols; line-writing form. 1914, 16, 266-270; 477-485; 569-576; 723-730.

BELL, Alexander G. Utility of action and gesture. 1915, 17, 13-18.

DELAND, Fred. An early use of the Melville Bell symbols with the deaf. 1915, 17, 487-489.

ANDREWS, Harriet U. The Melville Bell symbols, tried and true. 1916, 18, 311-312.

_____ Melville Bell symbols. 1918, 20, 65; 71; 88; 498; 582.

DELAND, Fred. The Bell Telephone memorial. 1918, 20, 231-236.

Bell Family (Contd.)

THE VOLTA REVIEW (Contd.)

_____ In memoriam; Alexander Graham Bell. 1922, 24, 307.

TAYLOR, Harris. Dr. Bell, the great, the good, the lovable. 1922, 24, 345-346.

_____ Tributes to Dr. Bell. 1922, 24, 346-349; 365-379.

DELAND, Fred. An ever-continuing memorial. 1922, 24, 351-363; 413-422; 465-471; 1923, 25, 34-39; 90-99; 145-152; 190-197.

YALE, Caroline A. Dr. Bell's connection with Clarke School. 1922, 24, 364-365.

YALE, Caroline A. Mabel Hubbard Bell--1859-1923. 1923, 25, 105-110.

DELAND, Fred. The telephone, the radiophone, the graphophone, the music record, and modern lip-reading. 1924, 26, 251-253.

TAYLOR, Harris, et al. Alexander Graham Bell memorial session. 1925, 27, 61-65.

DELAND, Fred. Alexander Graham Bell's benefactions to aid the hard of hearing adult. 1928, 30, 440-442.

MAYNE, Richard E. The Bell family and English speech. 1929, 31, 453-456.

MONTAGUE, Harriet. A man who loved deaf children. 1938, 40, 74-77; 116.

MONTAGUE, Harriet. Mr. Bell's private school. 1940, 42, 325-326.

GROSVENOR, Melville B. Memories of my grandfather. 1940, 42, 621-622.

GROSVENOR, Elsie B. My father, the Volta Bureau, and the association. 1950, 52, 112-114.

GROSVENOR, Elsie M. My father, Alexander Graham Bell. 1951, 53, 349; 386-388.

_____ Monument erected honoring Alexander Graham Bell. 1954, 56, 9-10.

MURPHY, Albert. Dr. Bell and Boston University. 1954, 56, 249-250.

SILVERMAN, S. Richard. The legacy of Mr. Bell. 1957, 59, 103-104.

GROSVENOR, Mrs. Gilbert. Mrs. Alexander Graham Bell--a reminiscence. 1957, 59, 299-305.

Bell Family (Contd.)

THE VOLTA REVIEW (Contd.)

_____. Dr. Bell, pioneer of a new era. 1958, 60, 110-111; 141.

_____. A Bell bibliography. 1960, 62, 111-112; 139.

BELL, Alexander G. The Sanders Reader (reproduction of excerpts from the original written by Mr. Bell in 1872-73). 1964, 66, 122-123.

BENTLEY, Keilor. Monument to a genius--the Alexander Graham Bell Museum at Baddeck, Nova Scotia. 1965, 67, 188-190.

_____. Dr. Bell's legacy to parents of deaf children. 1969, 71, 145-147.

_____. Alexander Graham Bell and the Volta Bureau. 1970, 72, 144-152.

DELAND, Fred. Dr. Bell's private school. 1972, 74, 145-149.

BRUCE, Robert B. Excerpts from Bell: Alexander Graham Bell and the conquest of solitude. 1973, 75, 146-154.

FELLENDORF, G.W. 75 years of excitement. 1976, 78, 100-103.

ANNALS OF THE DEAF

MITCHELL, Sue H. The haunting influence of Alexander Graham Bell. 1971, 116, 349-356.

Careers/Vocational Education

THE VOLTA REVIEW

DAVIDSON, S. G. A vocation school for deaf and hearing boys. 1905, 7, 32-43.

Careers/Vocational Education (Contd.)

THE VOLTA REVIEW (Contd.)

ANDREWS, Harriet U. Deaf girls as hospital nurses. 1910, 12, 471-476.

NITCHIE, Edward B. Unemployment, the tragedy of deafness. 1911, 13, 217-219.

ADAMS, Mabel E. Welfare work at Horace Mann School. 1911, 13, 381-386.

COGSWELL, Frank H. Co-operation between school and shop. 1913, 15, 137-139.

HAYS, Harold. The social and economic importance of deafness. 1913, 15, 303-310.

WRIGHT, John D. The economic significance of deafness. 1914, 16, 28-31.

CARTER, E. The training of girls. 1914, 16, 187-192.

PIERCE, J. A. The economic efficiency of the deaf. 1914, 16, 260-266.

DYER, Helen L. Vocational suggestions for the adult deaf. 1915, 17, 9-11.

DYER, Helen L. Aiming toward independence. 1915, 17, 465-470.

SALADE, Robert F. Printing: an ideal vocation for the deaf. 1916, 18, 59-63.

DELAND, FRED. War deafness. 1917, 19, 493-496.

_____. The plan of reconstruction of the defects in hearing and speech. 1918, 20, 457-460.

RICHARDSON, Charles W. Re-education of soldiers with defective hearing and speech. 1918, 20, 511-513.

FERRALL, John A. Cast down your bucket where you are! 1919, 21, 12-15.

PHILLIPS, Wendell C. The re-education of deaf soldiers. 1919, 21, 89-91.

DELAND, Fred. The rearranging of affairs after hearing vanishes. 1919, 21, 320-323.

BRUHN, Martha E. The hard of hearing as wage-earners and home-makers. 1919, 21, 574-576.

Careers/Vocational Education (Contd.)

THE VOLTA REVIEW (Contd.)

FERRALL, John A. The employment question. 1919, 21, 704-706.

MORRISON, J. Stuart. Industrial training: what shall we subtract and what shall we add in the new century of the education of the deaf. 1920, 22, 222-231.

POPE, Alvin E. Correlation of industrial and academic work. 1920, 22, 539-546.

DUFF, Jessie. Triumph over handicap. 1922, 24, 242-246.

SAMUELSON, Estelle E. Employment services for the deafened. 1923, 25, 488-498.

MCDERMOTT, Valeria D. Vocational studies for the deafened. 1923, 25, 503-505.

DE YOUNG, Dirk P. What can't a deaf man do? 1925, 27, 136-138.

PATTERSON, Alpha W. Printing as a trade for the deaf. 1926, 28, 649-652.

WOODBURG, Max W. The placement of the graduates of the Utah School for the Deaf. 1926, 28, 762-766.

SULLIVAN, Oscar M. Vocational training of the deafened. 1929, 31, 107-110.

PETERSON, P. N. Principles of vocational guidance. 1930, 32, 572-576.

HICKER, H. D. Vocational rehabilitation and the deaf. 1932, 34, 487-491.

TURNER, Wallace R. Starting a print shop. 1935, 37, 159-161; 196-197.

BREESE, Estelle. Vocational language problems. 1936, 38, 695; 748.

LEMLEY, Herman A. Relationship between vocational and academic departments. 1936, 38, 696-697.

GREENMUN, Robert M. A deaf newspaper editor. 1937, 39, 140-142; 181-182.

DE LA BAT, G. Vocational interchange. 1937, 39, 615-617; 662-663.

BLUETT, Charles G. Objective tests in vocational interviews. 1937, 39, 636-638; 657-658.

Careers/Vocational Education (Contd.)

THE VOLTA REVIEW (Contd.)

BLUETT, Charles G. Selecting vocations for the deaf. 1937, 39, 677-679.

WASHINGTON, Margaret L. Rehabilitation and the hard of hearing. 1938, 40, 36-37.

CHAMBLESS, Elizabeth. Rehabilitation can rehabilitate. 1938, 40, 345-346; 371.

CHAMBLESS, Elizabeth. Rehabilitation is a two-sided affair. 1938, 40, 584-585.

NITKIN, Nathaniel. Rehabilitation and personality. 1939, 41, 17-19; 56.

BLUETT, Charles G. Objective analysis in vocational placement. 1939, 41, 133-135; 179.

MONTAGUE, Harriet. Jobs for the hard of hearing. 1939, 41, 219-222; 250-251.

BLUETT, Charles G. Vocational survey of the graduating class of the California School for the Deaf. 1939, 41, 549-555; 615-620; 662.

LINDQUIST, Ida P. Rehabilitation of the hard of hearing. 1940, 42, 95-99; 115.

HOWARD, Jay C. The deaf and the deafened in industry. 1940, 42, 845-846; 87?.

ETTER, Carl L. Philosophy of vocational rehabilitation. 1941, 43, 251-254; 276-278.

FLANGE, C. S. Selecting a career. 1944, 46, 72-74; 126.

NELSON, Boyd E. Objectives of vocational training. 1944, 46, 389-390; 428-432.

AMATO, David. The District of Columbia's rehabilitation program. 1947, 49, 79; 94-96.

KROL, S. T. Blessing in disguise. 1949, 51, 604-605; 628-630.

BRANSON, Helen K. For the handicapped, what kind of job? 1951, 53, 247-248.

GREEN, Ruth. Employment counseling for the hard of hearing. 1954, 56, 209-212.

Careers/Vocational Education (Contd.)

THE VOLTA REVIEW (Contd.)

MURPHY, Albert T. Personal relations in a profession. 1954, <u>56</u>, 261-262.

ALSBERG, Julia. Vocational guidance. 1955, <u>57</u>, 119-120.

BECKER, V. A. California's rehabilitation program for the deaf. 1956, <u>58</u>, 73-74.

HOWARD, Petra F. A deaf person learns from his job. 1956, <u>58</u>, 201-204.

LEE, John J. Time and tide in developing services for the handicapped. 1960, <u>62</u>, 403-409.

JENKS, Monica K. Guidance and rehabilitation. 1960, <u>62</u>, 411-412.

REID, Harry W. New offerings and trends in vocational education. 1961, <u>63</u>, 287-288; 301.

ROSENSTEIN, Joseph. Social and vocational planning for the adolescent. 1962, <u>64</u>, 433-442.

ROSENSTEIN, Joseph. Social and vocational assessment. 1963, <u>65</u>, 542-547.

CONNOR, Leo, and ROSENSTEIN, Joseph. Vocational status and adjustment of deaf women. 1963, <u>65</u>, 585-591.

ALPINER, Jerome G., and WALKER, Richard A. A residential vocational rehabilitation program for young adults with severely impaired hearing. 1964, <u>66</u>, 118-121; 163.

BROWN, Donald W. Vocational preparation for the world of tomorrow. 1964, <u>66</u>, 368-372.

ELSTAD, Leonard M. Vocational competence through academic preparation. 1964, <u>66</u>, 372-376.

OWSLEY, Peter J. Academic-vocational education of hearing handicapped children. 1964, <u>66</u>, 551-555.

KHAN, Evelyn. The economic rehabilitation of the educated deaf. 1964, <u>66</u>, 562-565.

GARRETT, Charles W. Quo vadis. A pilot study of employment opportunities for the hearing impaired. 1964, <u>66</u>, 669-677.

NACE, John G. A superintendent looks ahead at the future of vocational technical education. 1965, <u>67</u>, 688-692.

Careers/Vocational Education (Contd.)

THE VOLTA REVIEW (Contd.)

VAUGHN, Gwenyth R. Hearing impaired students benefit from supportive programs. 1968, 70, 14-23, 58-66.

MATHAS, Chrysoula, and MOREHOUSE, William. A work-study program for hearing impaired students. 1969, 71, 553-556.

WYKS, Hollis W. Vocational education for the noncollege bound youth. 1970, 72, 97-101.

CRAIG, William N., et al. A progress report--post-secondary opportunities for deaf students. 1970, 72, 290-295.

FELLENDORF, George W. Technical training for deaf students at a community college. 1970, 72, 296-302.

GREENLEAF, Gene. A trade and technical institute program for deaf and hard of hearing students. 1970, 72, 357-361.

MARGOLIUS, Ellen. Affirmative action: does this mean more job opportunities for deaf individuals? 1975, 77, 318-322.

WENTLING, Tim R., BUTTERWECK, Thomas C., and ZOOK, George A. Career education and evaluation for hearing impaired adolescents: an example program. 1976, 78, 144-151.

LLOYD, Glenn T., and WATSON, Douglas. Social and rehabilitation services: an emerging force in deafness. 1976, 78, 34-41 (monograph).

ANNALS OF THE DEAF

BALIS, Sylvia C. Industrial education. 1893, 38, 15-20.

PORTER, George S. The deaf in business. 1901, 46, 141-149.

GRADY, Theodore. The deaf in the legal profession. 1901, 46, 429-434.

RICHARDSON, P. L. The industrial training of the deaf. 1904, 49, 260-268.

HANSON, Olof. The industrial problem among the American deaf. 1904, 49, 363-369.

Careers/Vocational Education (Contd.)

ANNALS OF THE DEAF (Contd.)

EURITT, Guilford D. Technical training for the deaf. 1905, 50, 365-370.

SIMPSON, Emmette W. Agricultural education for the deaf. 1912, 57, 305-313.

PETERSON, P. N. The influence of manual training upon the mental development of the deaf. 1915, 60, 119-129.

STUTSMAN, Grace T. Farming for the deaf. 1916, 61, 142-150.

MANNING, A. C. Reconstruction of deafened American soldiers. 1920, 65, 74-85.

HOPSON, A. B. Effects of trade training on the school life and after-school life of our deaf girls. 1920, 65, 481-486.

UNDERHILL, Odie W. The deaf man and the printing trade. 1923, 68, 317-330.

GRIFFIN, Mary E. Industrial training for deaf girls. 1925, 70, 340-350.

THOMPSON, Hazel N. Vocational training for girls. 1928, 73, 393-419.

DRIGGS, Frank M. Deafness as a social problem--the industrial side. 1929, 74, 113-124.

SULLIVAN, Oscar M. Vocational guidance for the deaf. 1929, 74, 386-389.

ANDERSON, Tom L. The need for occupational studies in relation to vocational guidance for boys. 1929, 74, 407-410.

BETTS, Otis A. Vocational training for the deaf. 1930, 75, 95-103.

DIVINE, L. R. The finishing touches to vocational education. 1934, 79, 238-243.

HJORTH, Ernst. A few remarks on vocational education. 1934, 79, 244-254.

FUSFELD, Irving S. A study of the vocations taught in American schools for the deaf. 1934, 79, 377-382.

ANDERSON, Tom L. Vocational needs of today. 1935, 80, 105-115.

Careers/Vocational Education (Contd.)

ANNALS OF THE DEAF (Contd.)

LAURITSEN, Wesley. Helping our graduates secure positions. 1936, 81, 126-135.

BUTLER, Stahl. Agricultural training for the deaf. 1937, 82, 262-271.

HELMLE, Margarette B. Employment, replacement training, and vocational counseling for the deaf. 1937, 82, 411-424.

ORR, John P. The deaf and their vocational problems. 1939, 84, 124-131.

STEPHENS, Alfred E. Labor legislation affecting the deaf. 1939, 84, 132-136.

HICKER, H. D. Coordination of services for vocational adjustment of the deaf. 1939, 84, 322-331.

CRAMMATTE, Alan B. Vocational guidance in schools for the deaf. 1939, 84, 392-404.

BARNES, Harvey B. The need for separating advanced vocational training from the elementary school atmosphere. 1940, 85, 449-451.

JONES, Uriel C. A critical survey of vocational guidance in schools for the deaf. 1940, 85, 471-486.

BARNES, Harvey B. Public employer relations and a job training center for the deaf. 1941, 86, 134-136.

_____. Positions for which deaf-mutes may be considered. 1942, 87, 288-290.

PARRISH, O. G. The vocational training program of the New Jersey School for the Deaf. 1943, 88, 122-126.

HOWARD, Jay C. Training and placing the deaf in industry. 1944, 89, 160-166.

LAVOS, George, and JONES, Earl W. The deaf worker in industry. 1946, 91, 154-176.

WILLIAMS, Boyce R. Essential characteristics (qualifications) of a rehabitable deaf or hard of hearing individual. 1947, 92, 215-226.

SHORTLEY, Michael J. Rehabilitation for the deaf and the hard of hearing. 1948, 93, 42-47.

Careers/Vocational Education (Contd.)

ANNALS OF THE DEAF (Contd.)

WILLIAMS, Boyce R. Cooperative school and rehabilitation programs, their organization and factors of effectiveness. 1948, 93, 165-173.

PHILLIPS, Richard M. A career information program for schools for the deaf. 1952, 97, 301-309.

WILLIAMS, Boyce R. Vocational rehabilitation. 1953, 98, 383-387.

KNIEVEL, William R. A vocational aptitude test battery for the deaf. 1954, 99, 314-319.

BOATNER, Maxine T. Vocational education under the Gallaudets. 1957, 102, 300-311.

DOANE, Ray C. Suggestions for improving vocational training. 1957, 102, 356-358.

SCHOWE, B. M. The deaf at work. 1958, 103, 283-292.

WILLIAMS, Boyce R. Resource needs of the deaf and ways to resolve them. 1958. 103, 293-299.

MCCLURE, William J. Accomplishments of the deaf. 1958, 103, 365-371.

PHILLIPS, Richard M. Community obligations to the deaf. 1958, 103, 378-381.

KENNEDY, W. Richard. Rehabilitation for the deaf. 1958, 103, 389-392.

DIMICHAEL, S. G. Understanding and counseling the adult deaf: an overdue mission of our time. 1958, 103, 393-398.

ALTSCHULOR, David, and ZABELL, Emil. Cooperative arrangement between division of vocational rehabilitation and a private agency. 1958, 103, 399-402.

FRIEDMAN, Max. The feelings and attitudes of the deaf towards vocational rehabilitation counselors and their programs. 1958, 103, 403-408.

SEAL, Albert G. Maximum use of community resources in the rehabilitation of the deaf. 1958, 103, 414-423.

STELLE, Roy M. Vocational rehabilitation as opportunity for the deaf. 1958, 103, 424-433.

Careers/Vocational Education (Contd.)

ANNALS OF THE DEAF (Contd.)

FUSFELD, Irving S. Suggestions regarding failure to follow the trade learned in school. 1959, 104, 277-281.

SWITZER, Mary E. Identification of researchable rehabilitation problems of the deaf. 1960, 105, 337-370.

WILLIAMS, Boyce R. Guidelines for the establishment of rehabilitation facilities for the deaf. 1961, 106, 341-364.

FALBERG, Roger M. An adventure into adult education of the deaf. 1962, 107, 329-338.

FESSANT, John M. Application of programmed learning for deaf children to industrial arts. 1963, 108, 241-244.

VERNON, McCay, and FISHLER, Thomas. Vocational needs in educational programs for deaf youth. 1966, 111, 444-451.

CRAIG, William N., and SILVER, Norman H. Examination of selected employment problems of the deaf. 1966, 111, 544-549.

BASILIER, Terje. Motivating and training the institutionalized deaf person. 1969, 114, 60-63.

BOWE, Frank G., Jr. Non-white deaf persons: educational, psychological, and occupational considerations, a review of the literature. 1971, 116, 357-361.

DUPREZ, Daryl. Occupational prestige and its correlates as conceived by deaf female vocational students. 1971, 116, 408-412.

LENOX, J., and HAMILTON, R. Mediates career education at the Marie H. Katzenbach School for the Deaf. 1973, 118, 531-537.

GREENSPAN, Stanley, and HORVATH, Richard. A public school program of economic independence for special education students. 1973, 118, 567-584.

MUNSON, Harold, HOAG, Ralph, and HOWARD, William. Career development in the education of the deaf: a program model. 1973, 118, 592-600.

FRISINA, Robert. Careers, technology and NTID. 1973, 118, 601-606.

Communication

THE VOLTA REVIEW

Aural/Oral

TILLINGHAST, Edward S. The oral method of education of the deaf. 1917, 19, 457-462.

BELL, Alexander G. The Association and its purposes. 1940, 42, 622-625.

MCLAUGHLIN, H. F. The advantage of the oral method. 1955, 57, 209-210.

O'CONNOR, Clarence D. To promote oral education for the deaf, 1956, 58, 287-288.

O'CONNOR, Clarence D. Benefits of an oral climate for all deaf children. 1957, 59, 335-336.

PRATT, George T. Oral education for deaf children: why and how. 1961, 63, 480-483.

SISTER ANNA ROSE. Oralism at St. Joseph Institute for the Deaf. 1962, 64, 496-499.

YOUNG, Ellery. Oral education in Louisiana. 1965, 67, 208-209.

STONE, Alice V. Oral education: a challenge and a necessity. 1968, 70, 289-292.

MILLER, June B. Oralism. 1970, 72, 211-217.

SCHMAEHL, Otto. Samuel Heinicke and the education of the deaf. 1970, 72, 237-241.

DICARLO, Louis M. A rationale for the oral method. 1970, 72, 280-285.

UDEN, Anthony v. New realizations in the light of the pure oral method. 1970, 72, 524-537.

FELLENDORF, George W. Is oralism worth the effort? 1971, 73, 352c-352d.

SIMMONS, Audrey A. Are we raising our children orally? 1971, 73, 439-446.

_____. Influential factors in our education to communicate with the world. 1971, 73, 468-480.

OWRID, H. L. Education and communication. 1972, 74, 225-234.

Communication (Contd.)

THE VOLTA REVIEW (Contd.)

Aural/Oral

JOHANSEN, Elizabeth B. A plea for communication. 1972, 74, 412-415.

_____. Audition, speech, and methodology, panel presentation. 1972, 74, 528-563.

SIMMONS-MARTIN, Audrey. The oral/aural approach: theoretical basis and rationale. 1972, 74, 540-551.

RUPP, Ralph, and MIKULAS, Marguerite. Some thoughts on handling the communication needs of the very young child with impaired hearing. 1973, 75, 288-295.

ERBER, Norman, and GREER, Carole W. Communication strategies used by teachers at an oral school for the deaf. 1973, 75, 480-485.

GRAMMATICO, Leahea F. The development of listening skills. 1975, 77, 303-308.

_____. Characteristics of an adequate auditory/oral program--a guide for parents and educators. 1975, 77, 431-435.

CALVERT, Donald R. Communication practices: aural/oral and visual/oral. 1976, 78, 76-81 (monograph).

LANE, Helen S. Thoughts on oral advocacy today...with memories of the Society of Oral Advocates. 1976, 78, 136-140.

GOLDSTEIN, Max A. Excerpts from: The Society of Progressive Oral Advocates: its origin and purpose--1917. 1976, 78, 140-143.

ROSS, Mark. Verbal communication: the state of the art. 1976, 78, 324-328.

LANE, Helen S. The profoundly deaf: has oral education succeeded? 1976, 78, 329-340.

Communication (Contd.)

THE VOLTA REVIEW

Manual

HANSON, Olof. The sign-language in American schools. 1901, 3, 223-226; 1902, 4, 129-131; 1903, 5, 195-196; 1904, 6, 150-151; 1905, 7, 327-328; 1906, 8, 162-163; 1907, 9, 384; 1908, 10, 282.

SUTERMEISTER, Eugene. Is the sign-language a necessity called forth by nature and circumstances? 1908, 10, 365-380.

DICARLO, Louis M. Much ado about the obvious. 1966, 68, 269-273.

OWRID, H. L. Studies in manual communication with hearing impaired children. 1971, 73, 428-438.

STUCKLESS, E. Ross. Manual and graphic communication. 1976, 78, 96-101 (monograph).

THE VOLTA REVIEW

Simultaneous

WRIGHT, John D. The "combined system" diagnoses its own case with remarkable truth and frankness. 1914, 16, 699-701.

WILLIAMS, Mary E. The betterment of a speech environment in a combined-system school. 1915, 17, 182-184.

WRIGHT, John D. A weak spot in the combined system. 1916, 18, 3-5.

ROE, W. Carey. Dr. Forchhammer's mouth-and-hand system: a discussion. 1918, 20, 175-177.

VERNON, McCay. Mind over mouth: a rationale for "total communication." 1972, 74, 529-540.

THE VOLTA REVIEW (Contd.)

Communication (Contd.)

Simultaneous

DRUMM, Philip R. "Total communication"--fraud or reality? 1972, 74, 564-569.

NIX, Gary W. Total communication: a review of the studies offered in its support. 1975, 77, 470-494.

GARRETSON, Mervin D. Total communication. 1976, 78, 88-95 (monograph).

THE VOLTA REVIEW

Comparisons

MULHOLLAND, Ann M. Communication: a review of current research. 1963, 65, 513-522.

ANNALS OF THE DEAF

Aural/Oral

WESTERVELT, Z. F. The natural method as applied to the instruction of young children. 1880, 25, 212-216.

STORRS, Richard S. Deaf-mutes and the oral method. 1883, 28, 145-168.

BLATTNER, J. W. The natural method. 1891, 36, 1-11.

KIRKHUFF, J. D. The natural method. 1891, 36, 120-128.

WESTERVELT, Z. F. American Association to Promote the Teaching of Speech to the Deaf. 1891, 36, 222-224.

Communication (Contd.)

ANNALS OF THE DEAF (Contd.)

Aural/Oral

GILLESPIE, Frances E. The theory and practice of instruction for an oral class of beginners. 1901, 46, 492-507; 1902, 47, 233-242.

FERRERI, Guilio C. The oral method: its fitness for the deaf. 1902, 4, 344-353.

BINET, A., and SIMON, Th. An investigation concerning the value of the oral method. 1910, 55, 4-33.

FERRERI, Guilio. Mistaken investigation concerning the value of the oral method. 1910, 55, 34-38.

DROUOT, E. The Binet investigation of the oral method. 1910, 55, 307-324.

CROUTER, A. L. The possibilities of oral methods. 1911, 56, 390-407.

GOLDSTEIN, M. A. The Society of Progressive Oral Advocates: its origin and purposes. 1917, 19, 443-447.

REINHARDT, Anna C., et al. Schools where deaf children talk and talk and where no use is made of the sign-language or the finger alphabet. 1918, 20, 476-484.

_____. Proceedings of the first annual convention of the Society of Progressive Oral Advocates. 1919, 21, 95-120; 57-183.

_____. Proceedings of the second annual convention of Progressive Oral Advocates. 1919, 21, 629-660; 716-746; 759-796.

STEWART, R. B. By ear alone. 1968, 113, 147-155.

BRAINERD, Susan H. Are audiologists strict oralists? 1975, 120, 489-492.

Communication (Contd.)

ANNALS OF THE DEAF

Manual

PEET, Harvey P. Words not "representatives" of signs, but of ideas. 1859, 11, 1-8.

JACOBS, J. A. The relation of written words to signs, the same as their relation to spoken words. 1859, 11, 65-78.

PEET, Isaac L. Initial signs. 1861, 13, 171-184.

KEEP, John R., and HUBBARD, Gardiner G. The language of signs. 1869, 14, 89-95.

HUTTON, George. The practicability and advantage of writing and printing natural signs. 1869, 14, 157-182.

HOLLISTER, H. H. The manual alphabet. 1870, 15, 88-93.

COCHRANE, W. A. Methodical signs instead of colloquial. 1871, 16, 11-17.

KEEP, John R. Natural signs--shall they be abandoned? 1871, 16, 17-25.

GALLAUDET, Edward M. Is the sign-language used to excess in teaching deaf-mutes? 1871, 16, 26-33.

KEEP, John R. The sign language. 1871, 16, 221-234.

PETTENGILL, B. D. The instruction of the deaf and dumb. 1872, 17, 21-33.

PETTENGILL, B. D. The sign language. 1873, 18, 1-2.

DEHEARNE, D. The natural language of signs. 1875, 20, 73-86; 137-153; 216-277; 1876, 21, 11-16.

TYLOR, Edward B. The gesture-language. 1878, 23, 162-178; 251-260; 1879, 24, 39-45.

FAY, O. Gilbert. The sign-language the basis of instruction for deaf-mutes. 1882, 27, 208-211.

WHITE, Harry. The influence of signs upon the study of language. 1884, 29, 174-178.

GALLAUDET, Edward M. The value of the sign-language to the deaf. 1887, 32, 141-147.

Communication (Contd.)

ANNALS OF THE DEAF (Contd.)

Manual

TILDEN, Douglas. Signs and words. 1887, 32, 176-179.

HASKINS, C. N. The sufficiency or insufficiency of signs--which? 1890, 35, 27-30.

WHITE, Henry C. Spelling versus signs. 1890, 35, 111-114.

GEORGE, D. W. Signs and finger spelling. 1890, 35, 115-117.

DRAPER, Amos G. How to teach and use the manual alphabet. 1897, 42, 370-371.

GALLAUDET, Edward M. Must the sign-language go? 1899, 44, 221-229.

SMITH, James L. The abuse of the sign-language. 1902, 47, 157-182.

LONG, T. Schuyler. The sign language: a manual of signs. 1908, 53, 230-249; 438-448; 1909, 54, 23-37; 140-160; 263-281; 339-347; 420-438; 1910, 55, 142-155.

STEPPUHN. Our present attitude with respect to the sign language. 1911, 56, 127-142.

JENKINS, Weston. The sign language: what is it? 1911, 56, 461-468.

FITZGERALD, Edith. Manual spelling and English. 1912, 57, 197-203.

THOMAS, Margaret L. An appeal for manual spelling in manual classes. 1926, 71, 213-218.

ANDERSON, Tom L. What of the sign language? 1938, 83, 120-130.

COATS, G. Dewey. Manual English. 1948, 93, 174-177.

FUSFELD, Irving S. How the deaf communicate--manual language. 1958, 103, 264-282.

ABERNATHY, Edward B. An historical sketch of the manual alphabets. 1959, 104, 232-239.

SCOUTEN, Edward L. Helping your deaf child to master English through finger-spelling. 1960, 105, 226-229.

ROWE, Frederick, et al. Communication through gestures. 1960, 105, 232-237.

Communication (Contd.)

ANNALS OF THE DEAF (Contd.)

Manual

FANT, Louie, and ROY, Howard. Programmed lessons for the language of signs. 1961, 106, 484-486.

ADLER, Edna P. Reading out loud in the language of signs. 1964, 109, 364-366.

STUCKLESS, E. Ross, and BIRCH, Jack W. The influence of early manual communication on the linguistic development of deaf children. 1966, 111, Part I, 452-460; Part II, 499-504.

SIGER, Leonard. Gestures, the language of signs, and communication. 1968, 113, 11-28.

MEADOW, Kathryn. Early manual communication in relation to the deaf child's intellectual, social and communicative functioning. 1968, 113, 29-41.

VERNON, McCay. Early manual communication and deaf children's achievement. 1970, 115, 527-536.

CASTLE, Diane L. Misinformation among advocates of non-oral methodologies. 1970, 115, 666-667.

BERGMAN, Eugene. Autonomous and unique features of American sign language. 1972, 117, 20-24.

BORNSTEIN, Harry. A description of some current sign systems designed to represent English. 1973, 118, 454-463.

BRAGG, Bernard. Ameslish--our American heritage: a testimony. 1973, 118, 672-674.

SANBORN, Donald E., SANBORN, Charlotte J., SEIBERT, Dean J., and PYKE, Harold F. Teaching sign language by interactive television. 1975, 120, 58-62.

STOKOE, William. The use of sign language in teaching English. 1975, 120, 417-421.

HOWLAND, Carroll R. Literature can live through signs. 1975, 120, 558-563.

REICH, Peter A., and BICK, Margaret. An empirical investigation of some claims made in support of visible English. 1976, 121, 573-577.

Communication (Contd.)

ANNALS OF THE DEAF

Simultaneous

HIRSCH, D. Mr. Hirsch's views of the "combined method" for the deaf and dumb. 1869, 14, 48-53.

SISTER MARY A. BURKE. Views on the combined method. 1880, 25, 172-174.

WILKINSON, Warring. The development of speech and of the sign language. 1881, 26, 167-178.

STORRS, Richard S. Semi-deaf, semi-mute and the combined method. 1883, 28, 21-36.

STORRS, Richard S. Deaf-mutes and the combined method. 1883, 28, 77-94.

GALLAUDET, Edward M. The combined system of instruction. 1892, 36, 255-266.

DUDLEY, D. C. Signs in oral schools. 1894, 39, 37-40.

_____. The Rochester method, an oral multisensory approach for instructing prelingual deaf children. 1967, 112, 50-55.

SCOUTEN, Edward L. The prelingual deaf child and his oral education in a new perspective. 1969, 114, 770-776.

FURFEY, Paul Hanley. Total communication and the Baltimore deaf survey. 1974, 119, 377-382.

MCCLURE, William J. The Rochester method and the Florida school. 1975, 120, 331-340.

LETOURNEAU, Nora, and YOUNG, Virginia. Total communication shuffles off to Buffalo. 1975, 120, 493-496.

BECKMEYER, Ted. Receptive abilities of hearing impaired students in a total communication setting. 1976, 121, 569-572.

Communication (Contd.)

ANNALS OF THE DEAF

Comparisons

WRIGHT, John D. Combined but not commingled. 1917, 62, 209-210.

MONTGOMERY, G. W. G. The relationship of oral skills to manual communication in profoundly deaf adolescents. 1966, 111, 557-565.

MOORES, Donald F. Oral vs. manual ... old prejudices die hard but die they must. 1970, 115, 667-669.

VERNON, McCay, and KOH, Soon D. Effects of oral preschool compared to early manual communication on education and communication in deaf children. 1971, 116, 569-574.

HIGGINS, Earl. An analysis of the comprehensibility of three communication methods used with hearing impaired students. 1973, 118, 46-49.

WHITE, Alfred H., and STEVENSON, Vivian M. The effects of total communication, manual communication, oral communication and reading on the learning of factual information in residential school deaf children. 1975, 120, 48-57.

CHASEN, Barbara, and ZUCKERMAN, William. The effects of total communication and oralism on deaf third-grade "rubella" students. 1976, 121, 394-404.

COLLINS, James L., and ROSE, Susan. Communicative interaction patterns in an open environment for deaf high school students. 1976, 121, 497-501.

MAYBERRY, Rachel. An assessment of some oral and manual language skills of hearing children of deaf parents. 1976, 121, 507-512.

JORDAN, S. K., GUSTASON, Gerilee, and ROSEN, Roslyn. Current communication trends at programs for the deaf. 1976, 121, 527-532.

Curriculum

THE VOLTA REVIEW

Art

MCCOWEN, Mary. Dramatization as a factor in education. 1904, <u>6</u>, 109-115.

BERRYMAN, Florence S. Art as compensation for the deafened. 1927, <u>29</u>, 58-59.

STEVENS, Kelly H. Finger painting for little deaf children. 1946, <u>48</u>, 445-447; 484-486.

SCHILLING, B. W. Another key: art. 1958, <u>60</u>, 437-438; 464.

SILVER, Rawley. Art for the deaf child--its potentialities. 1963, <u>65</u>, 408-413; 417.

ARNOLD, N. Hillis. A deaf sculptor. 1967, <u>69</u>, 378-381.

HARRINGTON, John D., and SILVER, Rawley A. Art education and the education of deaf students. 1968, <u>70</u>, 475-480.

THE VOLTA REVIEW

Mathematics

SENSENIG, Barton. Methods in arithmetic. 1903, <u>5</u>, 132-139.

ADAMS, Ida H. Arithmetic taught by constructive measuring. 1906, <u>8</u>, 238-241.

KENT, Eliza. Primary work in arithmetic. 1907, <u>9</u>, 104-110.

DOWNING, A. U. Arithmetic--the equation method. 1907, <u>9</u>, 191-198.

SENSENIG, Barton. Equational methods. 1911, <u>13</u>, 91-95.

ARCHER, Tunis V. Some points to emphasize in teaching arithmetic. 1912, <u>14</u>, 25-30.

COBB, Jennie. Beginning arithmetic. 1912, <u>14</u>, 679-680.

Curriculum (Contd.)

THE VOLTA REVIEW (Contd.)

Mathematics

SENSENIG, Barton. An outline in arithmetic and methods of presenting the subject. 1914, 16, 21-26; 60-64.

SENSENIG, Barton. An outline of third-year work in arithmetic, with methods. 1914, 16, 154-159.

NEWLEE, Clara E. The Cleveland arithmetic test. 1918, 20, 212-222.

TAYLOR, Annah S. A helpful device for teaching the formal skills of arithmetic. 1919, 21, 554-555.

SENSENIG, Barton. Training for number work. 1920, 22, 767-778.

TAYLOR, Annah S. A project for eighth grade mathematics. 1921, 23, 297-299.

_____. Arithmetic. 1925, 27, 40-47.

MORRIS, Dorothy. Mathematics in the grammar school. 1926, 28, 148-149.

DRISCOLL, Anita. Arithmetic in the Lexington Avenue School. 1926, 28, 303-304.

LEWIS, Sarah E. Primary number work. 1926, 28, 587-588.

HAYNES, Carrie A. A problem analysis. 1926, 28, 591-592.

BOOTH, Frank W. Teaching arithmetic objectively. 1926, 28, 606-613.

MCLAUGHLIN, Clayton L. Practical mathematics. 1927, 29, 463-465.

MCMILLAN, K. Work with number combinations in the Alabama School. 1928, 30, 227-228.

DRISCOLL, Anita. Arithmetic. 1928, 30, 630-632.

CHRISTIAN, Harvey T. Beginning algebra taught objectively. 1929, 31, 117-120.

WELTY, Harry L. The teaching of numbers. 1929, 31, 312-320.

LONG, E. Florence. The logical way of teaching arithmetic. 1930, 32, 413-414; 429-430.

HEMBROOK, Margaret. The use of the model store. 1930, 32, 576-577.

Curriculum (Contd.)

THE VOLTA REVIEW (Contd.)

Mathematics

ELLIOTT, C. Evangeline. Arithmetic in the elementary grades. 1933, 35, 374-376.

ACKER, Lela. Making arithmetic attractive. 1934, 36, 709-711; 762.

ACKER, Lela. Devices to make arithmetic interesting. 1936, 38, 11-13; 61.

POULOS, Thomas H. Needs and objectives in teaching arithmetic to the deaf. 1953, 55, 452-455.

O'NEILL, Veronica. Number fun at home. 1955, 57, 257-259; 275.

NUMBERS, Leona P. The teaching of arithmetic in the primary and intermediate grades. 1958, 60, 210-212; 226-227.

BOWER, Dolores. Summer fun with numbers. 1961, 63, 284-286.

BROHMAN, Doris. Teaching modern math to linguistically impaired children. 1967, 69, 527-530.

WOODBY, Lauren G., and WIRTZ, Robert. Curriculum in school mathematics. 1968, 70, 419-425.

O'NEILL, Veronica. Developing deaf children's thinking through mathematics. 1968, 70, 426-430.

SUMMERS, Hubert D., and SWAIM, William D. Valuable characteristics of modern mathematics instruction for deaf students. 1968, 70, 431-436.

BARRON, Roberta. Helping deaf children learn to solve addition and subtraction verbal problems. 1975, 120, 346-349.

Curriculum (Contd.)

THE VOLTA REVIEW

Music and Rhythm

JORDAN, Sarah A. Rhythm as an aid to voice training. 1900, 2, 16-19.

_____. A military school for the deaf, and its band of deaf musicians. 1911, 13, 201-207.

DYER, Helen L. Harmonic gymnastics. 1914, 16, 5-12.

MONRO, Sarah J. A resume of the rhythmic work in the Horace Mann School, Boston. 1915, 17, 133-138.

MONRO, Sarah J. The priceless value of rhythm to deaf children. 1915, 17, 437-439.

MONRO, Sarah J. Rhythmic exercises. 1916, 18, 233-237.

MONRO, Sarah J. Rhythmic movements of the body. 1917, 19, 532-534.

MONRO, Sarah J. A plea for the use of the piano in speech and voice work. 1918, 20, 93.

MONRO, Sarah J. Rhythm. 1918, 20, 781-783.

GEDDES, Kathleen R. Music for the hard of hearing. 1920, 22, 73-74.

NEW, Mary C. Rhythm-work in the Alabama School for the Deaf. 1921, 23, 148-149.

KNIGHT, Augustus C. Why give up your music? 1924, 26, 297-299.

_____. Rhythm. 1925, 27, 47-49.

_____. Percussion orchestra for deaf children. 1926, 28, 93-94.

SANDBERG, Irene L. Rhythm. 1926, 28, 310-323.

BRADY, Wilma S. The development of tone and rhythm. 1926, 28, 323-332.

HAMMER, Helen. A project in rhythm. 1928, 30, 30-32.

FLANDERS, Gwendolyn A. Rhythm for deaf children of ungraded schools. 1928, 30, 477-481.

Curriculum (Contd.)

THE VOLTA REVIEW (Contd.)

Music and Rhythm

KENT, Margaret S. Primary and intermediate rhythm. 1929, <u>31</u>, 512-513.

RADCLIFFE, Edith. Advanced rhythm. 1929, <u>31</u>, 514-515.

CORNELL, Louise E. Rhythm in the kindergarten and junior primary departments. 1929, <u>31</u>, 782-784.

HENDERSON, Jennie M. The awakening of latent hearing by means of musical tones and vibrations. 1930, <u>32</u>, 185-187; 197-202.

MCKINNEY, Lettie W. Music appreciation. 1930, <u>32</u>, 189-190.

KETCHAM, Margaret B. Rhythm. 1931, <u>33</u>, 80-82.

JAYNE, Gladys G. Rhythm--our kindergarten bands. 1931, <u>33</u>, 387-388.

SUNSTROM, Florence. Our rhythm band. 1931, <u>33</u>, 488-489.

RICHARDSON, Beatrice E. Teaching rhythm visually, 1934, <u>36</u>, 405-407; 443.

VAN NEST, Mary R. Eurythmics. 1937, <u>39</u>, 337; 373.

KAWAKAMI, Marcia. We can still hear music. 1937, <u>39</u>, 584-585.

MCALISTER, Grace W. Rhythm and personality growth. 1938, <u>40</u>, 212-214.

GARBETT, Arthur S. Music for the hard of hearing. 1943, <u>45</u>, 571-575; 598-600.

GARBETT, Arthur S. Music and our hearing aids. 1944, <u>46</u>, 639-643; 662; 702-705; 732; 1945, <u>47</u>, 27-30; 50-52.

NIELSEN, Dorothy V. Gay, profitable rhythm classes. 1948, <u>50</u>, 17-18.

CAVANAGH, Anita, and WINTERS, Loretta M. We've got rhythm. 1949, <u>51</u>, 111; 146-148.

UDEN, A. v. Music and dancing for the deaf. 1949, <u>51</u>, 386-388.

UNHOLTZ, Louise, and NEGLEY, Katherine. Our children's heritage. 1953, <u>55</u>, 131; 170-172.

UDEN, A. v. An electrical wind-instrument for severely or totally deaf children, 1953, <u>55</u>, 241-242.

Curriculum (Contd.)

THE VOLTA REVIEW (Contd.)

Music and Rhythm

FAGAN, E. Choral speaking by deaf children. 1954, 56, 17-18.

SANDBERG, Mabel W. Rhythms and music for the deaf and hard of hearing. 1954, 56, 255-256.

WOJAN, Kathleen. Eurythmics. 1955, 57, 253-254.

SMITH, Meredith J. Songs for the primary grades. 1956, 58, 253-255.

MARKELL, Alan. Teaching deaf children to dance. 1961, 63, 176-177.

MAY, Elizabeth. Music for deaf children. 1961, 63, 220-223; 247.

FAVORS, A., and Krohn, E. Amahl and the night visitors. 1961, 63, 484-486; 509.

COSTELLO, Patrice. Music for the deaf. 1964, 66, 92-93.

BIRKENSHAW, Lois. Teaching music to deaf children. 1965, 67, 352-358; 387.

KHARASCH, Ethel N. Fun for the deaf child. 1965, 67, 376-378.

GILMORE, M. Elizabeth. Rhythm, language, and the deaf child. 1966, 68, 160-165.

HOGAN, Loretta C., et al. A music program for young deaf children --a "mod" approach. 1968, 70, 561-565.

HUMMEL, Cora J. The value of music in teaching deaf students. 1971, 73, 224-228; 243-249.

BRICK, SISTER ROSE MARIE. Eurhythmics: one aspect of audition. 1973, 75, 155-160.

VETTESE, Joseph. Instrumental lessons for deaf children. 1974, 76, 219-222.

STERN, Virginia. They shall have music. 1975, 77, 495-500.

Curriculum (Contd.)

THE VOLTA REVIEW

Hygiene, Physical Education

GREEN, Grace G. The importance of physical training for the deaf. 1907, 9, 180-188.

DALY, Margaret A. Physical training for the deaf child. 1913, 15, 131-136.

HINES, Edward J. Physical education. 1914, 16, 248-250.

DALLET, Jean. Physical education for the deaf child--is it worthwhile? 1934, 36, 331-335.

BLISH, Stanford C. Problems involved in sex education in residential schools for the deaf. 1940, 42, 133-138; 208-213; 246; 268-272; 310; 501-505; 550.

SWAIN, N. G. Teaching Red Cross first aid to deaf students. 1955, 57, 265-267.

CHAPLIN, Joyce W. Sex education of deaf children. 1957, 59, 201-203; 225.

MILLER, Anne S. Personal hygiene for teenagers. 1964, 66, 179-183.

WOLFRAM, Bonnie R. Health education: evolution or revolution? 1968, 70, 500-507.

KLINE, Lorraine F. A social hygiene program in a residential school for deaf children. 1968, 70, 509-512.

HILL, Arlene. Some guidelines for sex education of the deaf child. 1971, 73, 120-124.

MILLER, Anne Small. If I have a daughter. . . the sex education program for teenagers at Clarke School. 1973, 75, 493-503.

Curriculum (Contd.)

Reading

GAWITH, Frances W. Reading in intermediate grades. 1909, 11, 397-403.

FRITZ, Katherine. First lessons in reading. 1912, 14, 602-604.

ROBERTS, Linnaeus. Cultivation of the reading habit. 1914, 16, 82-85.

_____. Visual reading. 1916, 18, 430-434.

FORDYCE, Charles. Testing the efficiency in reading. 1917, 19, 518-520.

HILL, Miss W. Reading and language development. 1920, 22, 298-301.

YALE, Caroline A. Chart stories for class-room work with young children. 1920, 22, 579-580.

GATES, A. I. An experimental study of teaching the deaf to read. 1926, 28, 295-298.

KIDDER, K. B. One approach to the enjoyment of reading--dramatization. 1926, 28, 300-302.

JOINER, Enfield. The personal experience story. 1926, 28, 581-582.

ERVIN, Annie M. Training children to read. 1926, 28, 583-585.

ERVIN, Annie M. Reading--the open sesame to language. 1926, 28, 695-699.

FARQUHAR, Grover C. Reading for intermediate pupils. 1927, 29, 194-196.

HOWES, Esther C. Teaching young deaf children to read. 1928, 30, 19-20.

SERUMGARD, Inez M. Teaching the love of reading. 1928, 30, 333-334.

NEWLEE, Clara E. A study in silent reading with deaf children of kindergarten age. 1928, 30, 523-526.

DAVIS, M. V. A silent reading experiment in grade one. 1929, 31, 66-72.

Curriculum (Contd.)

THE VOLTA REVIEW (Contd.)

Reading

BELL, Alexander G. On reading as a means of teaching language to the deaf. 1929, 31, 191-195.

HAMMER, Helen. The second step in a silent reading experiment. 1929, 31, 196-198.

WHITMAN, Mabel P. Reading made interesting. 1929, 31, 199-200.

DEAN, Katherine S. Our first experience with reading. 1929, 31, 787-788.

GESNER, Elizabeth T. Some points on reading comprehension and vocabulary building. 1930, 32, 24-36.

MORROW, Elizabeth. An introduction to interpretative reading. 1930, 32, 277-281; 294.

ANDERSON, Effie W. Reading in the advanced department. 1930, 32, 403-409.

AVONDINO, Josephine. Silent reading. 1930, 32, 623-624.

HAMMER, Helen. A nature study unit in reading. 1931, 33, 101-102.

READ, Elizabeth. Cultivating the reading habit. 1931, 33, 125-126.

FOSMARK, Laura B. Reading for pleasure. 1931, 33, 214; 233.

CHURCH, Lilian L. Reading for the deaf adolescent. 1931, 33, 251-252; 279.

GRIFFITH, Mary J. Comparing results in speech-reading and in silent reading. 1931, 33, 270-272.

EICKHOFF, Arlington J. The library period. 1931, 33, 445-446.

MOSS, Margery. Reading. 1931, 33, 446-447.

SISTER M. DE LASALLE. Supervised reading in the high school. 1932, 34, 111-113.

NICOLL, Mildred G. Reading. 1932, 34, 623-624; 649.

RUTHVEN, Henrietta. Early steps in reading. 1933, 35, 216-217.

BENNETT, Josephine. Reading in the primary grades. 1934, 36, 337-339; 378; 1938, 40, 5-9.

Curriculum (Contd.)

THE VOLTA REVIEW (Contd.)

Reading

BRUCE, Lula M. Creating an interest in reading. 1934, 36, 588-591.

WRIGHT, Bruce, et al. The deaf child and the newspaper. 1940, 42, 5-8.

NEWTON, Mary G. Books for the hard of hearing child. 1943, 45, 455-458; 470-476.

PUGH, Gladys S. Appraisal of the silent reading abilities of acoustically handicapped children. 1946, 48, 197-198; 254.

_____. Good books for children's reading. 1946, 48, 199-200; 252-254.

MCLAUGHLIN, Harriet F., et al. A reading program. 1946, 48, 666-667.

WINTERS, L. Reading readiness and beginning reading in the pre-school. 1946, 48, 667-669.

CRANDELL, Marian P. Reading in the primary grades. 1946, 48, 669-671.

MCNEIL, Marie T. Group reading. 1946, 48, 671-673.

WILMAN, M. Catherine. Reading in the upper school. 1946, 48, 673-675.

KENNARD, Marie S. Exercises in reading readiness. 1947, 49, 213-214.

VERMILLION, F. F. Children's experiences in written form (chart stories). 1947, 49, 374; 382-384.

PUGH, Gladys S. Recreational and study-type reading. 1947, 49, 547-548; 582-584.

PUGH, Gladys S. Study-type reading. 1948, 50, 205-207; 242-244.

PUGH, Gladys S., et al. Reading for deaf children. 1948, 50, 426-431.

DAVIES, Rachel D. Silent reading but oral English. 1948, 50, 437-441.

PUGH, Gladys S. Recreational reading for deaf children. 1949, 51, 437-440; 484-486.

Curriculum (Contd.)

THE VOLTA REVIEW (Contd.)

Reading

DOCTOR, Powrie V. A lesson plan for teaching poetry in an advanced class. 1950, 52, 205-208.

MACDONALD, Nellie V. Books suitable for small deaf children. 1950, 52, 256; 292.

MILLER, Bertha. Poetry in the lives of the deaf. 1950, 52, 493; 532-534.

SISTER M. RENEE. Reading for deaf children. 1951, 53, 104-107; 134.

REISS, Madeline. Can the comics help? 1952, 54, 155-157; 186.

GODA, Sidney. Early reading for the hard of hearing child. 1953, 55, 97-98; 106-108.

DOCTOR, Powrie V. (moderator, panel). Reading for the deaf. 1953, 55, 132-143.

WOODWARD, Helen. Books for the deaf child. 1953, 55, 391-399.

CASEY, Sally L. Teaching reading to the hearing handicapped child. 1954, 56, 251-254.

GULICK, Mabel. A reading program for first-year deaf school children. 1954, 56, 447-448.

GROHT, Mildred. Some thoughts on reading. 1955, 57, 294-296.

CORY, Patricia B. Leisure reading for deaf children. 1955, 57, 449-451; 1956, 58, 33-34; 123-125; 169-171; 213-214; 267-269; 409-411; 447-448; 1957, 59, 27; 38; 72; 85; 217-219; 314-315; 365-366; 409-410; 1958, 60, 35-36; 178-179; 447-449; 503; 506; 547; 1959, 61, 35-36; 181-183; 187; 228-230; 239; 429; 1960, 62, 36-38; 521; 1961, 63, 244-245; 453; 464; 1962, 64, 45-46; 153; 570; 1963, 65, 245-246; 430-431.

SISTER ANNA ROSE. They can't help but read. 1956, 58, 381-385.

THOMAS, Alyce, et al. Reading for deaf children (panel discussion). 1956, 58, 429-431.

CORY, Patricia B. Library work with the deaf. 1957, 59, 169-173.

Curriculum (Contd.)

THE VOLTA REVIEW (Contd.)

Reading

RICHARDSON, Paul C. A reading lesson using the Fitzgerald key headings. 1957, 59, 255-256.

EDGE, Lillie K. Book week at Western Pennsylvania School for the Deaf. 1957, 59, 402-406.

STRICKLAND, Ruth G. The interrelationship between language and reading. 1958, 60, 334-336.

SISTER ANNE BERNADINE. A developmental curriculum. 1958, 60, 337-340.

FITZGERALD, Margaret H. Improving the reading ability of deaf children. 1958, 60, 341-343.

CORY, Patricia B. Recreational reading and library program. 1958, 60, 343-347.

GRIFFIN, Barbara. Reading evaluation: a continuing study. 1958, 60, 476-477; 506.

CORY, Patricia. A child's first books should be fun. 1959, 61, 411-412.

SINCLAIR, Margaret. Interesting the disinterested reader. 1960, 62, 488-492.

OSTERN, Beatrice. Home help with reading. 1960, 62, 494-496.

WOODWARD, Helen. Read with your children. 1960, 62, 517-519.

PUGH, Bessie. Teaching children to use the dictionary. 1961, 63, 178-185.

PUGH, Bessie. Utilizing research in teaching reading. 1962, 64, 379-387.

KENT, Alice. To each his own in reading. 1962, 64, 387-389.

MANGAN, Kenneth R. An optimistic outlook toward teaching reading to deaf children. 1962, 64, 392-393.

SCHOWE, Ben M., Jr. Projecting books as an aid to teaching reading. 1962, 64, 421-422.

BECKMEYER, Theodore. Application of programed instruction to remedial reading for the deaf. 1963, 65, 415-417.

Curriculum (Contd.)

THE VOLTA REVIEW (Contd.)

Reading

CORY, Patricia. Special library reading project for teenagers. 1964, 66, 63-66.

NEWTON, Mary G. Readers, not leaf-turners. 1964, 66, 67-69.

MAGNER, Marjorie E. Reading: goals and achievements at Clarke School for the Deaf. 1964, 66, 464-468.

WITHROW, Margaret S. The augmented Roman alphabet--can it be used for teaching the deaf? 1964, 66, 540-543.

KAUFMAN, Maurice. A reading consultant in a school for the deaf. 1965, 67, 197-200.

STERNE, Lillian C. Using context clues in a reading program for the deaf. 1965, 67, 371-375.

FLINT, Richard W., et al. 1965 NDEA Institutes in Linguistics and Reading: The University of Kansas Institute in Reading. 1965, 67, 618-623.

NAIMAN, Doris. A different emphasis in reading for deaf children. 1965, 67, 632-634; 651.

RUDLOFF, Joseph S. The hearing handicapped retarded reader. 1966, 68, 567-571.

BALOW, Bruce, et al. Reading comprehension skills among hearing impaired adolescents. 1971, 73, 113-119.

PETERS, Nathaniel, and PETERS, Juanita. Better reading materials for the content areas, criteria for better use and annotated bibliography. 1973, 75, 375-387.

PETERS, Nathaniel, and PETERS, Juanita. Better reading materials for the content areas annotated bibliography--social studies. 1973, 75, 445-448.

PETERS, Nathaniel, and PETERS, Juanita. Better reading materials for the content areas, (language and guidance). 1973, 75, 509-513.

HARGIS, Charles H., EVANS, Carole C., and MASTERS, Carolyn. A criticism of the direct discourse form in primary level basal readers. 1973, 75, 557-563.

Curriculum (Contd.)

THE VOLTA REVIEW (Contd.)

Reading

PETERS, Nathaniel, and PETERS, Juanita. Better reading materials-consumer education, miscellaneous reading. 1973, 75, 564-567.

HINEY, Esther. World Traveler in the classroom: 1969-1974. 1974, 76, 368-373.

LANE, Helen S. and BAKER, Dorothea. Reading achievement of the deaf: another look. 1974, 76, 489-499.

PETERS, Nathaniel, and PETERS, Juanita. Better reading materials for the content areas. 1974, 76, 500-507.

HART, Beatrice O. Learning to read begins at birth. 1975, 77, 168-172.

BALOW, Irving H., and BRILL, Richard G. An evaluation of reading and academic achievement levels of 16 graduating classes of the California School for the Deaf, Riverside. 1975, 77, 255-266.

THE VOLTA REVIEW

Science

ANDREWS, Harriet U. The deaf child and nature. 1913, 15, 387-393.

ANDREWS, Harriet U. The importance of nature study for deaf children. 1914, 16, 192-198.

ANDREWS, Harriet U. In the woods in August. 1914, 16, 503-515.

CHURCH, Lilian L. Methods used in presenting practical science problems to the deaf child. 1925, 27, 215-217.

CHURCH, Lilian L. Problems illustrating the project method of teaching science. 1925, 27, 379-381.

CHURCH, Lilian L. The project method of teaching the science of common things. 1925, 27, 539-541; 711-713.

Curriculum (Contd.)

THE VOLTA REVIEW (Contd.)

Science

CHURCH, Lilian L. The project method of teaching practical science. 1926, 28, 46-48; 94-96; 338-340.

HOWES, Annette S. Science as it is taught in the Grammar Department of Clarke School. 1926, 28, 149-150.

HOWSON, James W. Some aspects of science teaching. 1926, 28, 652-654.

SHIELS, Katherine. General science. 1930, 32, 139-141.

WILSON, Amy E. Nature study in the primary grades. 1931, 33, 442-443.

BLAIR, Mary. A series of elementary science lessons. 1936, 38, 570-572; 616-618; 644-647; 715-718; 760.

KENNARD, M., and FITZGERALD, E. Outline of nature study for deaf children. 1941, 43, 429; 448-452.

ELIAS, Hans. A method of teaching science to the deaf. 1941, 43, 584-587.

PHILLIPS, F. I., and PETERSON, W. A planetarium visit. 1953, 55, 435-438.

ECKSTROM, Faith F. Studying science in the lower grades. 1956, 58, 75-76.

HAYDEN, Jean S., and WOODWARD, Helen M.E. Rationale for a science program. 1968, 70, 159-165.

HEDGES, H. G. Natural science for all students. 1968, 70, 379-384.

FITZGERALD, Sister M. Ambrosia. Trends in science education. 1968, 70, 385-388.

OWSLEY, Peter J. Development of the cognitive abilities and language of deaf children through science. 1968, 70, 389-393.

DEWALT, Patricia A. Adaptations of the scientific method for the deaf child. 1968, 70, 394-398.

Curriculum (Contd.)

Social Studies

SMITH, James L. Current history in the schoolroom. 1903, 5, 112-118.

GAWITH, Frances W. Geography and history for intermediate grades. 1907, 9, 135-142.

STRICKLAND, Elizabeth H. Hints on how to teach geography. 1911, 13, 403-409.

LONG, T. Schuyler. The teaching of history. 1920, 22, 550-557.

BEATTIE, Grace M. Geography. 1920, 22, 648-654.

HARRIS, James C. The heavens. 1921, 23, 284-292.

RENARD, Ella S. Some suggestions for teaching history. 1926, 28, 206-207.

SAVAGE, Julia W. Current events in advanced classes. 1926, 28, 251-253.

COWLES, Katherine. Vitalizing geography. 1926, 28, 585-586.

KING, Kate L. Making geography the most interesting subject. 1926, 28, 708-710.

STRICKLAND, Elizabeth H. Geography notes. 1927, 29, 750-754; 1928, 30, 101-106; 168-172; 232-234; 291-294; 391-393; 436-439; 482-485; 809-814; 1929, 31, 201-204; 322-325; 427-444; 1930, 32, 37-40; 147-149.

O'CONNELL, Agnes. A history project in sixth grade. 1928, 30, 33-34.

HARWOOD, Viola. History for the deaf. 1928, 30, 340-341.

_____. History (Virginia teachers). 1928, 30, 625-629.

COFFEY, M. Adelaide. Fourth grade geography. 1928, 30, 806-808.

DONALDSON, Elizabeth M. Geography for young minds. 1929, 31, 252-254.

MORRISON, Jessie S. Geography in departmental grades. 1929, 31, 254-256.

Curriculum (Contd.)

THE VOLTA REVIEW (Contd.)

Social Studies

MOORE, Helen T. Methods and devices for teaching current events and history. 1931, 33, 128-129.

FULLINGTON, Angeline. A history project. 1931, 33, 316-318.

SISTER M. ALBERT. Seventh grade geography. 1932, 34, 109-110.

MILLER, Ada R. A seventh grade study of Europe. 1933, 35, 25-26.

FRECK, Phyllis. Geography in the grammar grades. 1933, 35, 249-251.

JONES, Anne. A Holland project. 1932, 34, 390-392.

WOOD, Doris E. A language-geography project in 2B. 1934, 36, 524-526.

ARNOLD, Allie. Beginning history. 1934, 36, 647-649; 694.

KIRKLEY, J. R. Outline maps and current events. 1936, 38, 332; 368-369.

DICKEY, Dorothy B. Place geography. 1936, 38, 546-547.

COLLINS, Marcella. A spin around the world. 1936, 38, 573-575; 615.

CLATTERBUCK, M. B. Social studies in the Oregon School. 1939, 41, 136-138.

FOUTS, Mildred. Vitalizing the geography dosage. 1947, 49, 456; 490-492.

OLANOFF, Rose S., and MCCORMICK, Margaret. The house I live in (unit on brotherhood). 1953, 55, 75-76.

TIMBERLAKE, Josephine B. History is a continuous process. 1953, 55, 337-339.

POULOS, T. H. Planning a social studies program for the deaf. 1954, 56, 443-446.

BLISH, Isabel S. Creating social awareness through social studies. 1959, 61, 366-373.

HAABY, Lawrence O. Changing social studies programs--trends, 1968, 70, 399-404.

Curriculum (Contd.)

THE VOLTA REVIEW (Contd.)

Social Studies

WOODWARD, Helen M. E. The social studies in a school for deaf children. 1968, 70, 405-409.

BEHRENS, Thomas R., and MEISEGEIER, Richard W. Social studies in the education of deaf children. 1968, 70, 410-414.

BLISH, Isabel S. The social studies: a challenge. 1968, 70, 415-418.

ANNALS OF THE DEAF

Art

CLARKE, Francis D. Mechanical drawing for the deaf. 1887, 32, 1-6.

BEATTIE, Mary B. Drawing and painting as aids to expression and development of the child. 1912, 57, 167-177.

PINTNER, Rudolf. Artistic appreciation among deaf children. 1941, 86, 218-224.

LAMPARD, Marie T. The art work of deaf children. 1960, 105, 419-423.

HAYS, David. The National Theatre of the Deaf--present and future, 1967, 112, 590-592.

DAVIS, Jackson. A survey of theatre activities in American and Canadian schools for the deaf 1965-1970. 1974, 119, 331-341.

Curriculum (Contd.)

ANNALS OF THE DEAF

Mathematics

KEEP, John R. Addition, how it may be taught. 1856, 8, 110-113.

WAIT, Selah. Method of teaching the fundamental rules of arithmetic. 1869, 14, 239-245.

STORRS, Richard S. Arithmetic for deaf-mutes. 1871, 16, 143-160.

BIRD, William L. Preparatory drill in figures. 1879, 24, 1-9.

GREENBERGER, D. Arithmetic. 1882, 27, 12-28.

WALKER, S. Tefft. The teaching of numbers. 1882, 27, 224-227.

EDDY, Jonathan H. Arithmetic in the education of the deaf. 1887, 32, 93-98.

HASKINS, C. N. Mental arithmetic. 1887, 32, 156-161.

GREENBERGER, D. Form study. 1888, 32, 234-241.

SMITH, J. L., et al. A course in arithmetic. 1888, 33, 197-199.

DENISON, James. A new arithmetical device. 1891, 36, 129-136.

JENKINS, Weston G. The teaching of arithmetic. 1892, 37, 9-14.

BOOTH, F. W. Primary arithmetic: the notation of money. 1893, 38, 1-4.

FREEMAN, Samuel M. Addition and subtraction for beginners. 1901, 46, 159-166.

STAFFORD, May M. Some possibilities of arithmetic. 1901, 46, 526-531.

REED, Katharine F. Devices for primary number work. 1905, 50, 173-177.

SOWELL, James W. Arithmetic. 1905, 50, 279-293.

KENT, Eliza. Primary arithmetic. 1906, 51, 315-320.

SENSENIG, Barton. Errors in arithmetical methods. 1906, 51, 370-375.

FULLINGTON, Angeline. Primary arithmetic. 1908, 53, 137-141.

HARVEY, A., et al. Arithmetic in the intermediate and advanced departments of the Pennsylvania institution. 1909, 54, 197-237.

Curriculum (Contd.)

ANNALS OF THE DEAF (Contd.)

Mathematics

BEMIS, Luna A. Early steps in number work for deaf children. 1916, 61, 134-136.

DEEM, Harriet L. Primary arithmetic. 1922, 67, 112-116.

O'DONNELL, Francis H. Four arithmetic formulas. 1922, 67, 117-124.

ANDREWS, Harriet E. Primary arithmetic. 1922, 67, 232-235.

SENSENIG, Barton. Practical arithmetic. 1923, 68, 287-300.

CALDWELL, Wm. A. A device for teaching numeration. 1926, 71, 268-270.

GLENN, Sallie. Some devices in arithmetic. 1928, 73, 249-251.

SMITH, James L. "Too much arithmetic?" 1934, 79, 205-209.

VERMILLION, Frances F. A key to the language of arithmetic--an aid in teaching the fundamental processes. 1936, 81, 209-211.

MOSSEL, Max N. Dealing with zeros in the minuend. 1938, 83, 218-224.

WOLACH, Marvin. Visualizing the units of measure. 1952, 97, 341-347.

NEWMAN, Lawrence. Meaningful mathematic problem work for the deaf. 1957, 102, 293-299.

KENNEDY, Eloise. Teaching beginning number work to deaf children. 1967, 112, 56-59.

HARGIS, Charles H. The grammar of the noun phrases in arithmetic instruction for deaf children. 1969, 114, 766-769.

BEHRENS, Thomas R., et al. Mathematics curriculum supported by computer assisted instruction. 1969, 114, 889-892.

Curriculum (Contd.)

ANNALS OF THE DEAF

Music and Rhythm

TURNER, W. W., and BARTLETT, D. E. Music among the deaf. 1849, 2, 1-6.

LUDLOW, Fitz H. The music essence. 1872, 17, 94-126.

MONRO, Sarah A. The piano as an aid to speech. 1901, 46, 166-169.

PORTER, Sarah H. Musical vibrations for the deaf. 1912, 57, 137-158.

FULLER, Millicent B. Rhythm. 1917, 62, 257-261.

STEVENSON, Elwood A. Musical rhythm. 1919, 64, 196-204.

FISKE, Stella A. The place that hand training plays in the education of the deaf. 1922, 67, 175-182.

THORNTON, Marjorie. An outline of rhythm work and its application to schoolroom work. 1926, 71, 361-386.

CARTER, Maud. Rhythm outline. 1931, 76, 397-402.

JAYNE, Gladys G. Rhythm and its relation to the training of the deaf. 1939, 84, 137-150.

WECKER, Karl. Music for deaf children. 1939, 84, 151-155.

GAY, Ruth C. Some values of the rhythm orchestra in schools for the deaf. 1940, 85, 351-354.

MILLS, Mary M. Voice and rhythm in the primary grades of the New Jersey School for the Deaf. 1942, 87, 331-341.

ROSENSTEIN, Joseph. Tactile perception of rhythmic patterns by normal, blind, deaf, and aphasic children. 1957, 102, 399-403.

SWAIKO, Nancy. The role and value of an eurhythmics program in a curriculum for deaf children. 1974, 119, 321-324.

Curriculum (Contd.)

ANNALS OF THE DEAF

Hygiene, Physical Education

ERD, Robert. The place of physical education in a school for the deaf. 1909, 54, 393-401.

GUEDEL, A. E. Physical training. 1914, 59, 172-180.

LEWIS, Bertha. Health education for the deaf at the elementary level. 1958, 103, 564-571.

APPLEMAN, Karen. Seattle's summer recreation program for hearing impaired children. 1974, 119, 724-726.

FITZ-GERALD, Max, and FITZ-GERALD, Della. Sex education survey of residential facilities for the deaf. 1976, 121, 480-483.

ANNALS OF THE DEAF

Reading

CAROLL, David H. Teaching deaf-mutes to read. 1875, 20, 228-229.

WHITE, Henry. Reading as a means of acquiring a good command of language. 1879, 24, 100-104.

DENISON, James. Reading for the higher classes. 1888, 33, 89-96.

ROBERTS, Linnaeus. A reading experiment. 1889, 34, 117-120.

BELL, Alexander G. Reading before writing. 1891, 36, 141-142.

SMITH, James L. Reading for the little ones. 1891, 36, 190-193.

HASENSTAB, Philip J. An instructor in reading. 1892, 37, 183-188.

ALLABOUGH, B. R. Reading as an aid to language-teaching. 1893, 38, 118-124.

STONE, Elizabeth A. Reading for the deaf. 1914, 59, 131-134.

BUELL, Edith M. Reading for the deaf. 1915, 60, 1-5.

Curriculum (Contd.)

ANNALS OF THE DEAF (Contd.)

Reading

SMITH, James M. Reading in the schoolroom. 1915, 60, 242-253.

LUCAS, Frances. Articulation and lip-reading in the advanced dept. 1916, 61, 330-332.

JONES, John W. Reading the road to language. 1918, 63, 237-249.

TAYLOR, Nellie M. Teaching the deaf to read. 1919, 64, 374-379.

NORTHROP, Helen. Reading for the deaf. 1924, 69, 401-425.

FITZGERALD, Margaret H. Silent reading. 1924, 69, 448-454.

FARQUHAR, Grover C. A study of a reading test. 1928, 73, 264-272.

RICHARDS, Edith. Flash cards for silent reading. 1930, 75, 201-203.

PATTEN, Helen T. Reading (incidental uses of reading seat work activities). 1930, 75, 196-200.

NEWLEE, C. E. Reading as a means of teaching language to the deaf. 1930, 75, 345-361.

HURST, Fannie D. On teaching reading. 1932, 77, 161-180.

HURST, Fannie D. Chart work in reading. 1932, 77, 202-205.

BERG, Lloyd E. Some oral reading problems in the education of the deaf. 1932, 77, 257-260.

BENNING, Doris B. An outline of reading for the first year. 1934, 79, 109-119.

KENDALL, Elsie P. A reading and language unit--the three bears. 1934, 79, 214-222.

PARKS, Roy G. Objectives and skills in teaching reading in schools for the deaf. 1937, 82, 425-432.

BENNING, Doris B. A unit of reading for deaf children. 1937, 82, 440-444.

KIRKLEY, James R. What should be done about reading in our schools for the deaf. 1938, 83, 197-208.

HURST, Fannie D. A reading project. 1938, 83, 338-342.

Curriculum (Contd.)

ANNALS OF THE DEAF (Contd.)

Reading

FARQUHAR, Grover C., and GOUGH, John. An experiment in controlled reading. 1940, 85, 355-361.

BRILL, Richard G. The prognosis of reading achievement of the deaf. 1941, 86, 227-241.

BRILL, Richard G. Measurement of progress in reading. 1942, 87, 135-139.

WOOD, M. W. A comparison of techniques for increasing the rate of comprehension in reading by deaf children. 1944, 89, 111-131; 182-213.

KRAFT, Dorothy G. Reading for the deaf. 1945, 90, 164-173.

PUGH, Gladys S. Teaching reading to the deaf. 1945, 90, 180-187.

ROGERS, William B. Reading and the education of the deaf. 1945, 90, 221-236.

PUGH, Gladys S. Summaries from "Appraisal of the silent reading abilities of acoustically handicapped children". 1946, 91, 331-349.

CROSBY, Laura L. Books of high interest and low vocabulary level to meet the needs of deaf students in grades seven through twelve. 1948, 93, 339-359.

HEINL, S. S., et al. Books for recreational reading of primary grades in the Illinois School for the Deaf, Jacksonville, Illinois, a library project to determine suitability of. 1951, 96, 447-466; 524-543.

STREETER, Helen M. A study of the dependent clause in primary reading of the deaf. 1956, 101, 288-297.

FITZGERALD, Margaret H. Reading--the key to progress for deaf children. 1957, 102, 404-415.

KENNEDY, Eloise. Teaching the deaf child to read. 1959, 104, 372-382.

FESSANT, John M. Application of programmed learning for deaf children to industrial arts. 1963, 108, 241-244.

Curriculum (Contd.)

ANNALS OF THE DEAF (Contd.)

Reading

SANFORD, Adrian B. The learner and the printed page--the place of graphics in a learning system. 1966, 111, 626-632.

WALTER, Jean. The reading of paragraphs. 1969, 114, 71-75.

HAMMERMEISTER, Frieda K. Reading achievement in deaf adults. 1971, 116, 25-28.

MCCARR, Dorothy. Individualized reading for junior and senior high school students. 1973, 118, 488-495.

MAXWELL, Madeline. Teaching reading as a problem-solving activity. 1974, 119, 721-723.

MCLAUGHLIN, Joseph, and ANDREWS, Jean. The reading habits of deaf adults in Baltimore. 1975, 120, 497-501.

CONLEY, Janet E. The role of idiomatic expressions in the reading of deaf children. 1976, 121, 381-385.

STARK, Bill. "Meanwhile. . .": a look at comic books at Illinois School for the Deaf. 1976, 121, 470-477.

HENDERSON, John M. Learning to read: a case study of a deaf child. 1976, 121, 502-506.

ANNALS OF THE DEAF

Science

CLARKE, F. D. Science for the deaf and dumb. 1871, 16, 97-110.

GREENBERGER, D. Object lessons in science. 1886, 31, 254-259.

DAY, Herbert E. Science teaching in schools for the deaf. 1901, 46, 183-186.

DAY, Herbert E. Nature study in schools for the deaf. 1908, 53, 113-118.

Curriculum (Contd.)

ANNALS OF THE DEAF (Contd.)

Science

FOWLER, Frances Ellis. Nature study. 1909, 54, 166-172.

CARTER, W. H. Nature study. 1916, 61, 127-132.

——————————. Suggestions for the study of nature in primary grades. 1934, 79, 255-260.

OWSLEY, Peter J. Teaching science to deaf children. 1962, 107, 339-342.

GRANT, William D., ROSENSTEIN, Joseph, KNIGHT, David L. A project to determine the feasibility of BSCS's Me Now for hearing impaired students. 1975, 120, 63-69.

ANNALS OF THE DEAF

Social Studies

JENKINS, Weston. About teaching geography. 1886, 31, 101-107.

NEWCOMBE, F. C. Introduction to the study of geography. 1886, 31, 107-110.

WHITE, Henry C. How history may be taught. 1889, 34, 185-190.

FLETCHER, Katharine. Some reasons for teaching history. 1892, 37, 177-182.

SUTTON, Estella V. History-teaching--facts or philosophy? 1895, 40, 130-137.

FLETCHER, Katharine. Text-books in history. 1897, 42, 179-198.

DRIGGS, Frank M. Geography teaching. 1897, 42, 299-316.

GOGGIN, Anne P. The cultivation of the reading habit and of a taste for history in the primary grades. 1900, 45, 441-445.

ROBINSON, Warren. History. 1903, 48, 18-22.

Curriculum (Contd.)

ANNALS OF THE DEAF (Contd.)

Social Studies

MASHBURN, Arthur G. Geography teaching. 1903, 48, 440-451.

READ, Elmer D. Geography. 1905, 50, 502-509.

REED, Katharine F. Suggestions for geography teaching. 1906, 51, 136-141.

JENKINS, Weston. The place of history study. 1907, 52, 213-223.

READ, Elmer D. Problems met in teaching history. 1908, 53, 202-207.

GOGGIN, Anne P. Teaching geography. 1912, 57, 369-379.

RHODES, Elizabeth. Illustrative charts for geography teaching. 1915, 60, 137-139.

ADAMS, Mabel E. A lesson in preparatory history in a fifth grade in a school for the deaf. 1915, 60, 273-277.

WHITCHER, Cora M. Devices used in teaching geography. 1916, 61, 408-411.

ADAMS, Mabel E. History teaching. 1920, 65, 414-424.

ERVIN, Annie M. Teaching current history. 1923, 68, 134-142.

CURTISS, Louise A. History in the grammar grades. 1928, 73, 246-248.

SMITH, Minnie E. Projects in geography--grade 4A. 1928, 73, 254-256.

READ, Elmer D. Objective tests in history. 1930, 75, 252-273.

READ, Elmer D. Subject-matter plan for teaching history. 1932, 77, 211-231.

SISTER M. CONSTANTIA. The teaching of social studies in schools for the deaf. 1934, 79, 310-314.

Deaf-Blind

THE VOLTA REVIEW

WADE, W. The deaf-blind. 1901, 3, 41-42.

DONALD, Dora. Linnie Haguewood. 1901, 3, 97-105.

FERRERI, Giulio. The development of intelligence in the case of one deprived of both sight and hearing. 1905, 7, 440-448.

FERRERI, Giulio. The possibility of the education of the blind-deaf. 1907, 9, 363-369.

CZILY, Prof. A. Conversing with the blind-deaf. 1910, 12, 77-85.

LANGE, Paul. The truth about Helen Keller. 1910, 12, 750-754.

RIEMANN, G. (Trans. by Brill, T.). The care of the blind-deaf children. 1910, 12, 766-771.

PITROIS, Yvonne. The Heurtin family. 1911, 12, 733-749.

FERRERI, Giulio. Principles for the instruction of the blind-deaf as given in the work of the Abbé Deschamps. 1913, 15, 35-37.

DELAND, Fred. Helen Keller's flag. 1914, 16, 357-360.

FEARON, J. Charlie Crane: a deaf-blind boy. 1917, 19, 83-86.

DELAND, Fred. Sarah Fuller as Helen Keller's teacher of speech. 1927, 29, 352-355.

SHAW, Janet P. Our Jess. 1927, 29, 370-374.

NEWELL, Nettie. The doubly handicapped child. 1929, 31, 257-258.

MONTAGUE, Harriet A. More about Helen Keller. 1930, 32, 53-56.

PITROIS, Yvonne. The sunbeam of the deaf-blind. 1930, 32, 181-184.

HANSEN, Anders. The first case in the world. 1930, 32, 223-228.

MONTAGUE, Harriet A. Penetrating the darkness. 1930, 32, 421-423; 425-426.

ALCORN, Sophia. Tad Chapman's demonstration. 1930, 32, 517-518.

ROCHELEAU, Corinne. The deaf-blind. 1930, 32, 518-524.

MERRY, Ralph V. Applying psychological tests to the deaf-blind. 1932, 34, 406-407.

HEIDER, Grace M. Leonard Dowdy's vocabulary. 1935, 37, 340-341; 388-389.

Deaf-Blind (Contd.)

THE VOLTA REVIEW (Contd.)

FARRAR, A. A nineteenth century educator and his interest in the deaf blind. 1937, <u>39</u>, 335-336.

MONTAGUE, Harriet A. Helen Keller's personal history, a review. 1938, <u>40</u>, 330-331; 376.

HEIDER, Grace M. Learning from the blind. 1939, <u>41</u>, 11; 51-53.

HALL, Inis B. More about Leonard Dowdy. 1939, <u>41</u>, 202-203; 243.

HALL, Inis B. Deaf-blind pupils at Perkins. 1940, <u>42</u>, 21-22; 52-53; 83-84; 116.

HALL, Inis B. The education of the blind-deaf. 1940, <u>42</u>, 681-684.

HARRIS, Lena. Meeting the challenge, the story of Jackie Coker-- deaf and blind. 1941, <u>43</u>, 24-25; 74.

BOWMAN, Dorothy L. Carol's first three years. 1945, <u>47</u>, 439-442; 472-478.

BLANKENHORN, M. D. Miracle for Angeliki. 1951, <u>53</u>, 157; 178.

MONTAGUE, Harriet A. Tad Chapman at home. 1952; <u>54</u>, 58-59; 86-88.

COHEN, Sonya S. Helen Keller visits Haifa, Israel. 1952, <u>54</u>, 377-378; 396-398.

CHAPMAN, W. C. Carrying out my plans. 1952, <u>54</u>, 382; 394.

KROHN, Emmylou. Out of the quiet shadows. 1956, <u>58</u>, 440-442.

_____. Operational deaf-blind centers. 1969, <u>71</u>, 441, 443.

_____. National Center for Deaf-Blind Youths and Adults. 1969, <u>71</u>, 505.

DANTONA, Robert. Regional centers for deaf-blind children--a new hope. 1971, <u>73</u>, 411-415.

WIEDENMAYER, Joseph. Look or listen. 1973, <u>75</u>, 89-96.

HENRY, Virginia, and LYALL, Jerry H. Ability screening and program placement for deaf-blind children and adults. 1973, <u>75</u>, 227-231.

VERNON, McCay. Overview of Usher's syndrome. 1974, <u>76</u>, 100-105.

Deaf-Blind (Contd.)

ANNALS OF THE DEAF

PORTER, Samuel. Particulars respecting James Mitchell, a person deaf, dumb and blind from birth. 1847, 1, 246-258.

BURNET, John R. The case of Laura Bridgman. 1856, 8, 159-172.

HOWE, Samuel G. Laura Bridgman and Oliver Caswell. 1875, 20, 100-110.

HALL, G. Stanley. Laura Bridgman. 1879, 24, 202-228.

FAY, E. A. Blind and deaf persons. 1887, 32, 233-236.

FULLER, Sarah. How Helen Keller learned to speak. 1892, 37, 23-30.

WILLIAMS, Job. Is Helen Keller a fraud? 1892, 37, 156-159.

SULLIVAN, Annie M. How Helen Keller acquired language. 1892, 37, 127-154.

FOX, Thomas F. Miss Helen Adams Keller's first year of college preparatory work. 1897, 42, 387-401.

ROBINSON, Stanley. The education of the deaf-blind at the New York Institution. 1900, 45, 376-383.

BARRETT, E. M. The importance of early training for the deaf blind. 1903, 48, 149-155.

MORRIS, Minnie E. The training of a congenitally deaf-blind child. 1904, 49, 167-171.

FOX, Thomas F. The education of deaf-blind children in the New York Institution for the Instruction of the Deaf and Dumb. 1904, 49, 240-251.

NORDIN, Elizabeth A. The care and instruction of the blind-deaf. 1905, 50, 125-140.

JONES, J. W. The education of the deaf-blind. 1906, 51, 359-366.

WADE, William. The senses of the blind-deaf. 1909, 54, 451-455.

KELLER, Helen. The value of the sense of smell to the blind-deaf. 1910, 55, 282-284.

BOLTON, Thaddeus L. The psychology of the deaf-blind. 1915, 60, 222-227.

BALIS, Sylvia C. They who see darkly. 1922, 67, 99-111.

Deaf-Blind (Contd.)

ANNALS OF THE DEAF (Contd.)

FRICK, Kathryne M. Shall the deaf-blind be educated in residential schools for the deaf? 1931, 76, 496-497.

NEUSCHUTZ, Louise I. Proposed measures for the relief of the deaf-blind. 1933, 78, 427-430.

FARRELL, Gabriel. Extension of the work of Perkins Institution. 1935, 80, 157-159.

FISH, Anna G. Laura Bridgman. 1937, 82, 402-405.

_____. A study of the proceedings of the Convention of the American Instructors of the Deaf, 1850-1949: deaf-blind. 1950, 95, 303-306.

DINSMORE, Annette B. National approach to the education of deaf-blind children. 1953, 98, 418-430.

TWEEDIE, David. Observing the communication behavior of deaf-blind children. 1974, 119, 342-347.

BLEA, William. Deaf/blind news. 1976, 121, 458-463.

Deaf Youth and Adults

THE VOLTA REVIEW

ROGERS, Francis L. Teachers and night schools for the adult deaf. 1924, 26, 509-511.

BARROWS, Albert L. Work of the National Research Council on Problems of the Deaf. 1928, 30, 531-536.

THOMPSON, Richard. Ups and downs in the hearing world. 1949, 51, 5-6; 54.

_____. The Clarke School Alumni. 1952, 54, 363-369; 402.

SIMON, Arthur B. Wanted: a program for the adult deaf. 1956, 58, 256.

Deaf Youth and Adults (Contd.)

THE VOLTA REVIEW (Contd.)

JUSTMAN, Joseph, MOSKOWITZ, Sue. Graduates of P.S. #47--a half century report. 1965, 67, 275-280.

WAHLER, John J. An odyssey in deafness. 1966, 68, 154-158.

SIMON, Arthur B. The deaf college student in 1984. 1966, 68, 289-292.

_____. Deaf graduates of schools for the hearing. 1967, 69, 15-35; 1969, 71, 34-63; 1971, 73, 282-319.

MCARTHUR, Linda. Learning to be self-sufficient. 1967, 69, 259-261.

_____. A deaf man's experiences in a hearing world. 1967, 69, 652-655.

ELLIOTT, Holly. How to succeed in college without really hearing. 1970, 72, 157-160.

KISOR, Henry. A minority of one. 1971, 73, 19-22.

KRAMER, Morton C., and GUERTIN, Ralph, Ph.D. Portrait of an oral deaf adult. 1973, 75, 216-219.

SIMON, Arthur B. Ten years of ODAS in retrospect. 1974, 76, 274-279.

BLADON, Matthew. The vital link. 1974, 76, 374-378.

HARRIS, Mark. Walking toward a goal. 1975, 77, 312-317.

ANNALS OF THE DEAF

FALBERG, R. An adventure into adult education of the deaf. 1962, 107, 329-338.

LEVINE, Edna S., and SUSSMAN, A. (eds.). Institute of Deaf Professional Persons. 1968, 113, 42-87.

BLOCK, Samuel A. Problems of deaf professional persons. 1968, 113, 60-69.

Deaf Youth and Adults (Contd.)

ANNALS OF THE DEAF (Contd.)

WILLIAMS, Boyce R. Role and responsibilities of deaf professional persons. 1968, 113, 70-72.

SANDERSON, Robert G. Carrying out leadership influences and responsibilities. 1968, 113, 73-76.

SUSSMAN, Allen E., and BURKE, Douglas J. N. Summary--problems of deaf professional persons with the hearing community. 1968, 113, 77-87.

PANARA, Robert F. The deaf writer in America from colonial times to 1970. 1970, 115, Part I, 509-513; Part II, 673-679.

JACOBS, Leo. The community of the adult deaf. 1974, 119, 40-46.

HENDERSON, Rance. Community education and the North Carolina School for the Deaf. 1974, 119, 727-728.

JOHNSON, Donald D. Communication characteristics of a young deaf adult population: techniques for evaluating their communication skills. 1976, 121, 409-424.

Early Detection/Diagnosis

THE VOLTA REVIEW

REINHARDT, Anna C. The early recognition of deafness. 1920, 22, 74-77.

GOLDSTEIN, Robert. Detection and assessment of auditory disorders in children less than three years old, a critical review. 1955, 57, 215-219.

MCGROSKEY, Robert L., and BELL, Marian M. An annotated bibliography of publications on testing the hearing of infants. 1965, 67, 548-558.

NOBER, E. Harris. Diagnosis and meaning of deafness. 1966, 68, 482-490.

Early Detection/Diagnosis (Contd.)

THE VOLTA REVIEW (Contd.)

FERDINAND, Oldrich. Causes of late recognition of deafness in children. 1966, 68, 547-551.

JOHNSON, E. W. Let's look at the child not the audiogram. 1967, 69, 306-310.

FRISINA, Robert. Diagnostic evaluation and recommendation for placement. 1967, 69, 436-442.

DOWNS, Marion P. Identification and training of the deaf child-- birth to one year. 1968, 70, 154-158.

GOODHILL, Victor. Deafness research: where are we? 1968, 70, 620-629.

MCCROSKEY, Robert L., and CORY, Martha W. An annotated bibliography of publications on testing the hearing of infants, II. 1969, 71, 27-32.

ASBED, Ruth-Alice, et al. Early case finding of children with communication problems: report of a community screening program. 1970, 72, 23-49.

LLOYD, Lyle L., and DAHLE, Arthur J. Detection and diagnosis of a hearing impairment in the child. 1976, 78, 12-22 (monograph).

LEVIN, Susan, and ERBER, Norman P. A vision screening program for deaf children. 1976, 78, 90-99.

BECKER, Sheila. Initial concern and action in the detection and diagnosis of a hearing impairment in the child. 1976, 78, 105-115.

ANNALS OF THE DEAF

GOLDSTEIN, Robert. Differential classification of disorders of communication in children. 1958, 103, 215-223.

POLLARD, Gerald, and NEUMAUR, Richard. Vision characteristics of deaf students. 1974, 119, 740-745.

Education

THE VOLTA REVIEW

PERRY, Charles S. Training period of our deaf as compared with our hearing youth. 1899, 1, 150-157.

JENKINS, Weston. Use and abuse of memory in education. 1900, 2, 6-15.

BINGHAM, Katherine T. All along the line. 1900, 2, 20-29.

TAYLOR, Harris. The male teacher. 1900, 2, 363-366.

BELL, Alexander G. The International Congress. 1900, 2, 427-437.

FERRERI, Giulio C. Some didactic questions. 1903, 5, 254-263.

FERRERI, Giulio C. Teachers and physicians. 1903, 5, 423-430.

HOFFMAN, Hugo. The division of pupils in the instruction of the deaf according to their capacity. 1904, 6, 35-40.

_____. The Annals statistics. 1904, 6, 93-95.

DANGER, O. The education of the deaf for life in human society. 1904, 6, 101-108.

MCCOWEN, Mary. Dramatization as a factor in education. 1904, 6, 109-115.

CROUTER, A. L. Examinations, promotions and grading. 1905, 7, 107-120.

WINNIE, A. J. What a study of the deaf child will do for the hearing child. 1905, 7, 137-144.

DELAND, Fred. The real romance of the telephone, or why deaf children need no longer be dumb. 1905, 7, 306-326; 389-399; 1906, 8, 1-27; 120-135; 205-222; 329-334; 406-427; 1907, 9, 324-335; 401-419; 505-520; 1908, 10, 1-35; 123-137; 233-239; 343-348; 449-454; 1909, 11, 1-12.

REINHARDT, Anna C. What has been done with one deaf child in his own home. 1906, 8, 36-39.

ARCHER, T. V. The summer school at Northampton. 1906, 8, 40-46.

_____. The deaf before and after attendance at school. 1906, 8, 243-248.

Education (Contd.)

THE VOLTA REVIEW (Contd.)

BELL, Alexander G. Special report upon the deaf, based on the returns of the twelfth census. 1906, 8, 351-370; 442-469; 1907, 9, 336-356; 427-444; 533-545; 1908, 10, 36-47; 138-147; 240-255; 349-364; 455-464.

DEVRIES, J. G. The fear of the written word. 1908, 10, 174-185.

_____. The education of the deaf. 1910, 12, 180-181.

DAVIDSON, S. G. Pessimism of parents and teachers. 1910, 12, 363-366.

LOVE, J. K. Education of the very young deaf child. 1910, 12, 602-603.

FULLINGTON, Angeline B. Some principles of teaching. 1911, 12, 622-625.

_____. Analysis of the Annals statistics (pupils and teachers in American schools for the deaf, 1893 through 1910). 1911, 12, 719-720.

BELL, Alexander G. Simple experiments. 1912, 14, 103-106.

STORY, Arthur J. The approach to the normal. 1913, 15, 111-116.

LEONARD, Eleanor C. "When?" and "where?" in the education of the deaf child. 1913, 15, 180-182.

WRIGHT, John D. Extracts from report submitted to the Board of Education of Massachusetts. 1913, 15, 183-194.

MANNING, Clarence A. School hours: academical and industrial. 1913, 15, 245-250.

DRIGGS, Frank M. Curriculum and texts. 1913, 15, 288-293.

WRIGHT, John D. The disadvantages of private instruction in the home. 1913, 15, 352-356.

RITTENHOUSE, Marion F. Experimental teaching. 1913, 15, 361-365.

DELAND, Fred. The Volta Bureau. 1913, 14, 605-621.

REED, Katherine F. The teacher's relation with the parents of deaf children. 1913, 14, 634-636.

HAYCOCK, George S. The early education of young deaf children. 1914, 16, 33-43.

Education (Contd.)

THE VOLTA REVIEW (Contd.)

ARBAUGH, Laura L. Training the deaf child. 1914, 16, 687-689.

WRIGHT, John D. Are the taxpayers getting what they pay for? 1915, 17, 73-75.

STORY, Arthur J. Analysis and synthesis in teaching methods. 1915, 17, 95-96.

ROBERTS, Emma. Training the deaf child. 1915, 17, 305-311.

HILLIARD, Ethel M. Practical demonstration with pupils of Central Institute for the Deaf: St. Louis. 1915, 17, 305-311.

WRIGHT, John D. The dual system eventually: why not now? 1915, 17, 369-370; 387-388.

FAY, Edward A. Progress in the education of the deaf. 1916, 18, 71-76.

BELL, Alexander G. Auto-education continued in the primary school. 1916, 18, 135-142.

ROE, W. Carey. The inquisitive habit. 1916, 18, 161-165.

NUMBERS, F. C. Objects of study. 1916, 18, 180-182.

TILLINGHAST, Edward S. The drift of opinion as to pure oral departments in combined system schools. 1917, 19, 1-3.

WRIGHT, John D. A fair chance for every deaf child. 1917, 19, 3-9.

DELAND, Fred. The Abbé de l'Epée. 1917, 19, 40-45.

HILL, A. C. The school journal as a factor in the education of the deaf. 1917, 19, 190-192.

MACLOINGSIGH, Peadar. Teaching deaf children. 1917, 19, 231-233.

KEARNS, C. W., et al. Statements by experienced teachers. 1917, 19, 319-329.

BARNES, F. G. Talks to young teachers. 1917, 19, 367-370.

WRIGHT, John D. A common platform on which all can stand. 1917, 19, 452-455.

HARMAN, Augusta. A vacation pupil. 1917, 19, 698-700.

HILL, A. C. From the notebook of an inspector. 1918, 20, 223-227; 315-316; 397-401.

Education (Contd.)

THE VOLTA REVIEW (Contd.)

WRIGHT, John D. Proper teaching of deaf children. 1918, 20, 473-475.

BICKLEY, Celia. Inasmuch. 1918, 20, 624-626.

SYLVESTER, Elfrieda. Betty thinks. 1918, 20, 675-679.

NEWLEE, Clara E. About compulsory education for deaf children. 1919, 21, 1-3.

MCDOWELL, Evelyn. A charming southern school. 1919, 21, 231-236.

DELAND, Fred. Working in behalf of deaf children. (or how, when, and why the American Association to Promote the Teaching of Speech to the Deaf was organized). 1919, 21, 523-530; 581-585; 663-669; 701-702.

GOLDSTEIN, M. A. The deaf child. 1920, 22, 347-354.

DELAND, Fred. Pedro Ponce De Leon (born, 1520). Juan Pablo Bonet (author, 1620). 1920, 22, 391-421.

HALL, Percival. Retrospect and prospect. 1920, 22, 546-550.

PINTNER, Rudolf. Standardization of schools for the deaf. 1920, 22, 662-669.

GRUVER, Elbert A. Training of backward deaf children. 1920, 22, 687-699.

STEED, Lyman. The education of the deaf. 1921, 23, 18-20; 25-29.

BOOTH, Frank W. The education of the deaf. 1921, 23, 25-29.

PANCONCELLI-CALZIA, G. What experimental phonetics has accomplished for the instruction of the hard of hearing and the deaf. 1921, 23, 417-422.

NEVILE, Miss B. Our greatest need in the schools. 1922, 24, 105-108.

LEONARD, Myrtle H. The deaf child and something of his early training. 1922, 24, 150-152.

COOPER, Helen M. The deafened at play. 1923, 25, 299-303; 378-381; 467-470; 530-532; 1924, 26, 27-30.

_____. Compulsory education of the deaf. 1924, 26, 77-80.

Education (Contd.)

THE VOLTA REVIEW (Contd.)

STURDIVANT, Elizabeth. The deaf child's heritage. 1925, 27, 385-387.

BETTERLY, E. J. Ye that are deaf. 1925, 27, 447-449.

MADISON, J. L. The Iowa convention. 1925, 27, 483-492.

YALE, Caroline A. Special training for the deaf child: when shall it begin? when shall it end? 1926, 28, 139-142.

HURD, Anna C. Home life in the school, an important factor in the education of the deaf child. 1926, 28, 243-246.

FARRAR, A. The deaf in medieval times. 1926, 28, 389-391.

PALEN, Imogen B. The grade teacher and the deafened child. 1926, 28, 437-440.

BREITWIESER, J. V. The conservation of energy in the training of the deaf. 1926, 28, 642-648.

DUNLAP, Mary M. Two helpful projects. 1927, 29, 98-100.

REINHARDT, Anna C. Progressive education for the deaf. 1927, 29, 204-206.

ARBAUGH, Laura L. Making drill work pleasant. 1928, 30, 284-290.

TILLINGHAST, Edward S. School home ideals. 1928, 30, 355; 360; 472-477; 1929, 31, 12-15.

BUELL, Edith M. Which subjects should receive special emphasis? 1928, 30, 577-579.

DANIEL, Elizabeth. Work and play in our junior classes. 1928, 30, 802-806.

KINSLEY, Grace. Beginning study periods. 1929, 31, 250-251.

CLAYTON, Nellie C. Seat work as a normalizing agent for deaf children. 1929, 31, 728-730.

HAMMER, Helen L. A project in community life, an opportunity for the teacher of the deaf. 1930, 32, 217-220.

EGAN, Ann R. We learn by doing. 1930, 32, 409-411.

BLAIR, Mary. Projects in first and second grades. 1932, 34, 59; 85.

Education (Contd.)

THE VOLTA REVIEW (Contd.)

MONTAGUE, Harriet. The education of the deaf in the United States. 1933, 35, 338-342.

FOSS, Bertha M. Current events in Rhode Island. 1933, 35, 372-374.

WALL, Alice P. Projects for the special class. 1933, 35, 418-420.

MCMANAWAY, Howard M. New objectives in the education of the deaf. 1934, 36, 5-6.

JOINER, Enfield. Shall we or shall we not? (rewards). 1934, 36, 73-74.

_____. Prepared by research dept. of Clarke School. Abstracts of scientific studies (Clarke). 1934, 36, 408-411; 474-475; 506; 663-665; 1935, 37, 25; 56-57; 289; 320-322; 412-413; 441; 529; 553.

DUNLAP, Mary M. Activities with a special group. 1935, 37, 461-462; 497.

EVANS, Mildred. Common sense in modernization. 1935, 37, 510-511; 558-559.

EARHART, E. K., MCCAIN, M., et al. New things we have undertaken. 1935, 37, 519-520; 566-568; 586-587; 623; 655-656; 708-709.

NUMBERS, Mary E. Broader horizons. 1936, 38, 629-632; 684.

BERRY, Gordon. Deafness in the United States, a statistical review. 1938, 40, 69-71; 120.

LEE, John J. A new challenge in education. 1938, 40, 261-263; 309-312.

GRUVER, Elbert A. Stands and trends in the education of the deaf. 1938, 40, 621-626.

BODYCOMB, Margaret, et al. Can children who enter school without speech and apparently without hearing ever leave school "hard of hearing" rather than "deaf"? 1938, 40, 729-740.

PINTNER, Rudolf. Report of Clarke School research. 1940, 42, 767-768; 812.

WHILDIN, Olive A. Modern education of the deaf. 1942, 44, 618-620.

INGRAM, Christine P. Trends in special education. 1944, 46, 197-199; 252-254.

Education (Contd.)

THE VOLTA REVIEW (Contd.)

O'CONNOR, Clarence D. Some modern trends in the education of the deaf. 1945, 47, 197-200; 248-250.

GROHT, Mildred. Hearing children and deaf children: helping the two groups to understand each other. 1945, 47, 204-205; 236.

NELSON, Boyd E. The classroom tells about the teacher. 1945, 47, 557-558.

GUTHRIE, Virginia S. Creative and expressive activities for young deaf children. 1945, 47, 679-682; 724-728; 1946, 48, 14-17; 54-58.

NELSON, Boyd E. Habits in handwriting. 1947, 49, 72; 106.

PUGH, Bessie. Twentieth century trends in the education of the deaf. 1947, 49, 261-262; 300-302.

O'CONNOR, Clarence D. How our schools can solve some of today's problems. 1948, 50, 399-402.

DEWAR, Dorothy G. Educating deaf children for democracy. 1949, 51, 157-158.

SIMON, Arthur B. An answer to a teacher of the deaf. 1950, 52, 157-159; 196-198.

SILVERMAN, S. Richard (moderator). Education of the deaf today-- an assessment and a look into the future. 1953, 55, 187-207.

O'CONNOR, Clarence D. What is "special" about the education of the deaf? 1954, 56, 291-292; 318.

KEASTER, Jacqueline. How shall the deaf child be educated? 1954, 56, 293-297.

STELLE, Roy M. (moderator, panel discussion). Where should the deaf child be educated? 1954, 56, 297-313.

O'CONNOR, Clarence D. Children with impaired hearing. 1954, 56, 433-439.

FUSFELD, Irving S. The academic program of schools for the deaf. 1955, 57, 63-70.

GRUVER, Margaret H. Educating the profoundly deaf child. 1955, 57, 243-247.

REED, Nell D. They are prepared. 1955, 57, 247-250.

Education (Contd.)

THE VOLTA REVIEW (Contd.)

MURPHY, Albert T. The educational needs of the acoustically handicapped. 1955, 57, 301-304.

_____. Slow learning deaf children can learn. 1956, 58, 101-102.

STRENG, Alice. Curriculum in schools for the deaf. 1957, 59, 291-296.

STAHLEM, Evelyn M. Major problems in the instruction of the deaf. 1958, 60, 248-251; 279.

MILLER, June B. Academic achievement. 1958, 60, 302-304.

CONNOR, Leo E. Diagnostic teaching--the teacher's new role. 1959, 61, 311-315.

CHAMBERLAIN, Naomi H. A screening outline for determining group readiness. 1959, 61, 455-457; 476.

JOLLY, Faith. Educating the deaf and hard of hearing in our 50th state. 1960, 62, 158-160.

SISTER MARY WALTER. Individual instructional seatwork. 1960, 62, 162-165.

GOLDBERG, Herman R. Administering curriculum change. 1960, 62, 378-383.

SIMON, Arthur B. Helping your deaf child grow up--let him experiment and explore. 1961, 63, 35-39.

JONES, Kate H. Communication skills. 1961, 63, 72-77; 94.

CRUM, Carole. The normality of deaf children. 1961, 63, 231-232; 249.

SISTER M. HENRIELLA. The slow-learning deaf child. 1961, 63, 380-384; 444-448.

WILSON, D. K. The hearing team. 1962, 64, 22-25.

HOROWITZ, Leola S., and REES, Norma S. Attitudes and information about deafness. 1962, 64, 180-189.

HARDY, William G. Human communication--ordered and disordered. 1962, 64, 354-362.

WITHROW, Frank B. A special education program in a state residential school for the deaf. 1962, 64, 431-433.

Education (Contd.)

THE VOLTA REVIEW (Contd.)

RICHARDSON, Paul C. Developing natural time expressions. 1962, 64, 543-545; 574.

DEHAVEN, Mabel. Our mail: a visit to the post office. 1962, 64, 595-598.

LESHIN, George J., and STAHLECKER, Lotar V. Academic expectancies of slow-learning deaf children. 1962, 64, 599-602.

HARRELL, Hattie. The education of the deaf in Oregon. 1963, 65, 349-350.

CONNOR, Leo E. Research in the education of the deaf in the United States. 1963, 65, 523-534.

_____. Council on Education of the Deaf, Indianapolis, Ind. Minutes of the annual meeting. 1964, 66, 213-216.

OWSLEY, Peter J. Issues in the education of the deaf. 1964, 66, 308-311.

O'CONNOR, Clarence D. The role of the deaf academic classroom teacher. 1964, 66, 397-398.

SCHUNHOFF, Hugo F. Comprehensive programming to meet today's needs for all deaf children. 1964, 66, 410-414.

PECK, B. J. The residential school community. 1964, 66, 425-429.

JONES, Christina C. Curriculum controls. 1964, 66, 431-434.

MILLER, Reid C. Adequate programming on a junior and senior high school level. 1964, 66, 439-445.

QUICK, Marion A. Development and presentation of classroom observations; 1964, 66, 449-452.

MANGAN, Kenneth R. Six weeks is not enough. 1964, 66, 452-455.

KOPP, Harriet G. Elementary school subjects in the curriculum for the deaf. 1964, 66, 474-480.

LANE, Helen S. Research and its application to the classroom. 1964, 66, 480-490.

STOLP, Lauren E. A curriculum for the slow-learning deaf child. 1964, 66, 494-498.

WARNER, Larae. Community living as a basis of a curriculum. 1964, 66, 499-503.

Education (Contd.)

THE VOLTA REVIEW (Contd.)

WASELL, Irene T. Discipline in the classroom--a positive factor. 1964, 66, 514-517.

RUSHFORD, Georgina. Glossary of terms relating to children with hearing problems. 1964, 66, 750-753.

CONNOR, Leo E. Secondary education of deaf children. 1965, 67, 126-132; 165.

_____. Education of the deaf in the United States. The advisory committee's report. 1965, 67, 345-351.

KEASTER, Jacqueline. Educational recommendations. 1965, 67, 545-547; 589.

MILLER, June B. Educational assessment. 1965, 67, 676-680; 701.

DUFFY, John K. /i/t/a and the hearing impaired child. 1966, 68, 150-153.

_____. Education of the deaf in the United States: the review and recommendations. 1966, 68, 210-213.

DALE, D. M. C. Units for deaf children. 1966, 68, 496-499.

LORENE, SISTER JAMES. "Cook book" compositions. 1966, 68, 506-512.

GRAY, Virginia Q. Curriculum for older low-achieving hearing impaired students. 1966, 68, 634-638.

STRENG, Alice H. The swing of the pendulum. 1967, 69, 94-101.

WAITE, Helen E. 100 years of the conquest of silence. 1967, 69, 118-126.

GOLDSTEIN, Leonore. Great oaks from little acorns grow. 1967, 69, 148-154.

KOPP, Harriet G. Curriculum as a process. 1968, 70, 376-378.

ROSENSTEIN, Joseph, and MCGEE, Donald I. Curriculum, learning theory, and instruction. 1968, 70, 440-446.

GRIFFING, Barry L. Supervision of instruction: guiding innovation and change in instruction for deaf children. 1968, 70, 678-684.

ROSENSTEIN, Joseph. Curriculum and cognition. 1971, 73, 481-496.

NORTHCOTT, Winifred H. Tutoring a hearing impaired student in the elementary grades. 1972, 74, 432-435.

Education (Contd.)

THE VOLTA REVIEW (Contd.)

BERNSTEIN, H. William. Special approaches in learning processes for the deaf. 1974, <u>76</u>, 42-51.

MUIR, Priscilla Pittenger. "Deaf education." 1974, <u>76</u>, 88-92.

BALDWIN, Richard L. Characteristics of quality programs for hearing impaired children. 1975, <u>77</u>, 436-439.

BOSCH, Bart. A letter to his former schoolmates. 1976, <u>78</u>, 44-46.

CRAIG, William N. Curriculum: its perspectives and prospects. 1976, <u>78</u>, 52-59 (monography).

BRUCE, Wallace T. Trends in education. 1976, <u>78</u>, 318-323.

ANNALS OF THE DEAF

WOODRUFF, Lucius H. Primary instruction of the deaf and dumb. 1848, <u>1</u>, 46-55.

RAY, Luzerne. Historical sketch of the instruction of the deaf & dumb before the time of De l'Epée. 1848, <u>1</u>, 197-208.

AYRES, J. A. A complete education for the deaf and dumb. 1849, <u>2</u>, 24-32.

TURNER, W. W. Courses of instruction. 1849, <u>2</u>, 97-105; 217-232.

PEET, Harvey P. Memoir on the origin & early history of the art of instructing the deaf and dumb. 1851, <u>3</u>, 129-160.

PEET, Edward. Biographical sketch of Dr. Itard. 1853, <u>5</u>, 110-124.

TALBOT, Benjamin. Responsibility of the teacher of the deaf and dumb. 1856, <u>8</u>, 82-93.

DALGARNO, Geo. Dalgarno's Didascalocophys (Didascalocophys, or the deaf and dumb man's tutor, reprinted from the 1680 edition). 1857, <u>9</u>, 14-64.

GREEN, Samuel A. The earliest advocate of the education of the deaf-mutes. 1861, <u>13</u>, 1-8.

GALLAUDET, Edward M. The American system, its defects and their remedies. 1861, <u>13</u>, 147-170.

Education (Contd.)

ANNALS OF THE DEAF (Contd.)

STONE, Collins. The history and methods of deaf-mute instruction. 1869, 14, 95-121.

LATHAM, W. H. Difficulties in deaf-mute instruction. 1870, 15, 104-111.

NOYES, J. L. Compulsory education as applied to deaf-mutes. 1870, 15, 216-223.

PEET, Isaac L. A practical view of deaf-mute instruction. 1871, 16, 69-97.

FAY, G. O. The methods of deaf-mute education. 1873, 18, 13-26.

VAISSE, Leon. Practical suggestions relating to the instruction of the deaf and dumb. 1874, 19, 10-20.

STORRS, Richard S. Methods of deaf-mute instruction. 1880, 25, 105-119; 233-250; 1881, 26, 141-160.

BELL, Alexander G. Fallacies concerning the deaf. 1884, 29, 32-60.

WING, George. The associative feature in the education of the deaf. 1886, 31, 22-35.

GALLAUDET, Edward M. History of the education of the deaf in the United States. 1886, 31, 130-147.

KIESEL, Theodore A. How to start the deaf child. 1887, 32, 6-10.

KIESEL, Theodore A. The early stages in the education of the deaf. 1891, 36, 211-221.

LANDIS, Kate S. Six months with a beginning class. 1892, 37, 189-198.

CLARKE, Francis D. The first year's work. 1894, 39, 209-225; 1895, 40, 14-30; 137-148; The second year's work. 1896, 41, 129-146; 242-251; 274-278; The third year's work. 1897, 42, 1-16; 75-83; 143-152; The fourth year's work. 1897, 42, 224-237; 317-325; 371-386; The fifth year's work. 1898, 43, 309-315; 360-380; 1899, 44, 7-23.

HURD, Anna C. Busy work for primary classes. 1896, 41, 88-97.

TILLINGHAST, E. S. Correlation of instruction and environment. 1898, 43, 22-32; 220-228.

Education (Contd.)

ANNALS OF THE DEAF (Contd.)

_____. The twelfth census of the deaf of the United States, 1900. 1906, 51, 288-296; 487-499; 1907, 52, 13-27; 158-167; 245-254; 1908, 53, 159-172.

BRECKINRIDGE, Mary S. Useful devices for a primary class. 1902, 47, 143-146.

SMITH, James L. Physical characteristics of pupils. 1902, 47, 301-323; 1903, 48, 1-18.

HANSON, Olof. Comparative statistics of methods of educating the deaf in the United States. 1902, 47, 349-357.

YEARSLEY, Macleod. The education of the deaf: its present state, with suggestions as to its future modifications and development. 1911, 56, 284-323; 484-499; 1912, 57, 23-31.

COBB, Jennie L. Schoolroom efficiency. 1913, 58, 207-213.

CROUTER, A. L. The vital point in our work and certain ways to reach it. 1914, 59, 6-14.

TAYLOR, Mrs. La Verne. Some problems confronting a teacher during the first few years in a school for the deaf, and how they may be met. 1914, 59, 15-19.

MORRIS, M. E. The conservation of material in the school. 1914, 59, 118-131.

SHERIDAN, Laura C. Schoolroom problems. 1914, 59, 205-214.

BALIS, Sylvia C. The deadness of education. 1914, 59, 253-259.

GALLAUDET, Edward M. The pre-natal history of the college. 1914, 59, 281-285.

SMITH, James L. Making education more practical. 1914, 59, 425-442.

WILLIAMS, Katherine. The correlation of all school work. 1914, 59, 461-471.

AVERY, Elizabeth B. Calling up visual memories to be used in educating the deaf. 1916, 61, 117-123.

HOWARD, Caroline M. The assigning of lessons. 1916, 61, 168-171.

DAVIS, W. M. Interest and attention. 1916, 61, 205-212.

THOLLON, B. The organization of schoolroom work. 1916, 61, 255-264; 434-443; 1917, 62, 130-134.

Education (Contd.)

ANNALS OF THE DEAF (Contd.)

THOLLON, B. Let us make haste. 1917, 62, 199-208.

LONG, J. Schuyler. Our aim in teaching the deaf. 1917, 62, 413-425.

JONES, John W. One hundred years of history in the education of the deaf in America and its present status. 1918, 63, 1-47.

WRIGHT, John D. Working suggestions. 1918, 63, 324-342.

GEMMILL, W. H. The state: its relation and obligations to the deaf child (Iowa). 1919, 64, 289-297.

FAY, Helen. Classroom suggestions. 1919, 64, 421-428.

KENNER, Marcus L. Preliminary education of deaf children. 1920, 65, 447-451.

FUSFELD, Irving S. Is the male teacher becoming an extinct species? 1921, 66, 21-32.

HOWSON, James W. Motivation in schools for the deaf. 1922, 67, 125-143.

BLATTNER, J. W. Problems of the deaf. 1925, 70, 130-139.

BRILL, Tobias. An outline for study for intermediate and advanced grades. 1925, 70, 140-163; 254-267; 1926, 71, 227-248; 419-430; 72, 437-445.

WRIGHT, John D. The fundamental principles that must underlie the successful education of the deaf. 1926, 71, 142-146.

PATTERSON, Robert. The romance of the education of the deaf. 1926, 71, 177-185.

GAULT, R. H. The use of the sense of touch. 1928, 73, 134-146.

HALL, Percival. Educational problems of the deaf. 1928, 73, 163-168

MCMANAWAY, Howard M. Recent educational advancements and our reactions to them. 1929, 74, 180-192.

DRIGGS, Frank M. Progress in the education of the deaf. 1929, 74, 351-373.

PATERSON, Donald G. Problems in the education of the deaf. 1929, 74, 373-385.

ASKEW, Louise M. Interesting slow pupils. 1930, 75, 2-5.

Education (Contd.)

ANNALS OF THE DEAF (Contd.)

BURNS, Margaret A. Are we so very different? 1932, 77, 315-321.

ELLIOTT, Ida D. Educational problems. 1933, 78, 96-100.

FUSFELD, Irving S. Dr. Goldstein's "Problems of the Deaf." 1933, 78, 352-358.

MOORE, L. M., and YALE, Caroline A. Pioneer and builder. 1934, 79, 189-196.

AURELL, Ernest. A new era in the history of the education of the deaf. 1934, 79, 223-230.

DEAN, Louise E. Experiments in the academic education of adolescent deaf pupils. 1934, 79, 292-305.

TILLINGHAST, Hilda. Progressive education in schools for the deaf. 1934, 79, 369-376.

WALKER, Isabelle, et al. The federal survey of the deaf and hard of hearing. 1935, 80, 116-125; 126-142; 200-242; 342-366; 295-407.

BRILL, Tobias. A guide to the literature on the deaf--particularly the education of the deaf. 1936, 81, 100-112.

ELLIOTT, A. Edwina. Teaching time relations to deaf children. 1937, 82, 168-175.

MORSH, Joseph E. A comparative study of deaf and hearing students. 1937, 82, 223-233.

_____. Project No. 6065, W.P.A.; A special report of retardation of children with impaired hearing in the N.Y.C. schools. 1937, 82, 234-243.

DIVINE, L. R. Revised curriculum, as compiled for the Southern Conference of Executives of Schools for the Deaf. 1938, 83, 103-113; 235-242; 1939, 84, 260-276; 432-444.

PINTNER, Rudolf. Ever-widening fields of research. 1938, 83, 225-234.

LARUE, Mary S. For variety in drill. 1938, 83, 367-371.

WILLIAMS, Boyce R. Making those leisure time hours count. 1939, 84, 377-382.

GRIFFING, W. T. The slow pupil. 1939, 84, 383-386.

ANDERSON, Tom L. Fair consideration for the profoundly deaf pupil. 1941, 86, 159-165.

Education (Contd.)

ANNALS OF THE DEAF (Contd.)

ZECKEL, Adolf. Research possibilities with the deaf. 1942, 87, 173-191.

SILVERMAN, S. Richard. Child-accounting in the administration of pupil personnel in public residential schools for the deaf. 1943, 88, 220-240.

RANKIN, C. E. The education of a child handicapped by a loss of hearing. 1945, 90, 276-283.

HIGGINS, F. C. The education of the deaf--the book mart. 1947, 92, 151-168; 1950, 95, 315-349.

DOCTOR, Powrie V., et al. The American Annals of the Deaf, 1847-1947; 1974, 92, 367-449.

KERR, M. M. Research in the education of the deaf. 1948, 93, 185-193.

JOHNSON, Elizabeth H. The ability of pupils in a school for the deaf to understand various methods of communication. 1948, 93, 194-213; 258-314.

COX, Ian. Deafness in young children. 1948, 93, 330-332.

FAUTH, Bette L., and WARREN, W. Methods of instruction. 1951, 96, 301-319.

MILLER, June. Hearing and speech program at the University of Kansas Medical Center. 1951, 96, 353-362.

DOCTOR, Powrie V. A guide to literature in journals, proceedings, indexes and abstracts on the education and welfare of the deaf. 1951, 96, 432-446.

MACKIE, Romaine P. The school building and the child with impaired hearing. 1951, 96, 494-501.

MYKLEBUST, Helmer R., and BRUTTEN, Milton. A survey of the research needs in the education of the deaf. 1951, 96, 512-523.

POULOS, Thomas H. Is our teaching meaningful? 1953, 98, 251-256.

DOZIER, J. D., and GETZ, S. B. Problems involved in the placement of a deaf Puerto Rican child in an educational environment in the United States. 1953, 98, 260-267.

QUIGLEY, Howard M., and ELSTAD, Leonard M. Educational problems of the deaf. 1953, 98, 431-476.

Education (Contd.)

ANNALS OF THE DEAF (Contd.)

TEMPLIN, Mildred C. A qualitative analysis of explanations of physical casualty. 1954, 99, Part I, 252-269; Part II, 351-362.

HARRIS, Nathan P. Some aspects of school placement of young deaf children. 1954, 99, 293-302.

BOATNER, Maxine T. The Washington life of Edward Miner Gallaudet. 1955, 100, 313-318.

TAYLOR, Sam D. A plea for the activity method of education. 1956, 101, 254-257.

WORTHINGTON, Anna M. Applying communication theory to education of the deaf. 1956, 101, 280-287.

PITTINGER, Priscilla. New approaches to teaching the young deaf children. 1956, 101, 340-348.

BLAIR, Francis X. A study of the visual memory of deaf and hearing children. 1957, 102, 254-263.

BINDON, D. Personality characteristics of rubella deaf children: implications for teaching of the deaf in general. 1957, 102, 264-270.

ELSTAD, Leonard M. Historical background of types of schools and methods of communication. 1958, 103, 300-308.

GREENMUN, Robert M. Society's attitudes and popular conceptions concerning the deaf. 1958, 103, 372-377.

GOETZINGER, C. P., and ROUSEY, C. L. Educational achievement of deaf children. 1959, 104, 221-231.

KENT, Margaret. Administrative procedures concerning admission of new students to residential schools for the deaf. 1959, 104, 271-276.

DOCTOR, Powrie, V. Deafness in the twentieth century. 1959, 104, 330-334.

FALCONER, G. A. A mechanical device for teaching sight vocabulary to young deaf children. 1961, 106, 251-257.

CONNALLY, Eileen E. Implications of research for the classroom teacher. 1961, 106, 397-404.

_____. The international congress on the education of the deaf. 1961, 106, 411-413.

Education (Contd.)

ANNALS OF THE DEAF (Contd.)

_____. Public Law 87-276, 87th Congress S. 336, 1961, 106, 481-483.

MCINTIRE, W. F. Leadership training in the area of the deaf. 1961, 106, 488-490.

HENDERSON, S., and FRANCIS, D. H. The meaning of deafness: the report of a workshop for audiologists. 1962, 107, 464-596.

SCHUNHOFF, Hugo F. Bases of a comprehensive program in the education of deaf children. 1964, 109, 240-247.

GOLDSTEIN, Hyman, and SCHEIN, Jerome D. First steps toward the collection of uniform statistics of severe hearing impairments and deafness in the United States. 1964, 109, 400-409.

POWERS, Margaret H. The prevalence of deafness in school-age children. 1964, 109, 410-417.

SILVERMAN, S. Richard. Report of the president, Council on Education of the Deaf. 1964, 109, 420-422.

DOCTOR, Powrie V. A liberal education for the deaf. 1964, 109, 423-426.

LLOYD, Glenn T. A proposal for better educational opportunity for the deaf child. 1966, 111, 505-509.

CARR, Josephine. Administrative problems in the education of the deaf. 1966, 111, 552-556.

_____. Library survey project. 1966, 111, 695-699.

SALEM, James M., and SMITH, Ada H. The development and operation of a state accredited high school program in a residential school for the deaf. 1968, 113, 2-9.

GONZALES, B. Robert. What is the role of the supervising teacher of the deaf? 1968, 113, 869-873.

CLOUSER, Richard A. The changing classroom. 1968, 113, 1007-1014.

BERENSON, Bertram. The educational implications of architecture for the deaf. 1968, 113, 1030-1039.

LEITMAN, Allan. The workshop classroom furnishings in the learning module. 1968, 113, 1056-1062.

BLACKWELL, H. Richard. Lighting in the learning module, 1968, 113, 1063-1074.

Education (Contd.)

ANNALS OF THE DEAF (Contd.)

RAY, Henry W. Creating environments for learning. 1968, 113, 1075-1085.

AGRON, George. Architecture for social needs. 1968, 113, 1086-1105.

GALLAGHER, James J. Better organization of the educational establishment to aid the handicapped. 1969, 114, 853-860.

YEAGER, John. A system for individualizing education. 1969, 114, 861-867.

CRAIG, William N., and COLLINS, James L. Analysis of communicative interaction in classes for deaf children. 1970, 115, 79-85.

CRAIG, Helen B. Reinforcing appropriate visual attending behavior in classes of deaf children. 1970, 115, 481-491.

COHEN, Oscar P., and LERMAN, Alan. Residential care, a new concept. 1971, 116, 369-371.

SCHERER, Patricia A. An open letter to educators of the deaf. 1971, 116, 404-407.

LOWELL, Edgar L. The new economics and the deaf. 1971, 116, 469-472.

WEINRICH, John E. Direct economic costs of deafness in the United States. 1972, 117, 446-454.

CRAIG, Helen B., and HOLMAN, Gary L. The "open classroom" in a school for the deaf. 1973, 118, 675-685.

ISSACS, Morton. Precision teaching of the deaf. 1973, 118, 686-690.

CULBERTSON, Lynda N. CAI--beneficial teaching tool at Texas School for the Deaf. 1974, 119, 34-40.

KELLER, James F., and MOORE, Marian B. Democracy in the hearing impaired classroom. 1974, 119, 307-313.

HUFF, Anna. Personnel survey of resource centers in schools for the deaf. 1974, 119, 358-360.

_____. Report of the Ad Hoc Committee to define deaf and hard of hearing. 1975, 120, 509-512.

DICKER, Leo. Intensive interpreter training. 1976, 121, 312-319.

PENDERGRASS, R. A., and HODGES, Marlis. Deaf students in group problem solving situations: a study of the interactive process. 1976, 121, 327-330.

Education (Contd.)

ANNALS OF THE DEAF (Contd.)

CURTIS, Marie. Counseling in schools for the deaf. 1976, 121, 386-388.

CURTIS, Jonathan J. Educators of the hearing prioritize the needs for instructional materials. 1976, 121, 486-488.

JONES, Peter Allen. An educational comparison of rubella and non-rubella students at the Clarke School for the Deaf. 1976, 121, 547-553.

LUETKE, Barbara. Questionnaire results from Mexican-American parents of hearing impaired children in the United States. 1976, 121, 565-568.

Foreign Programs/International Trends

THE VOLTA REVIEW

HOFFMAN, Hugo. The education of deaf mutes in Germany at the end of the nineteenth century. 1901, 3, 1-10.

DANGER, O. The "mixed method" and the "pure oral method" in Germany. 1901, 3, 411-417.

FERRERI, Giulio C. The oral method in the school of Frankfurt-on-the Main. 1902, 4, 1-6.

DANGER, O. Education of the deaf in Prussia. 1902, 4, 122-128; 201-207.

FORCHHAMMER, G. A new expedient for the teaching of the deaf. 1902, 4, 413-423.

SCHMIDT, A. Principal Italian institutions for the deaf. 1902, 4, 455-470.

STELLING, H. Schools for the weak minded in Denmark and Norway. 1903, 5, 16-24.

_____. Hungarian institutions for the deaf. 1904, 6, 191-197.

Foreign Programs/International Trends (Contd.)

THE VOLTA REVIEW (Contd.)

HOFFMANN, Hugo. Language and language teaching in German schools. 1908, 10, 265-271.

BODENSIEK, Gustav. The present status of the education of the backward deaf in Prussia. 1909, 11, 20-29; 91-102; 169-178.

WETTSTEIN, Carl T. School for the deaf in North Europe. 1911, 12, 605-612.

STORY, Arthur J. How London educates the deaf. 1912, 14, 263-299.

STORY, Arthur J. The English movement in favor of the earlier education of the deaf. 1913, 15, 7-11.

YEARSLEY, Macleod. The co-operation of the teacher and the doctor. 1913, 15, 374-377.

STORY, Arthur J. The Glasgow conference of teachers of the deaf. 1913, 15, 394-398.

PITROIS, Yvonne. The national institution for the deaf in Paris. 1913, 14, 710-718.

ADDISON, W. H. The present state of the education of the deaf in Scotland. 1914, 16, 165-173.

SWAINSON, Miss. The education of the deaf in India. 1914, 16, 173-177.

NELSON, William. A brief account of the principles of teaching in the Manchester school. 1914, 16, 251-257.

YEARSLEY, Macleod. Hard of hearing classes in London. 1915, 17, 41-48.

STEVENS, J. E. Schools for the deaf in Europe. 1915, 17, 221-225.

_____. War deafnesses. 1917, 19, 683-686.

SCRIPTURE, E. W. The laboratory of experimental phonetics at Hamburg. 1921, 23, 238-240.

ZEBROWSKI, Alexander. The institute for the instruction of the deaf in Warsaw (Poland). 1922, 24, 174-176.

ADAMETZ, Josef. The schools for hard of hearing children in Vienna, Austria. 1922, 24, 331-334.

HAYCOCK, George S. Training of teachers of the deaf in England. 1923, 25, 345-351.

Foreign Programs/International Trends (Contd.)

THE VOLTA REVIEW (Contd.)

WRIGHT, John D. Schools for the deaf in Italy. 1925, <u>27</u>, 91-97; 221-222; 282-284; 330-334; 383-385.

WRIGHT, John D. Speech reading in Switzerland for the adult deaf. 1925, <u>27</u>, 289-291.

WRIGHT, John D. Swiss schools for the deaf. 1925, <u>27</u>, 713-717.

STORY, Arthur J. The present position of the education of the deaf in Great Britain. 1926, <u>28</u>, 39-46.

WRIGHT, John D. Schools for the deaf in the Orient. 1926, <u>28</u>, 49-52.

WRIGHT, John D. Schools for the deaf in India. 1926, <u>28</u>, 348-355; 593-595; 769-770.

WRIGHT, John D. School for the deaf, Colombo, Ceylon. 1926, <u>28</u>, 415-417.

HANSEN, Anders. The Belgian method. 1928, <u>30</u>, 8-13.

KLOPFER, Stephen. The Belgian method. 1931, <u>33</u>, 245-247; 280-281.

WOLF, Edna L. Impressions gained through visits to schools for the deaf in Europe. 1932, <u>34</u>, 447-452.

FETTERLY, H. B. Social education in the Ontario school. 1933, <u>35</u>, 122-123.

RAU, E. F. Methods of educating very young deaf children (Translated from Russian by Helen G. Smith). 1935, <u>37</u>, 514-518; 579-583; 649-654; 700-701.

TIMBERLAKE, Josephine B. An educator of the deaf who has revolutionized his field. 1953, <u>55</u>, 148-149; 160.

NALL, Frances. History and operation of Ewing House. 1955, <u>57</u>, 145-146.

MAGNER, Marjorie E. An American teacher's comments on education of the deaf in England. 1956, <u>58</u>, 11-14.

MAGNER, Marjorie E. Home and parent guidance in England. 1956, <u>58</u>, 341-345; 348.

WILLIAMS, Howard. Speech and language for the deaf in Russia. 1957, <u>59</u>, 387-390.

PASCOE, D. A new school in Venezuela. 1958, <u>60</u>, 21-23.

Foreign Programs/International Trends (Contd.)

THE VOLTA REVIEW (Contd.)

JONES, Lilian G. Education of the deaf behind the Iron Curtain. 1958, 60, 152-155; 203-205; 222-225; 260-266.

WALTER, Jean. Supervision in Australian schools for the deaf. 1958, 60, 361-365.

HUNT, J. F. Education of the deaf in the U.S.S.R. 1959, 61, 356-363; 390.

UDEN, A. v. Observations of education of the deaf in The Netherlands and the U.S.A. 1960, 62, 10-14.

MORKOVIN, Boris V. Experiment in teaching deaf preschool children in the Soviet Union. 1960, 62, 260-268.

TAYLOR, W. W., and I. W. The education of the deaf in Western Europe. 1962, 64, 487-495.

BUCHLI, M. J. Home education of deaf children in The Netherlands. 1963, 65, 279-285; 316.

WATSON, T. J. Research in the education of the deaf outside the United States. 1963, 65, 535-541.

YUNGHANS, Marian. Teaching art to the deaf in Nigeria. 1964, 66, 275-279.

PRETTYMAN, Eileen. The education of the deaf in Toronto. 1965, 67, 420-421.

PERELLÓ, Jorge. From Spain: a method of liminal audiometry for children. 1965, 67, 588-589.

QUIGLEY, Stephen P. Language research in countries other than the United States. 1966, 68, 68-83.

OWSLEY, Peter J. Education of hearing impaired children in Europe. 1966, 68, 655-659.

THOMASIA, SISTER M. Teaching lipreading in a school in South Africa. 1967, 69, 45-49.

PITCHERS, B. J. The educational treatment of deafness in Kent. 1968, 70, 577-580.

GEISPERGER, Friedrich. Use of tape recordings in Germany for auditory training and auditory education. 1969, 71, 308-313.

HÄRTEL, Herbert. The German Museum of Information on Deaf-mutes. 1969, 71, 369-372.

Foreign Programs/International Trends (Contd.)

THE VOLTA REVIEW (Contd.)

GULDAGER, Lars. Denmark's cottage system offers home environment to deaf children. 1969, <u>71</u>, 405-407.

HERRICK, Helen M., and KAPUR, Y. P. Education of the deaf in India. 1969, <u>71</u>, 492-499.

LUNDSTRÖM, Karin. Special education in Sweden. 1969, <u>71</u>, 528-538.

MEADOW, Kathryn P., and LLOYD. The treatment of deafness in England-- a comparison with the American scene. 1970, <u>72</u>, 242-251.

DALVI, Kunda. Teaching the deaf in India. 1970, <u>72</u>, 272-277.

PARSONS, Michael. The New Zealand approach to screening babies for deafness. 1971, <u>73</u>, 233-235.

FELLENDORF, George W. A look at services for preschool hearing impaired children in Sweden. 1973, <u>75</u>, 282-287.

UDEN, the Rev. Anthony v. Education of the deaf at St. Michielsgestel, The Netherlands. 1973, <u>75</u>, 440-444.

NAKANO, Yoshitatsu. Oral education for hearing impaired children in Japan. 1975, <u>77</u>, 291-295.

FELLENDORF, George W. International trends. 1976, <u>78</u>, 42-46. (monograph).

ANNALS OF THE DEAF

DECONDILLAC, E'tienne B. (1715-1780); The language of action (a translation by Mrs. E. M. Gallaudet). 1886, <u>13</u>, 35-41.

NORRIS, Anne C. With American educators in Europe. 1929, <u>31</u>, 50-54.

HÖXTER, Richard. The Bárczi method and its application in the School for the Deaf of the Alliance Israélite Universelle. 1938, <u>83</u>, 383-403.

Foreign Programs/International Trends (Contd.)

ANNALS OF THE DEAF (Contd.)

EWING, Irene, and A. W. G. Educating the deaf in Britain. 1949, 94, 318-324.

TAYLOR, Sam D. Education for the deaf in England. 1953, 98, 240-248.

GODIN, Leonid. Professions for deaf citizens in the USSR. 1967, 112, 593-594.

GODIN, Lev. Interpreters for the deaf in Russia. 1967. 112, 595-596.

AMCOFF, Sven. Programmed instruction for Swedish children aged 7-10 years who are deaf or hard of hearing. 1968, 113, 318-326.

──────────────. Training for deaf welfare in Britain. 1968, 113, 874-877.

BERGER, Kenneth W. A history of the education of the deaf in the Philippines. 1969, 114, 79-94.

MEADOW, Kathryn, and Lloyd. The education of deaf children in England. 1969, 114, 777-785.

D'AUDNEY, Weslee W. The Soviet search and research for new methods in deaf education. 1975, 120, 42-47.

Hard of Hearing

THE VOLTA REVIEW

FERRERI, Giulio C. Children who are hard of hearing. 1902, 4, 232-239.

LEIGHTON, Etta V. The hard of hearing child in the public school. 1913, 14, 672-679.

TRASK, Alice N. A plea for the hard of hearing. 1914, 16, 693-696.

BRUHN, Martha E. The hard of hearing adult. 1915, 17, 381-385.

WRIGHT, John D. The partially deaf child: a school problem. 1917, 19, 449-452.

WALKER, Jane B. An open door for the hard of hearing. 1917, 19, 439-441.

Hard of Hearing (Contd.)

THE VOLTA REVIEW (Contd.)

──────────────. Extracts from the proceedings of the Second Annual Meeting of the American Association for the Hard of Hearing. 1921, 23, 471-491; 525-531; 1922, 24, 16-28; 54-64; 79-87.

──────────────. Extracts from the proceedings of the Third Annual Meeting of the American Federation of Organizations for the Hard of Hearing, Inc., Toledo, Ohio. 1922, 24, 308-330; 397-407; 441-450.

HOWE, Alice G. The hard of hearing child in the public schools of Rochester, N.Y. 1923, 25, 40-43.

SAMUELSON, Estelle E. The hard of hearing child from the social worker's viewpoint. 1923, 25, 44-47.

EVANS, Florence L. Voice placing and enunciation for the hard of hearing. 1923, 25, 203-204.

PECK, Annetta W. Organizations for the hard-of-hearing; their history, purpose and promotion. 1923, 25, 391-395.

EUBANK, Earle E. The need of educational preparation for social work with the hard-of-hearing. 1923, 25, 450-453.

──────────────. Proceedings of the Fifth Annual Conference of the American Federation of Organizations for the Hard of Hearing, Inc. 1924, 26, 385-477.

DELAND, Fred, and SPOFFORD, Florence P. Public school pupils with imperfect hearing. 1925, 27, 414-417.

──────────────. Proceedings of the Sixth Annual Conference of the American Federation of Organizations for the Hard of Hearing, Inc. 1925, 27, 545-665.

TROLL, George D. The hard of hearing adolescent. 1926, 28, 221-223.

NORRIS, Mrs. James F. Committee on the Survey of Hard of Hearing Children. 1926, 28, 451-461.

DURFEE, Marion A. Public school teaching of hard of hearing adults and children. 1927, 29, 565-572.

BERRY, Gordon. Problems of the hard of hearing. 1928, 30, 127-136.

BELLOWS, Howard P. The harsh voice of the hard of hearing. 1929, 31, 393-394.

Hard of Hearing (Contd.)

THE VOLTA REVIEW (Contd.)

DELANY, Elizabeth G. The problems of the hard of hearing and how we meet them. 1935, 37, 545-546; 564.

MONTAGUE, Harriet. What can a hard of hearing person do? 1935, 37, 743-746.

CLOUD, D. T. Meeting the problem of the hard of hearing child. 1937, 39, 487-489; 540.

CRAIG, Sam B., et al. What should be done for the hard of hearing child in a school for the deaf? 1937, 39, 490-493; 536.

FRUEWALD, E. The hard of hearing child in a school for the deaf. 1939, 41, 325-327; 375.

NELSON, Boyd E. Hard of hearing pupils in schools for the deaf. 1942, 44, 325-328; 368.

NEW, Mary C. Speech for the hard of hearing. 1945, 47, 282-284.

REEVE, Jesse W. A five-day school for the hard of hearing. 1953, 55, 208-209; 228; 248-249; 264-266; 298-299; 320-322; 349-350; 406.

BROWN, Ruth. Hard of hearing children among the deaf. 1953, 55, 289-291; 324.

MACNUTT, Ena G. Program for the hard of hearing child in the public school. 1953, 55, 385-386.

_____. Hard of hearing child (questions and answers). 1953, 55, 401-405.

KELLY, J. C. The older hard of hearing child. 1954, 56, 403-405.

MILLER, June. Classroom methods and materials for hard of hearing children. 1957, 59, 343-345.

DRENNEN, Genevieve. Preparing teachers for hard of hearing in public schools. 1959, 61, 111-114.

THORNE, Bert. The problem of the marginally deaf. 1961, 63, 133-134; 146.

GILDSTON, Phyllis. The hard of hearing child in the classroom--a guide for the classroom teacher. 1962, 64, 239-245.

GOETZINGER, Cornelius P. Effects of small perceptive losses on language and on speech discrimination. 1962, 64, 408-414.

Hard of Hearing (Contd.)

THE VOLTA REVIEW (Contd.)

GOETZINGER, Cornelius P., et al. Small perceptive hearing loss: its effect in school-age children. 1964, 66, 124-131.

THOMAS, Donald. Separate programming for the deaf and hard of hearing. 1964, 66, 436-438.

WHORTON, Gladys P. The hard of hearing child: a challenge to educators. 1966, 68, 351-353.

KENNEDY, Mildred, and WHITEHURST, Mary W. Suggestions for friends and relatives of the hard of hearing. 1969, 71, 81-88.

WITCHER, Betty. "She's not deaf, she's hard of hearing." 1974, 76, 428-434.

ANNALS OF THE DEAF

WRIGHT, John D. The partially deaf child--a school program. 1917, 62, 321-329.

STEVENSON, Elwood A. Are our deaf all deaf? 1919, 64, 351-359.

Health Care/Medical

THE VOLTA REVIEW

LOVE, J. K. The deaf child from the view-point of the physician and of the teacher. 1910, 12, 143-154.

DELAND, Fred. Keep the nose clean and free from obstructions. 1921, 23, 3-4; 82-84; 159-161.

NEWHART, Horace. The responsibility of the physician in otology. 1921, 23, 170-173.

Health Care/Medical (Contd.)

THE VOLTA REVIEW (Contd.)

CRAMP, Arthur J. Deafness--cure quackery and pseudo-medicine. 1926, 28, 497-504.

_____. The otologist and the deaf child. 1953, 55, 15-16.

HOLOWACH, Jean. The pediatrician and the deaf child. 1955, 57, 121-122.

MACAULEY, Dorothy. What I wish my doctor had told me. 1956, 58, 310-311; 316.

BROBERG, Rose F. Guidelines for nurses working with hearing impaired children. 1968, 70, 552-558.

MCGEE, T. Manford. Ototoxic antibiotics. 1968, 70, 667-671.

HERRELL, Wallace E. Progress in control of viral infections. 1968, 70, 707-710.

BALLER, Warren R., and GIANGRECO, C. Joseph. Correction of nocturnal enuresis in deaf children. 1970, 72, 545-549.

HINEY, Esther. To the parent of a deaf adolescent--drug awareness. 1973, 75, 296-298.

OSBERGER, Mary Joe, and DANAHER, Ellen Martin. Temporary conductive loss in students with severe sensorineural deafness. 1974, 76, 52-56.

SHIMIZU, Hiroshi. Acupuncture treatment for deafness: an eyewitness report. 1974, 76, 290-292.

ROSEN, Samuel, M.D. Acupuncture and Chinese medical practices. 1974, 76, 340-350.

CHERRY, James D. Rubella: past, present, and future. 1974, 76, 461-465.

JENSEMA, Carl. Post-rubella children in special educational programs for the hearing impaired. 1974, 76, 466-473.

CHAPMAN, Jean. Special health needs of the hearing impaired. 1975, 77, 35-44.

LEIGH, Irene W. The impact of a hearing loss on health care of the infant or preschool child. 1975, 77, 46-52.

Health Care/Medical (Contd.)

THE VOLTA REVIEW (Contd.)

HINCKLEY, Robert F., M.D. The silent school bell: health care and the school-age hearing impaired child. 1975, <u>77</u>, 53-56.

MILLER, Lucille V. The adult and the elderly: health care and hearing loss. 1975, <u>77</u>, 57-63.

STEWART, Joseph L. Provision of health care to underserved populations. 1975, <u>77</u>, 64-71.

FELLENDORF, George W. Trends and future goals. 1975, <u>77</u>, 73-77.

GLASSOCK, Michael E. Medical intervention. 1976, <u>78</u>, 2-5 (monograph).

FELLENDORF, George W. Project feedback (editorial). 1976, <u>78</u>, 135.

Hearing Aids/Group Systems

THE VOLTA REVIEW

HANSON, Earl C. The vactuphone--an electric hearing aid employing the vacuum-tube amplifier. 1921, <u>23</u>, 331-333.

_____. Investigation of hearing devices for the deafened. 1926, <u>28</u>, 84-86.

MACFARLAN, Douglas. The report of the committee appointed to survey the instrumental aids to hearing. 1927, <u>29</u>, 592-629.

HALLER, G.L., and LYBARGER, S.F. Selection of electrical apparatus for auricular training. 1933, <u>35</u>, 295-298; 316.

FERRERI, Giulio. The audiphone-stroboscope. 1934, <u>36</u>, 133-138.

KNUDSEN, Vern O. Artificial aids to hearing. 1934, <u>36</u>, 581-587; 630.

WATSON, Ruth B., and Norman, A. Hearing aids in schools for the deaf. 1937, <u>39</u>, 261-266; 314-315.

PLESS, Marie A., et al. Our hearing aid consultation service. 1937, <u>39</u>, 512-513; 529-530.

Hearing Aids/Group Systems (Contd.)

THE VOLTA REVIEW (Contd.)

O'CONNOR, Clarence D. What every superintendent of a school for the deaf should know about hearing aids and their use. 1938, 40, 710-717.

BRALY, Kenneth. Fitting hearing aids. 1938, 40, 777-779; 808.

WATSON, Norman A. Selective amplification. 1939, 41, 338-340; 371.

CROUTER, Alan Y. Exploring with a hearing aid. 1941, 43, 93-94; 156-157.

DE LA BAT, G. Individual hearing aids for children. 1941, 43, 125-127.

CRUTCHETT, Ralph. Just how should hearing aids be fitted, an explanation. 1941, 43, 546-548.

CAVALIERE, R. A., and CUTLER, S. James. Rehabilitating with hearing aids. 1943, 45, 635-639.

BARRETT, Katherine. The value of individual hearing aids--a comparative study of selective achievements of two groups of school children. 1944, 46, 553-557; 608; 628-631; 668-670; 681-685; 728.

TABER, Frank A. The audiometer and our hearing aids. 1945, 47, 453-454; 464.

GALLOWAY, James H. The value of individual hearing aids in a school for the deaf. 1945, 47, 617-618.

LEVINE, Edna S., and NESS, Agnes D. Personal hearing aids for deaf children. 1945, 47, 619-620.

MONTAGUE, Harriet. Hearing aids for deaf children. 1946, 48, 9-13; 60.

WHILDIN, Olive A. Hearing aid service for children. 1946, 48, 23-26.

RIGHTER, George J., and WINKLER, Pauline K. Observations on grade school children wearing hearing aids. 1946, 48, 568-570; 594.

DI CARLO, Louis M. Hearing aids: factors in adjustment. 1946, 48, 647-649.

BRADFORD, Charles A. Hearing aids in schools for the deaf. 1946, 48, 649-651.

Hearing Aids/Group Systems (Contd.)

THE VOLTA REVIEW (Contd.)

HUDGINS, Clarence V. Testing the performance of hearing aids. 1947, 49, 5-6; 60-62.

JOHNSON, Elizabeth H. Audiometric testing of hearing aids. 1947, 49, 7-12.

MOORE, Charles E. Selecting hearing aids for high school. 1947, 49, 504; 536-538.

OLSON, Florence, and SOISSONS, Margaret. Problems in the selection of hearing aids for children. 1948, 50, 478-484.

CORLISS, Edith L. How are hearing aids tested? 1948, 50, 567-568; 598; 600; 602; 604. Part II: 613-615; 646; 648.

LASSMAN, Grace, and MONTAGUE, Harriet. Hearing aids and young deaf children. 1949, 51, 447-449; 478; 518-520; 524-526.

TIMBERLAKE, Josephine B. Hearing aids on their fiftieth anniversary. 1951, 53, 507-510; 534-538.

WOODWARD, Helen. A child and his hearing aid. 1952, 54, 261-262; 288-290.

SCOTT, Duncan R. C. The hearing aid is not enough. 1952, 54, 379-381; 394; 396.

HUDGINS, Clarence V. Modern hearing aid equipment in schools for the deaf. 1953, 55, 185-186.

CARTER, Howard A. Something new in hearing aids. 1953, 55, 357-358.

YENRICK, D. E. The hearing aid--its acceptance and use. 1954, 56, 171-172.

HARDY, William G. Hearing aids for deaf children. 1954, 56, 355-358.

WINCHESTER, R. A., et al. Hearing aids for children. 1955, 57, 357-359.

PRALL, Josephine. Hearing aid selection and use. 1955, 57, 390-392.

HASKINS, Harriet. Listening with the help of a hearing aid. 1955, 57, 408-410; 417.

ROTTER, Paul. A guide to group hearing aids. 1956, 58, 23-27.

Hearing Aids/Group Systems (Contd.)

THE VOLTA REVIEW (Contd.)

SORTINI, Adam J. Hearing aids for preschool children. 1956, 58, 103-106; 130.

_____. Group hearing aids in the schools. 1956, 58, 208-212.

GOLDSTEIN, Robert. Relation of some audiologic findings to the use of hearing aids. 1958, 60, 404.

BENDER, Ruth E., and WIIG, Elisabeth. Binaural hearing aids for young children. 1960, 62, 113-115.

NELSON, Max. Public school audiometry. 1961, 63, 282-283; 305.

REEVES, J. K. Some parental and social attitudes towards children using hearing aids. 1962, 64, 314-316; 331.

LEWIS, Dorothy N., and GREEN, Ruth R. Value of binaural hearing aids for hearing impaired children in elementary schools. 1962, 64, 537-542; 571.

HAUG, O., et al. A comparison of hearing aid evaluation test instruments and aids purchased from dealers. 1963, 65, 26-29.

VICTOREEN, J. A. The audiologist and the hearing instrument dispenser. 1963, 65, 76-78; 87.

CALVERT, Donald R. A comparison of auditory amplifiers in the classroom in a school for the deaf. 1964, 66, 544-547.

LING, Daniel. Implications of hearing aid amplification below 300 CPS. 1964, 66, 723-729.

WATSON, T. J. The use of hearing aids by hearing impaired pupils in ordinary schools. 1964, 66, 741-744; 787.

POLLACK, Doreen C., and DOWNS, Marion P. A parent's guide to hearing aids for young children. 1964, 66, 745-749.

FELLENDORF, George W. Interest in the hearing aid and its user (The Alexander Graham Bell Association for the Deaf). 1964, 66, 767-769.

WALKER, Crayton. Interest in the hearing aid and its user (The American Hearing Society). 1964, 66, 769-771.

VENTRY, Ira M. Interest in the hearing aid and its user (The American Speech and Hearing Association). 1964, 66, 771-773.

Hearing Aids/Group Systems (Contd.)

THE VOLTA REVIEW (Contd.)

HARRINGTON, Donald A. Interest in the hearing aid and its user (The Children's Bureau). 1964, 66, 774-775.

BURGER, Richard. Interest in the hearing aid and its user (The Hearing Aid Industry Conference). 1964, 66, 775-778.

KENWOOD, John C. Interest in the hearing aid and its user (The Society of Hearing Aid Audiologists). 1964, 66, 778-779.

BELLEFLEUR, Philip A., and MCMENAMIN, Sayre B. Problems of inductance loop amplification. 1965, 67, 559-563; 579.

FOGEL, Howard H. The role of the modern hearing aid dealer. 1965, 67, 566-569.

BELLEFLEUR, Philip A. Inductance loop amplification: its adaptation to television for the deaf. 1966, 68, 561-565.

LECKIE, Doris, and LING, Daniel. Audibility with hearing aids having low frequency characteristics. 1968, 70, 83-86.

RISBERG, Arne. A critical review of work on speech analyzing hearing aids. 1971, 73, 23-25.

SMITH, Gale M. Coupling hearing aids to the telephone. 1971, 73, 47-50.

LING, Daniel. Conventional hearing aids: an overview. 1971, 73, 343-352.

VERNON, Jack, et al. Evaluation of an implantable type hearing aid by means of cochlear potentials. 1972, 74, 20-29.

ZINK, G. David. Hearing aids children wear: a longitudinal study. 1972, 74, 41-51.

BISHOP, Milo E., et al. A study of amplification systems used in schools for the deaf. 1972, 74, 111-121.

HASKINS, Harriet L. Aids to hearing. 1972, 74, 417-425.

SUNG, Richard J., SUNG, Grace S., and HODGSON, William R. Telecoil versus microphone, performance in hearing aids. 1973, 75, 417-424.

ROSS, Mark, et al. The use of a rating scale to compare binaural and monaural amplification with hearing impaired children. 1974, 76, 93-99.

Hearing Aids/Group Systems (Contd.)

THE VOLTA REVIEW (Contd.)

HANNERS, Barbara A., and SITTON, Ann B. Ears to hear: a daily hearing aid monitor program. 1974, 76, 530-536.

ISRAEL, Richard H. The hearing aid. 1975, 77, 21-26.

FELLENDORF, George W. Hearing aids and young hearing impaired children in Sweden and the United States. 1975, 77, 410-415.

BERGER, Kenneth W. From telephone to electric hearing aid. 1976, 78, 83-89.

LYBARGER, Samuel F. Personal hearing aids. 1976, 78, 113-120 (monograph).

ANNALS OF THE DEAF

POPE, Alvin E. The use of hearing tests and hearing aids in the education of the deaf. 1936, 81, 323-332.

STEVENSON, Elwood P. Hearing aids--the deaf--the hard of hearing. 1939, 84, 3-7.

KNUDSEN, Vern O. Hearing aids today and tomorrow. 1939, 84, 316-321.

GALLOWAY, James H. A hearing-aid-testing clinic. 1941, 86, 429-440.

MYKLEBUST, Helmer R. The use of individual hearing aids in a residential school for the deaf. 1943, 88, 270-278.

MYKLEBUST, Helmer R. The use of individual hearing aids in a residential school for the deaf with implications for acoustic training. 1946, 91, 255-261.

LORGE, Irving. Gains in hearing capacity in a two year period for hearing aid and control groups. 1946, 91, 391-396.

SILVERMAN, S. Richard. The implications for schools for the deaf of recent research on hearing aids. 1949, 94, 325-339.

REITER, F. H. Hearing aids not a substitute for lack of hearing. 1950, 95, 249-253.

Hearing Aids/Group Systems (Contd.)

ANNALS OF THE DEAF (Contd.)

SILVERMAN, S. Richard, and HARRISON, C. E. The National Research Council Group Hearing Aid Project, a progress report. 1951, 96, 420-431.

PRALL, Josephine. Group and wearable hearing aids in a residential school for the deaf. 1957, 102, 240-250.

BOYD, John, and JAMROZ, Anthony. A comparison of group hearing aid systems. 1963, 108, 245-250.

BØRRILD, Knud. Experience with the design and use of technical aids for the training of deaf and hard of hearing children. 1968, 113, 168-177.

MINAMI, Kyusaburo, and KATSURAYAMA, Keiko. Frequency shift type aid and an utterance trainer. 1968, 113, 307-319.

NIEMOLLER, Arthur F. Acoustical design of classrooms for the deaf. 1968, 113, 1040-1045.

HIRSH, Ira J. Use of amplification in educating deaf children. 1968, 113, 1046-1055.

BELLEFLEUR, Philip A. Critique on current auditory training equipment. 1969, 114, 790-795.

MATKIN, Noel D., and OLSEN, Wayne C. Response of hearing aids with induction loop amplification systems. 1970, 115, 73-78.

VANDENBERG, D. Marjorie. Relationship between extent of hearing-aid use and language and academic achievement. 1972, 117, 14-19.

PORTER, Thomas A. Hearing aids in a residential school. 1973, 118, 31-33.

Heredity/Etiology

THE VOLTA REVIEW

DANGER, O. The heredity of deafness. 1900, 2, 343-348.

LOVE, James K. The study of the deaf child: being a researcher on deaf-mutism. 1907, 9, 449-462.

BELL, Alexander G. A few thoughts concerning eugenics. 1908, 10, 166-173.

GOLDSTEIN, M. A. The physician and the deaf child. 1910, 12, 279-287.

LOVE, James K. The medical inspection of school children. 1911, 13, 332-343.

HICKERNELL, W. F. Eugenics and the United States census. 1911, 13, 399-402.

ROBERTS, Linnaeus. Heredity and intermarriage: factors in deafmutism. 1912, 14, 184-186.

DELAND, Fred. Marriages of the deaf. 1912, 14, 186-189.

_____. Graphical studies of marriages of the deaf. 1913, 15, 80-91.

BELL, Alexander G. Graphical studies of marriages of the deaf. 1913, 15, 146-152; 196-203; 230-238; 280-287; 322-329; 366-373; 408-415.

DRIGGS, Frank M. The causes of deafness. 1913, 15, 330-334.

_____. Genealogy and eugenics. 1915, 17, 361-363.

ROTT, O. M. The prevention of deafness in children and the teacher's responsibility thereto. 1924, 26, 495-500.

BELL, Alexander G. Marriage--an address to the deaf. 1935, 37, 457-460; 491.

SATALOFF, Joseph. The Rh factor in congenital deafness. 1950, 52, 311; 332.

BROCKMAN, Seymour J. Recent advances in experimental otologic research. 1957, 59, 105-110.

BRILL, Richard G. Hereditary aspects of deafness. 1961, 63, 168-175.

SANK, Diane, and KALLMAN, Franz J. The role of heredity in early total deafness. 1963, 65, 461-470.

Heredity/Etiology (Contd.)

THE VOLTA REVIEW (Contd.)

MCCABE, Brian F. The etiology of deafness. 1963, 65, 471-477.

MCGEE, T. Manford. Otologic research. 1963, 65, 478-485.

SZANTON, Victor L., and Willette C. Allergic paracusis: new allergic syndrome. 1964, 66, 248-252.

MILLER, James R. Pediatrics and disorders in communication: some genetic counseling problems in families with congenital hearing defect. 1965, 67, 118-123; 165.

KONIGSMARK, Bruce W., and MCKUSICK, Victor A. Hereditary deafness. 1966, 68, 336-341.

STRESHINSKY, Shirley G. Does it run in the family? 1967, 69, 311-315.

LARSON, Carl A. Deafness and the planned family. 1970, 72, 83-87.

COOK, Robert C. A deaf variety of the human race. 1970, 72, 89-93.

NANCE, Walter E. Studies of hereditary deafness: present, past, and future. 1976, 78, 6-11 (monograph).

JONES, Peter Allen. Causative factors and prevention of childhood deafness. 1976, 78, 268-275.

ANNALS OF THE DEAF

TAYLOR, Harris. Hereditary deafness. 1892, 37, 249-259.

FAY, Edward A. Marriages of the deaf in America. 1896, 41, 22-31; 79-88; 171-183; 215-242; 299-331; 391-402; 1897, 42, 29-33; 96-109.

FAY, Edward A. Illegitimate unions. 1897, 42, 141-143.

COBB, Jennie L. The influence of heredity. 1911, 56, 253-259.

FOWLER, Edmund P. Prevention of diseases and disorders of the ears between the ages of three and twelve years (inclusive). 1938, 83, 306-319.

Heredity/Etiology (Contd.)

ANNALS OF THE DEAF (Contd.)

VERNON, McCay. Current etiological factors in deafness. 1968, 113, 106-115.

KLOEPHER, Warner H., et al. Genetic aspects of congenital hearing loss. 1970, 115, 17-22.

BASILIER, Ferge. The surdo-cardiac syndrome with prolonged Q-T interval. 1974, 119, 314-317.

BUDDEN, Sarajini S., ROBINSON, Geoffrey C., MACLEAN, C. Dunella, CAMBON, Kenneth G. Deafness in infants and preschool children. 1974, 119, 387-395.

JENSEMA, Carl, MULLINS, Jane. Onset, cause, and additional handicaps in hearing impaired children. 1974, 119, 701-705.

Higher Education

THE VOLTA REVIEW

FECHHEIMER, A. Lincoln. University experiences. 1899, 1, 27-34.

JOHANSEN, Donald. "Should I go to college in spite of my deafness?" 1925, 27, 505-507.

TIMBERLAKE, Josephine B., and HUNTER, Mabel R. Deaf graduates of hearing schools and colleges. 1928, 30, 449-450.

TIMBERLAKE, Josephine B. Deaf graduates of schools and colleges for hearing students. 1929, 31, 489-491.

_____. Deaf graduates of schools and colleges for hearing students. 1930, 32, 73-75; 1931, 33, 71-73; 527-529; 1932, 34, 631-633; 1933, 35, 400-501; 1934, 36, 715-720; 1935, 37, 725-729; 1936, 38, 703-705; 1937, 39, 687-689; 1938, 40, 773-775; 1939, 41, 690-691; 1940, 42, 515-518; 1941, 43, 716-720; 1943, 45, 686-691; 1944, 46, 691-694; 1945, 47, 693-696; 1946, 48, 770-773; 1947, 49, 552-555; 1949, 51, 10-16; 1950, 52, 7-11; 1951, 53, 58-61; 1952, 54, 113-118; 1962, 64, 299-313; 1963, 65, 363-375; 1965, 67, 30-81.

Higher Education (Contd.)

THE VOLTA REVIEW (Contd.)

ADAMS, Bradford C. The independent study plan for the deaf student at college (with discussion by Jerry A. Pierce). 1933, 35, 445-448; 474-475.

HEWARD, Mr. and Mrs. H. Oral education brings success in college. 1959, 61, 284-287.

BREUNIG, H. Latham. An analysis of a group of deaf students in colleges with the hearing. 1965, 67, 17-27; 94.

_____. The National Technical Institute for the Deaf. 1965, 67, 484-492.

ELLINGSON, Mark. The National Technical Institute for the Deaf. 1967, 69, 523-524.

FELLENDORF, George W. NTID--after one year. 1969, 71, 296-307.

CARVER, Vida, and HALES, G. W. Tuition and support services for the deaf in the open university. 1974, 119, 407-412.

ANNALS OF THE DEAF

BULL, J. C. A few suggestions on the higher education of deaf-mutes. 1870, 15, 224-231.

PETTENGILL, B. D. The higher education of deaf-mutes and semi-mutes. 1881, 26, 17-22.

PEET, Elizabeth. Gallaudet College: seventy-five years of higher education for the deaf. 1939, 84, 198-217.

FUSFELD, Irving S. Higher education for the deaf. 1945, 90, 142-153.

ELSTAD, Leonard M. Higher education. 1953, 98, 374-378.

_____. St. Joseph College for the Deaf. 1962, 107, 343.

SCHEIN, Jerome, and BUSHNAQ, Suleiman. Higher education for the deaf in the United States--a retrospective investigation. 1962, 107, 416-420.

Higher Education (Contd.)

ANNALS OF THE DEAF (Contd.)

FUSFELD, Irving S. A critique on the question of college enrollment for deaf persons in the United States. 1963, 108, 220-235.

STUCKLESS, E. Ross. Planning for individualized instruction of deaf students at NTID. 1969, 114, 868-873.

GREENBERG, Bernard L. and Sally H. The measurement of college potential in the hearing handicapped. 1971, 116, 372-381.

MERRILL, Edward C., Jr. A perspective on higher education for the deaf. 1972, 117, 597-605.

STUCKLESS, E. Ross. Post-secondary programs for deaf students in 1972. 1972, 117, 377-382.

CRAIG, William N., et al. An experiment in post-secondary education for deaf people. 1972, 117, 606-611.

CASTLE, William, and ARGENTO, Frank. The first six years at NTID-- a prologue for the future. 1974, 119, 472-477.

FORR, Donald. Gallaudet update. 1974, 119, 478-484.

RAWLINGS, Brenda W., and TRYBUS, Raymond J. Update on postsecondary programs for hearing impaired students. 1976, 121, 541-546.

Infant/Preschool

THE VOLTA REVIEW

RIDER, Edward C. Kindergarten work in schools for the deaf. 1899, 1, 34-41.

TAYLOR, Helen. The importance of a right beginning. 1899, 1, 158-161.

TAYLOR, Ellen E. Kindergartens for the deaf. 1903, 5, 1-11.

LOVE, J. K. Education of the very young deaf child. 1910, 12, 602-603; 621.

Infant/Preschool (Contd.)

THE VOLTA REVIEW (Contd.)

YEARSLEY, Macleod. The deaf child's proper school-age. 1910, 12, 695-699.

MARGULIES, Mrs. A. R. The Montessori method and the deaf child. 1912, 14, 74-85; 146-47; 1913, 15, 334-338.

ANDERSON, Mrs. J. S. The Montessori method of teaching hearing children. 1912, 14, 95-102; 154-168.

ANDERSON, Mrs. J. S. Proving the worth of the Montessori method. 1913, 15, 38-42.

REINHARDT, Anna C. The Home School for Little Deaf Children, Kensington, Maryland. 1913, 15, 51-55.

LONGWILL, Mrs. J. B. The training of children of tender years. 1913, 15, 398-402.

FAY, Edward A. Montessori training: oral teaching. 1914, 16, 387-388.

MCARDLE, S. M. Kindergarten methods. 1914, 16, 517-521.

HURD, Anna C. The Montessori method applied to deaf children. 1915, 17, 239-242.

DELAND, Fred. Home schools for little deaf children. 1915, 17, 440-442.

LEONARD, Eleanor C. Preparing a little deaf child for school. 1917, 19, 253-280.

WELSH, Eugenia T. Sense training. 1922, 24, 111-113.

BODYCOMB, Margaret. Sense training and hand work. 1928, 30, 579-581.

MOORE, Grace. The nursery school movement. 1928, 30, 583-588.

WELLS, Anita. Keeping beginners happy and interested. 1929, 31, 248-250.

BEARD, Richard O. Deafening in the pre-school child. 1929, 31, 457-460.

FORSYTHE, Kathrin B. The kindergarten circle. 1929, 31, 786-787.

THOMA, Florence B. The nursery school. 1933, 35, 369-371.

HOWES, Esther C. What the teacher can do for the pre-school child. 1933, 35, 413-414.

Infant/Preschool (Contd.)

THE VOLTA REVIEW (Contd.)

MONTAGUE, Harriet. The nursery school and the deaf child. 1935, 37, 207; 249-250.

YOUNG, Irene B. A nursery school experiment. 1935, 37, 208; 252-253.

MCNEIL, Naomi. Why wait until they are five? 1936, 38, 501-504; 542-543.

SISTER ROSE GERTRUDE. The preschool at St. Mary's. 1937, 39, 325-327; 376.

CROUTER, John Y. The nursery school in the education of the deaf. 1937, 39, 613-614.

SCYSTER, Margaret. Johnny is boss. 1939, 41, 14-15; 55.

HOFFMAN, Virginia. Preschool classes at the Lexington School. 1940, 42, 69-72; 118; 144-146; 182.

HOWARD, Evelyn S. The preschool department at the Rochester School. 1940, 42, 405-408; 440.

APPEL, Catherine R. Objectives of a preschool program. 1942, 44, 621-622; 662.

LANE, Helen S. Influence of nursery school education on school achievement. 1942, 44, 677-680.

_____. Nursery schools for deaf children: an association committee report. 1942, 44, 681-683; 718.

HEIDER, Grace, and Fritz. Studies of preschool deaf children. 1943, 45, 261-267.

HOWARD, Evelyn S. Nursery schools: their development and their functions. 1943, 45, 437-441; 466.

POORE, Mrs. H. T. The report on nursery schools for deaf children. 1943, 45, 620-621; 660.

WINTERS, Loretta M. Departmentalizing a nursery school. 1944, 46, 623-627; 660-662.

GUTHRIE, Virginia S. A history of preschool education for the deaf. 1945, 47, 5-9; 56-58; 72-76; 116-118; 142-146; 186-188.

EWING, Irene B. Training deaf babies. 1945, 47, 208-209; 254.

DAVIDSON, Helena M. Residential nursery schools? No! 1946, 48, 494-496.

Infant/Preschool (Contd.)

THE VOLTA REVIEW (Contd.)

_____. Residential nursery schools--a discussion. 1946, 48, 496-513; 542.

NEW, Mary C. The nursery school. 1946, 48, 631-632.

GESELL, Arnold. Normal and deaf child in the preschool years. 1946, 48, 633-636.

GREENAWAY, E. S. The properly organized nursery is the better home for the deaf child. 1947, 49, 121; 156-158.

GARDNER, Warren H. A pre-school demonstration class for deaf children. 1947, 49, 169-171; 200-201.

MACDONALD, Nellie. A new nursery school. 1948, 50, 63; 84-86.

AVERY, Charlotte B. The social competence of preschool acoustically handicapped children. 1948, 50, 256-257; 286-288.

_____. Nursery and preschool (panel discussion). 1948, 50, 403-414.

LASSMAN, Grace H. Lipreading in nursery school. 1948, 50, 445-449.

ADELSON, L., and COLEPAUGH G., et al. A new approach to the education of two and three year old deaf children. 1949, 51, 205-208; 256-258; 273-275; 308-310.

MENDELSON, N., and CANNON, Mary. Experiment in language development for kindergarten deaf children. 1950, 52, 65-66; 98-100.

MACDONALD, Nellie V. Home-made sense training material. 1951, 53, 8-9; 42; 44.

WARREN, Nell. Deaf children with hearing children: a nursery school experiment. 1951, 53, 199; 232-234.

WALLIN, Margaret. A new program of education. 1951, 53, 420-424.

MILLER, Jane (moderator). Nursery and preschool (panel discussion). 1952, 54, 421-434; 464-466.

O'HALLORAN, Dorothy M. A sense training program. 1953, 55, 491-492.

RANKIN, C. E. Preschool unit. 1953, 55, 495-496.

MILLER, June. Vocabulary needs of the preschool deaf child. 1954, 56, 58-62.

ROACH, Robert E. Severe deafness in the pre-speech years. 1954, 56, 153-157.

Infant/Preschool (Contd.)

THE VOLTA REVIEW (Contd.)

HEINRICHS, Eunice L. The nursery in a day school. 1954, 56, 390-392.

STONER, Marguerite. The development of early speech with emphasis on the Synthetic method. 1955, 57, 15-17.

ROTTER, Paul. The development of speech in young children. 1955, 57, 53-57.

LEVINE, Edna S., and GROHT, Mildred A. Nursery school and the deaf child. 1955, 57, 199-209.

GESELL, Arnold. The psychological development of normal and deaf children in their preschool years. 1956, 58, 117-120.

SHANAHAN, Minette. Teaching concepts to preschool deaf and hard of hearing children. 1956, 58, 121-122.

_____. Schools and classes for deaf children under six. 1957, 59, 157-164; 1959, 61, 264-275; 1961, 63, 272-281; 1965, 67, 512-524.

VORCE, Eleanor R. Speech in the preschool for the deaf. 1958, 60, 478-481; 504.

RICHARDSON, Paul C. Developing fundamental speech patterns. 1959, 61, 276-282.

CORY, Patricia B. A child's first books should be fun. 1959, 61, 411-412.

IANDOLI, Edward A., et al. The Albany Hospital Conservation of Hearing Center pre-school testing program. 1959, 61, 452-454; 1960, 62, 63-65; 271-273; 286.

CHAMBERLAIN, Naomi H. A screening outline for determing group readiness. 1959, 61, 455-457; 476.

MILLER, June. Speech and the preschool child. 1960, 62, 315-317.

WHITEHURST, Mary W. Testing the hearing of preschool children. 1961, 63, 430-432; 463.

BURNETT, Alice. Montessori education today and yesterday. 1963, 65, 235-239; 244.

ROBINSON, Geoffrey C. Hearing loss in infants and young preschool children with particular reference to medical participation. 1964, 66, 314-318.

Infant/Preschool (Contd.)

THE VOLTA REVIEW (Contd.)

GRIFFITHS, Ciwa. The auditory approach for preschool deaf children. 1964, 66, 387-397.

CAMBON, K. G. Otological considerations in a preschool hearing program. 1964, 66, 603-609; 651.

VARWIG, Renate. Pediatrics and disorders in communication: social considerations in the care of the preschool hearing handicapped child. 1965, 67, 434-438.

HARRIS, Grace M., and WEBER, Larry. Babies with hearing losses, 1967, 69, 604-609.

NORTHCOTT, Winifred N. Head start program--implications for deaf children. 1968, 70, 106-113.

BELL, Dorothy. Communication problems in preschool children. 1968, 70, 241-245.

STERN, Virginia W. Finger paint on the hearing aid. 1969, 71, 149-154.

STACK, SISTER PATRICIA MARIE. In our program--everyone gets into the act. 1973, 75, 425-430.

GRAMMATICO, Leahea F., and MILLER, Sophia D. Curriculum for the preschool deaf child. 1974, 76, 280-289.

URBAN, Beth. Identification and management of the hearing impairment. 1975, 77, 10-20.

CONNOR, Leo E. New directions in infant programs for the deaf. 1976, 78, 8-15.

KENNEDY, Patricia, NORTHCOTT, Winifred, MCCAULEY, Robert, and WILLIAMS, Susan Myklbye. Longitudinal sociometric and cross-sectional data on mainstreaming hearing impaired children: implications for preschool programming. 1976, 78, 71-81.

BRACKETT, Diane, and HENNIGES, Marian. Communicative interaction of preschool hearing impaired children in an integrated setting. 1976, 78, 276-285.

Infant/Preschool (Contd.)

ANNALS OF THE DEAF

WALDO, Mary S. Early home instruction of deaf-mutes. 1859, 11, 146-150.

PETTENGILL, B. D. The primary education of deaf-mutes and semi-mutes. 1879, 24, 197-202.

POYNTZ, Leonidas. The paramount importance of primary education. 1880, 25, 209-211.

SUTTON, Estella V. Kindergarten work in its relation to primary education. 1893, 38, 25-32.

HUDSON, Alice F. Kindergartens for the deaf. 1894, 39, 25-27.

SUTTON, Estella V. The desirability of kindergartens for the deaf. 1894, 39, 81-92.

MCALONEY, Thomas S. Kindergarten for the deaf. 1898, 43, 184-190.

KIESEL, Theodore A. First steps in teaching language to our little ones. 1906, 51, 208-225; 439-460; 1907, 52, 134-158.

JOHNSON, Richard O. Kindergarten work. 1908, 53, 378-380.

BINGHAM, Cornelia D. Flaws in kindergarten work. 1908, 53, 381-383.

LAMPRECHT, Emil. What games are suitable for little deaf children before the school age? 1911, 56, 472-478.

BATES, Laura M. Montessori models. 1913, 58, 16-25.

LONG, T. Schuyler. The Montessori method: a comparison. 1913, 58, 117-125.

WRIGHT, John D. Sense training. 1921, 66, 473.

TAYLOR, Harris. A proper adjustment of the course of study to meet the requirements of very young children. 1927, 72, 222-236.

ADAMS, Mabel E. A pre-school experiment. 1928, 73, 169-171.

HECTOR, Elizabeth R. The deaf child of preschool age. 1932, 77, 290-291.

KILPATRICK, W. M. Preschool needs of handicapped children--the deaf particularly. 1932, 77, 321-327.

MILLER, Malinda K. The status of the preschool deaf child. 1934, 79, 414-427.

WAGNER, Mary A. The experimental preschool group of Clarke School. 1935, 80, 391-394.

Infant/Preschool (Contd.)

ANNALS OF THE DEAF (Contd.)

SCYSTER, M. Summary of four years' experiment with preschool deaf children at the Illinois School for the Deaf. 1936, 81, 212-230.

BENNING, Doris B. Nursery schools for the deaf. 1938, 83, 417-424.

CLOUD, D. T. The Illinois preschool experiment and present plan. 1940, 85, 234-241.

HENDERSON, J. M. Preschool deaf children. 1944, 89, 297-302.

PATTAN, H. T. Preschool conservation of hearing program. 1955, 100, 319-320.

CRAIG, William N. Effects of preschool training on the development of reading and lipreading skills of deaf children. 1964, 109, 280-296.

RODDA, M., GODSAVE, B., and STEVENS, J. Some aspects of the development of young hearing-impaired children. 1974, 119, 729-735.

PETERSON, Lucy C., and JONES, Robert S. Community-based early childhood programs for the deaf in North Carolina. 1975, 120, 422-426.

SCHWIRIAN, Patricia M. Effects of the presence of a hearing-impaired preschool child in the family on behavior patterns of older "normal" siblings. 1976, 121, 373-380.

BEST, Barbara, and ROBERTS, Gail. Early cognition development in hearing impaired children. 1976, 121, 560-564.

Language Acquisition

THE VOLTA REVIEW

DAVIDSON, S. G. The relation of language to mental development and of speech to language teaching. 1899, 1, 129-139.

ADAMS, Mabel E. The reinforcement of speech by writing. 1899, 1, 144-149.

Language Acquisition (Contd.)

THE VOLTA REVIEW (Contd.)

SMITH, James L. Teaching idiomatic English to the deaf. 1904, 6, 18-34.

BOOTH, Frank W. Language learning by the intuitive method. 1905. 7, 215-224.

ROBINSON, Warren. Every-day language. 1906, 8, 223; 227.

BLISS, Susan E. Language work in intermediate grades. 1907, 9, 143-153.

DAVIDSON, S. G. The proper treatment of the verb. 1907, 9, 221-230.

MIRRIELEES, Ruchiel. The beginnings of language and reading. 1909, 11, 385-388.

HILLIARD, Ethel. Corrective work in language. 1909, 11, 388-397.

JONES, J. W. The development of language in the deaf child. 1910, 12, 299-306.

ROBINSON, Warren. The vocabulary of the deaf. 1910, 12, 553-560.

LEONARD, Eleanor C. Which tense? 1912, 14, 261-262.

BUELL, Edith M. Word-pictures as a means of mental development. 1912, 14, 495-499.

BLAIR, Cora L. Connected language. 1912, 14, 499-501.

GRUVER, Elbert A. The teaching of technical grammar. 1913, 15, 293-297.

BARNES, F. G. The development of language. 1914, 16, 177-187.

BABCOCK, E. J., and Jessie T. A plea for the play coefficient in teaching conversation to deaf children. 1914, 16, 613-616.

HIGGINS, Lydia F. Language in the home. 1915, 17, 442-444.

BENEDICT, A. L. English spelling. 1915, 17, 477-481.

BRUHN, Martha E. Practical exercises on advanced study of homophenous words. 1916, 18, 215-224; 331-339; 361-368; 447-453.

BARNES, F. G. Talks to young teachers of language. 1916, 18, 501-505.

WORCESTER, Eleanor R. Simple language for young children. 1917, 19, 673-679.

WALKER, Jane B. Winged words. 1918, 20, 631-633.

Language Acquisition (Contd.)

THE VOLTA REVIEW (Contd.)

PINTNER, Rudolf. The measurement of language ability and language progress of deaf children. 1918, 20, 755-766.

ROE, W. Carey. Language and the deaf child. 1919, 21, 49-52.

ROE, W. Carey. Reading and language development. 1920, 22, 80-84.

COX, Mary R. Improving the use of language by the deaf. 1920, 22, 188-193.

BENEDICT, A. L. The extent of the vocabulary. 1920, 22, 494-500.

DRIGGS, Frank M. The use of English in schools for the deaf. 1920, 22, 529-535.

JONES, Mabel K. Language development for primary grades. 1920, 22, 597-603; 680-684; 790-792.

JONES, J. W. Language for advanced grades of deaf pupils. 1920, 22, 655-662.

BROWN, J. The improved development and use of language by our deaf pupils. 1921, 23, 78-82.

GOODWIN, Elizabeth. An experiment in teaching languages on individual lines. 1921, 23, 435-445.

GUINNESS, S., GOODSPEED, E., and ATWOOD, M. Language in intermediate grades. 1922, 24, 1-9.

ERVIN, Annie M. Some language difficulties. 1922, 24, 64-70.

WETHERILL, Stella J. Technical language in an intermediate class. 1923, 25, 5-6.

FITZGERALD, Edith. Technical language work in the primary dept. 1923, 25, 205-214.

DIBOS, Lucille, et al. Language. 1925, 27, 24-30.

ADAMS, Mabel E. A symposium on "live language." 1925, 27, 30-40.

WILLOUGHBY, J. Evelyn. Suggestions for action work. 1925, 27, 273-276; 1926, 28, 145-147.

_____. A device for teaching months and seasons. 1926, 28, 101-112.

UPHAM, Louise. Language lessons for second year classes. 1926, 28, 193-195.

Language Acquisition (Contd.)

THE VOLTA REVIEW (Contd.)

BRUCE, M. Ethel. Application of language in the lower grades. 1926, 28, 198-200.

EVANS, Mildred. Sugar coated drills. 1926, 28, 201-203.

BEATTY, Mary M. Developing the power of thought in connection with language teaching. 1926, 28, 203-204.

THOMPSON, Etta M. The use of diaries in language work. 1926, 28, 205-206.

WELSH, Eugenia T. Teaching practical language. 1926, 28, 247-249.

BUELL, Edith M. Word pictures. 1926, 28, 289-295.

ROE, W. Carey. Language development. 1926, 28, 419-421.

MOORE, Helen T. Teaching news condensing. 1926, 28, 589-590.

DAWES, Rachel E. Primary language. 1926, 28, 691-693.

JOINER, Enfield. Original language in the primary grades. 1926, 28, 693-695.

MORRIS, M. Esther. Intermediate language in a special class. 1926, 28, 699-702.

DONALD, Ida M. English in the intermediate grades. 1926, 28, 702-705.

CALDWELL, William A. Devices for teaching English. 1926, 28, 706-707.

GUMMARUN, Mary D. A year of language projects. 1927, 29, 91-97.

ORR, Marie P. An exercise in connected language. 1927, 29, 102-103.

WETHERILL, Stella J. Intermediate language. 1927, 29, 250-253.

SWAYZE, Rachel H. How we can improve the language in the primary department of our school. 1927, 29, 356-358.

AVERY, Elizabeth B. Teaching the passive voice. 1927, 29, 473-477.

BANKS, Marjorie S. An amplified idea. 1927, 29, 696-698.

FITZGERALD, Edith. Direct and indirect discourse. 1927, 29, 700-703.

BRILL, Tobias. Direct and indirect discourse. 1928, 30, 49-51.

ROBERTS, M. Some special phases of language work in our primary and lower intermediate grades. 1928, 30, 222-223.

THORNTON, E. Classification and analysis of language errors. 1928, 30, 224-226.

Language Acquisition (Contd.)

THE VOLTA REVIEW (Contd.)

GORDON, Mary L. Thoughts on the articles. 1928, 30, 229-230.

WINSTON, Matie E. Classification of words. 1928, 30, 274-276.

BUELL, Edith M. Ask, say and tell. 1928, 30, 597-601.

KIRK, Louise. Teaching language to the deaf through poetry. 1929, 31, 33-35.

BLANKENSHIP, Ota C. A language game--primary work. 1929, 31, 113-114.

SMITH, Margaret C. Developing "have" and "be" by the Barry method. 1929, 31, 309-312.

HOBART, Elsa L. Devices for English teaching. 1930, 32, 136-138.

JACKSON, Anne W. Ladders to vocabulary building. 1930, 32, 170-172.

CLEARY, E. P. Teaching language to the deaf. 1930, 32, 174-175.

DUNLAP, S. C. Second grade language (third year). 1930, 32, 411-413.

HURST, Fannie D. Type-errors in language of the deaf. 1930, 32, 511-512.

SMITH, James L. Teaching idiomatic language. 1930, 32, 578-579.

STRONG, Arch. Action work in the fourth grade. 1930, 32, 580-581.

QUINN, Josephine. The use of symbols in language teaching. 1930, 32, 611-612.

KEEFER, M. B. Original language in the primary classes. 1930, 32, 619-622.

BUELL, Edith M. A comparison of the "Barry Five Slate System" and the "Fitzgerald Key." 1931, 33, 5-19.

DONEGHY, Lucy. Some helps in language teaching. 1931, 33, 122; 135.

BUELL, Edith M. In the classroom: adjective phrases (story suggested by pictures). 1931, 33, 248-250; 348-249; 367; 371; 502-506.

MOORE, Helen T. Corrective work on the passive voice. 1931, 33, 351-352; 367; 371.

WARD, R. H. Drill exercises in punctuation. 1931, 33, 388-389.

RUPLEY, Stella. Language games as a help in teaching language. 1931, 33, 394-395.

MITCHELL, Dorothy. Conjugations in the first grade. 1931, 33, 490-491.

Language Acquisition (Contd.)

THE VOLTA REVIEW (Contd.)

LEWIS, Sarah E. The Wing symbols. 1931, 33, 491; 507.

MCALONEY, Thomas S. The Barry (five) slate system. 1931, 33, 530-542.

WATROUS, Helen D. Primary language and reading. 1932, 34, 215-216.

LINDSTROM, Thure A. Learning language through reading. 1932, 34, 269-271.

GROHT, Mildred A. On making language natural. 1932, 34, 368-369.

MACMILLAN, Betty. The value of diagrams in teaching grammar. 1932, 34, 377-378.

STRAUCH, Genevieve B. Some phases of composition. 1932, 34, 613-617.

INGVARSSON, Ivar M. Language teaching in a school for the deaf. 1933, 35, 5-10; 346-350; 352.

BERRY, Helen. The Hayne grocery store (an activity). 1933, 35, 11-12; 41.

GARE, Marion W. Teaching the present perfect tense. 1933, 35, 73-77.

ROSE, Lillian. Duration of time. 1933, 35, 214-216.

EISEMAN, Marie H. Teaching the comparison of adjectives. 1933, 35, 218-219; 234-235.

GROHT, Mildred A. Composition in the grammar grades. 1933, 35, 251-254.

BENNETT, Josephine. "To have" and "to be" in the primary grades. 1933, 35, 254-258.

MAXSON, Kathryn P. Calendar work. 1933, 35, 258-259; 272.

ASHBY, Madelyn T. Language in the fifth grade. 1933, 35, 422-423.

KAWAMOTO, Unosuke. The psychological basis of teaching language to the deaf. 1934, 36, 12-16.

BUELL, Edith M. Lessons on relative pronouns. 1934, 36, 146-147; 184-185.

PETERSON, Edwin G. Itinerant teachers of language. 1934, 36, 197-198.

GROHT, Mildred A. Suggestions for teaching English. 1934, 36, 199-204; 244.

Language Acquisition (Contd.)

THE VOLTA REVIEW (Contd.)

BUELL, Edith M. Lessons on relative clauses. 1934, 36, 270-271; 312-313.

MURPHY, Margaret. A third grade lesson in questions. 1934, 36, 526-528.

GROHT, Mildred A. Individual language drill stories. 1934, 36, 528-530.

ORR, Marie P. Incentives to better English. 1934, 36, 592; 630.

GROHT, Mildred A. Oral English. 1934, 36, 650-654; 693.

MILLER, Marjorie. First steps in language development. 1934, 36, 665; 697.

CRAWFORD, May T. Three plans for teaching language. 1935, 37, 13-14; 51-52.

WELTY, Harry L. Teaching the use of the dictionary. 1936, 38, 133-136; 178-179.

SMITH, Gladys, E. Drill and non-drill verbs. 1936, 38, 270-273.

VAN NEST, Mary R. Language project (personal description). 1936, 38, 509; 544-545.

DAVIES, Rachel D. My new job. 1937, 39, 138-139.

GROHT, Mildred A. More notes on the teaching of language. 1937, 39, 197-200; 244.

QUINN, Josephine. First year's work. 1937, 39, 284-285; 316.

GROHT, Mildred A. Oral English. 1938, 40, 631-632.

FORD, Catherine. Language for the slow child. 1938, 40, 681-684.

HAMEL, Clara A. The teaching of high school English. 1938, 40, 685-688.

FINCH, Wallace J. The use of language in industry. 1938, 40, 688-689.

LACY, Mabel V. Language work in the Honolulu School for the Deaf. 1938, 40, 692-695.

QUINN, Josephine. Fundamental language. 1939, 41, 104-105; 243.

VINSON, Marietta R. English for the deaf. 1939, 41, 271-273.

Language Acquisition (Contd.)

THE VOLTA REVIEW (Contd.)

WHILDIN, Olive A. Language for the young deaf child in the school, in the home. 1940, 42, 641-648.

GROHT, Mildred A. Adjustment to industry through language. 1940, 42, 648-655.

WEAVER, James A. Teaching language in a school for the deaf. 1941, 43, 169-171; 210; 246-248; 280-282.

RICHARDS, Edith. A device for first year language work. 1941, 43, 174; 218.

CROUTER, Alan Y. Let's teach language. 1941, 43, 297-300; 340-342; 376-378; 399-400.

KNOX, Addie C. The teaching of common things. 1941, 43, 362-363.

HEIDER, Fritz, and Grace M. Comparison of sentence structure of deaf and hearing children. 1941, 43, 364-367; 406; 536-540; 564; 599-604; 628-630.

INGLE, Helen F. Language for the deaf child. 1941, 43, 645-648; 690; 726-728; 748.

HOLLEY, Minnie C. Developing a consciousness of language. 1941, 43, 660; 685-686.

MILLER, Marjorie. The present tense is alive. 1943, 45, 331; 370.

CRANDELL, Marian P. Natural language for the deaf. 1944, 46, 264-266; 304-306.

BENNETT, Josephine. A verb device. 1944, 46, 325-330.

COTA, Agnes. What can basic English offer us? 1944, 46, 441-443; 480.

STREETER, Helen M. Language in the primary dormitory. 1945, 47, 549-553; 596.

HARKNESS, Margaret M. Language in the pre-school and primary classes. 1946, 48, 676-677.

NUMBERS, Mary E. Language in the middle grades. 1946, 48, 677-679.

BRILL, Tobias. Language in advanced grades. 1946, 48, 680-681.

HEIDER, Fritz. On the construction of a language usage test for the deaf. 1946, 48, 742-744.

Language Acquisition (Contd.)

THE VOLTA REVIEW (Contd.)

KELLER, Lillian, et al. Language for the deaf. 1948, 50, 432-442.

DOCTOR, Powrie V. On teaching the abstract to the deaf. 1950, 52, 547-549; 568-572.

GROHT, Mildred A. Language for the deaf. 1953, 55, 243-246; 274-276.

GROHT, Mildred A. The teaching of vocabulary--an introduction. 1954, 56, 57.

SHELLGRAIN, Evelyn M. Realizing, enriching, and anticipating vocabulary for primary deaf classes. 1954, 56, 62-65.

NUMBERS, Mary E. A word is a word is a word. 1954, 56, 66-71.

PITTINGER, Priscilla. Preparation for the teaching of vocabulary. 1954, 56, 71-74.

TIBERIO, C. S. Teaching vocabulary in the school shop. 1954, 56, 75-77.

NEW, Mary C. The deaf child's speech vocabulary. 1954, 56, 105-108.

BUCHMAN, Martha. The role of language in speech training for the hearing impaired child. 1954, 56, 205-208.

DOCTOR, Powrie V. Bibliography for the teaching of vocabulary to the deaf. 1954, 56, 217-218.

MANNEN, Grace. Everyday expressions through speech: their understanding and use. 1956, 58, 57-60.

RICHARDSON, Paul C. Expressive writing for the deaf. 1956, 58, 161-163.

STRENG, Alice. Action verbs and their meanings. 1956, 58, 305-309.

GROHT, Mildred A. The language arts in a school for the deaf. 1957, 59, 337-342.

GIANGRECO, Marianne, and C. Joseph. Teaching English to teenagers. 1957, 59, 437-439.

PITTINGER, Priscilla. The development of language. 1958, 60, 12-20.

SISTER JEANNE d'ARC. The development of connected language skills. 1958, 60, 58-65.

PAULS, Miriam D. Language development through reading. 1958, 60, 105-107; 142.

Language Acquisition (Contd.)

THE VOLTA REVIEW (Contd.)

BOLLBACK, Betty L. Visual language. 1958, 60, 108-109.

STRICKLAND, Ruth G. The interrelationship between language and reading. 1958, 60, 334-336.

GROHT, Mildred A. Living language for the deaf. 1958, 60, 347-350.

STRENG, Alice. Language disability in children with hearing impairments. 1958, 60, 350-357.

TERVOORT, Bernard Th. Acoustic and visual language communicating systems. 1958, 60, 374-380.

SISTER MARY WALTER. The calendar dynamic. 1958, 60, 439; 464.

PITTINGER, Priscilla. What is a basic vocabulary. 1958, 60, 528-529; 531.

MANNEN, Grace. Conversational language (parts I-V). 1959, 61, 11-16; 66-70; 89; 137-141; 170-177; 225-227.

WOODWARD, Helen. Language and the elementary school curriculum. 1959, 61, 63-65; 89.

TAUSSIG, Eleanor. Language development as a factor in school placement. 1959, 61, 168-169; 193.

LORENE, SISTER JAMES. Pronouns puzzle primary pupils. 1960, 62, 17-19; 46.

SISTER ANNE BERNADINE. Let's increase their vocabularies. 1960, 62, 218-219.

WOOD, Nancy. Language in personality development. 1960, 62, 321-322.

CALDWELL, Elizabeth H. Some adventures in language development. 1961, 63, 60-64.

JONES, Kate-Helen. Communication skills. 1961, 63, 72-77; 94.

PUGH, Bessie. Teaching children to use the dictionary. 1961, 63, 178-185.

BOWN, Jesse C., and MECHAM, Merlin J. The assessment of verbal language development in deaf children. 1961, 63, 228-230.

FEHR, Joann D. Programing language for deaf children. 1962, 64, 14-21.

SCOTT, Elizabeth V. Language and reading. 1962, 64, 128-132.

Language Acquisition (Contd.)

THE VOLTA REVIEW (Contd.)

STUCKLESS, E. Ross, and BIRCH, Jack W. A programed approach to written language development in deaf children. 1962, 64, 415-417.

GOETZINGER, Cornelius P. Effects of small perceptive losses on language and on speech discrimination. 1962, 64, 408-414.

SIMMONS, Audrey A. A comparison of the type-token ratio of spoken and written language of deaf and hearing children. 1962, 64, 417-421.

WITHROW, Margaret S. Reinforcing speech and language in the family. 1962, 64, 422-424.

RICHARDSON, Paul C. Developing natural time expressions. 1962, 64, 543-545.

EWING, Alexander W. Linguistic development and mental growth in hearing impaired children. 1963, 65, 180-187.

BALTZER, Susanna. Language problems in speech therapy programs for teenagers. 1963, 65, 401-406.

FOY, Robert E. Teaching language appreciation to the deaf. 1964, 66, 205-207.

SISTER M. THERESE. Illustrated verbs. 1964, 66, 272-274.

GRAMMATICO, Leahea. Building a language foundation at the preschool level. 1964, 66, 378-381.

HART, Beatrice O. The language program at the Lexington School for the Deaf. 1964, 66, 468-473.

GANTENBEIN, Andrew. Expressive inner language for the deaf through a descriptive grammar program. 1964, 66, 521-525.

ELLIOTT, Shirley S. Structural language blocks. 1964, 66, 526-531.

MCGRADY, Harold J. The influence of a program of instruction upon the conceptual thinking of the deaf. 1964, 66, 531-536.

WITHROW, Frank B. Paired-associate learning of moving sequences by deaf children. 1964, 66, 555-557.

CALDWELL, Elizabeth H. The hyphenated subject. 1964, 66, 557-561.

HART, Beatrice O., and ROSENSTEIN, Joseph. Examining the language behavior of deaf children. 1964, 66, 679-682.

Language Acquisition (Contd.)

THE VOLTA REVIEW (Contd.)

GANTENBEIN, Andrew, and NOLLER, Joanne. Descriptive grammar, an approach to expressive language for the auditorially impaired. 1965, 67, 136-143.

HARRINGTON, D. A. Language and perception. 1965, 67, 191-196.

SISTER JAMES LORENE. Developing language through vertical learning and horizontal association. 1965, 67, 201-207.

BOONE, DANIEL R. Infant speech and language development. 1965, 67, 414-419.

MULHOLLAND, Ann M. The Columbia University Institute in Language. 1965, 67, 623-626.

MCNEILL, David. The capacity for language acquisition. 1966, 68, 17-33.

FURTH, Hans G. Research with the deaf: implications for language and cognition. 1966, 68, 34-56.

COOPER, Robert L., and ROSENSTEIN, Joseph. Language acquisition of deaf children. 1966, 68, 58-67.

SCHMITT, Philip J. Language instruction for the deaf. 1966, 68, 85-105.

SIMMONS, Audrey A. Language growth for the preschool deaf child. 1966, 68, 201-205.

NORTHCOTT, Winifred. Language development through parent counseling and guidance. 1966, 68, 356-360.

CARPENTER, Craig L. Patterns of language used by kindergarten children. 1966, 68, 574-578.

STUCKLESS, E. Ross. Objective evaluation of original written language of deaf students. 1966, 68, 679-685; 775-776.

PARSONS, Juanita L. Let the deaf create. 1967, 69, 58-60.

KATES, Solis L. The education of the deaf and the role of language. 1967, 69, 384-390.

SIMMONS, Audrey A. Teaching aural language. 1968, 70, 26-30.

BUCKLER, Sister Marie Suzanne. Expanding language through patterning. 1968, 70, 89-96.

Language Acquisition (Contd.)

THE VOLTA REVIEW (Contd.)

SIMMONS, Audrey A. Content subjects through language. 1968, 70, 481-486.

STRENG, Alice H. The language arts in the curriculum for deaf children. 1968, 70, 487-492.

SMULLEN, Hazel S. Beginning functional language. 1968, 70, 496-499.

BENDER, Ruth E. Teaching the nonverbal child. 1968, 70, 537-548.

MCCOMBS, Maxwell E. and Zoe. Descriptive style of deaf children. 1969, 71, 23-26.

SCHWARTZBERG, Joanne G. A young deaf child learns emotional concepts from stick figures and faces. 1969, 71, 228-232.

BELL, Janice W. Visual language. 1971, 73, 157-160.

RUSH, Mary Lou. Writing for children with language and reading deficiencies. 1972, 74, 492-501.

FLETCHER, J. D., and STAUFFER, C. M. Learning language by computer. 1973, 75, 302-311.

DRY, Edward B. The use of expressions in the classroom. 1973, 75, 486-492.

WILSON, Gary B., ROSS, Mark, and CALVERT, Donald R. An experimental study of the semantics of deafness. 1974, 76, 408-414.

HARGIS, Charles H., and LAMM, Carolyn O. Have and be: a lexicon of verb forms. 1974, 76, 420-424.

BECKER, Sheila. The performance of deaf and hearing children on a logical discovery table. 1974, 76, 537-545.

WILBUR, Ronnie B., and QUIGLEY, Stephen P. Syntactic structures in the written language of deaf children. 1975, 77, 194-203.

WOODWARD, Helen M. E. Criterion-referenced testing and the measurement of language growth. 1975, 77, 229-240.

WOODWARD, Helen M. E. Measuring language growth in older deaf children: a classified bibliography (August 1974). 1975, 77, 241-242.

HARGIS, Charles H. Just, even, and only: a lexicon of modifiers. 1975, 77, 368-374.

Language Acquisition (Contd.)

THE VOLTA REVIEW (Contd.)

KIELY, Arlene. Lend me your ears. . . or at least draw me a picture. 1975, 77, 423-430.

MOOG, Jean S. Language instruction determined by diagnostic observation. 1975, 77, 561-570.

KRETSCHMER, Richard R. Language acquisition. 1976, 78, 60-67 (monograph).

MENYUK, Paula. Cognition and language. 1976, 78, 250-257.

ANNALS OF THE DEAF

BARTLETT, D. E. The acquisition of language. 1851, 3, 83-92.

BURNET, John R., and PORTER, Samuel. Under what forms do deaf-mutes apprehend words? 1858, 10, 228-241.

BURNET, John R. Is it easier for deaf-mutes to spell words mentally, or to regard them as units? 1859, 11, 17-32.

PORTER, Samuel. The instruction of the deaf and dumb in grammar. 1869, 14, 30-48.

FAY, Edward A. The acquisition of language by deaf-mutes. 1869, 14, 193-204.

KEEP, J. R. How should deaf-mute children learn verbal language? 1870, 15, 28-41.

BARNARD, F. A. The difficulties of the deaf and dumb in the acquisition of language. 1870, 15, 161-165.

GILLET, H. S. Language. 1870, 15, 232-244.

PETTENGILL, B. D. The acquisition of written language by deaf-mutes. 1874, 19, 230-237.

PETTENGILL, J. H. Language: its nature and functions. 1875, 20, 1-26.

PETTENGILL, B. D. The natural method of teaching language. 1876, 21, 1-10.

Language Acquisition (Contd.)

ANNALS OF THE DEAF (Contd.)

PERRY, Charles S. The acquisition of language. 1877, 22, 72-73.

PORTER, Samuel. A method of teaching complex and compound sentences. 1877, 22, 232-233.

HODGSON, E. A. The division of words into syllables. 1882, 27, 142-146.

PETTENGILL, B. D. Methods of teaching language. 1882, 27, 203-208.

BELL, Alexander G. Upon a method of teaching language to a very young congenitally deaf child. 1883, 28, 124; 139.

MOFFAT, L. Voice, alphabetics, and language. 1885, 30, 111-121; 251-258; 1886, 31, 111-119; 180-191.

CALDWELL, William A. Expedients for teaching language. 1886, 31, 169-180.

WING, George. The theory and practice of grammatical methods. 1887, 32, 84-92.

WALKER, H. D. Sentence forms and analysis as set forth by symbols and diagrams. 1887, 32, 217-224.

JENKINS, William G. Teaching the relative pronouns. 1888, 33, 229-234.

FOX, Thomas F. The use of the dictionary in teaching language. 1888, 33, 259-262.

WALKER, H. D. Idioms. 1889, 34, 21-29.

MOSELY, T. F. Learn idioms by using them. 1890, 35, 14-19.

ASHLEY, J. B. Language for the deaf. 1890, 35, 250-255.

DODDS, P. The natural development of language: its effect on oral teaching. 1891, 36, 178-181.

HURD, Anna C. Asked, said, told. 1892, 37, 94-103.

PORTER, Sarah H. Language. 1892, 37, 219-227.

GILLESPIE, John A. The presentation of language. 1892, 37, 245-249.

GREENBERGER, D. Language-teaching. 1892, 37, 267-279.

ADAMS, Ida H. Primary conversation lessons. 1893, 38, 112-118.

Language Acquisition (Contd.)

ANNALS OF THE DEAF (Contd.)

ARCHER, Tunis V. The natural method of teaching language. 1893, 38, 254-256.

HUMASON, Thomas A. Words and language. 1894, 39, 249-258.

JENKINS, William G. Language and thought. 1895, 40, 1-14.

HURD, Anna C. An outline of primary language work. 1895, 40, 97-121; 187-206; 274-285.

WING, George. The acquisition of language by deaf-mutes. 1895, 40, 231-235.

FLETCHER, Katharine. Concerning aim and method in language teaching. 1896, 41, 1-12.

ADAMS, Mabel E. The language sense. 1896, 41, 278-292.

ADAMS, Mabel E. Natural language plus drill. 1897, 42, 160-179; 210-223.

ROBINSON, Warren. A new device in language teaching. 1898, 43, 78-87; 170-183.

HULL, Susanna E. The psychological method of teaching language. 1898, 43, 190-196.

GÖPFERT, E. The place of writing in the language instruction of the true deaf mutes, especially the less intelligent. 1899, 44, 92-110.

PUTNAM, George H. Lessons in language. 1900, 45, 7-16.

TILLINGHAST, Edward S. Memory training and the teaching of language. 1900, 45, 184-193.

SCOTT, Wirt A. Language teaching in connection with other studies. 1900, 45, 265-271.

DODDS, P. The teaching of language during the first, second, and third year of a deaf child's school life. 1900, 45, 275-296.

MCCLURE, George M. The correction of errors in language work. 1901, 46, 21-23.

MORRIS, Minnie E. The correction and prevention of mistakes in language. 1901, 46, 242-249.

JENKINS, Weston. The teaching of English. 1901, 46, 488-492.

Language Acquisition (Contd.)

ANNALS OF THE DEAF (Contd.)

PETERSON, Peter N. A plea for more technical language in the classroom. 1902, 47, 23-30.

TILLINGHAST, Edward S. Notes on language teaching. 1902, 47, 137-143; 1903, 48, 33-44.

BOOTH, Frank W. The lesson to be learned by the general teacher from teaching language to the deaf. 1902, 47, 323-330.

LONG, T. Schuyler. The story in language teaching. 1902, 47, 331-339.

ADAMS, Mabel E. Three years of language. 1904, 49, 209-229; 301-318.

REED, Katherine F. Language through the grades. 1904, 49, 252-260.

HURD, Anna C. Primary language. 1906, 51, 312-314.

STORY, Arthur J. Why the deaf do not use language. 1907, 52, 183-201.

BALDRIAN, Karl. Differences in the natural and artificial acquisition of language. 1908, 53, 7-15.

COBURN, Alice T. Language in the primary grades. 1908, 53, 466-473.

FONNER, Mary D. Primary language. 1908, 53, 473-478.

ADAMS, Mabel E. A way of imparting notions of tense to young deaf children. 1909, 54, 160-166.

REED, Katherine F. Material for language work. 1910, 55, 172-177.

JONES, John W. The development of language in the deaf child. 1910, 55, 353-363.

_____. The acquisition of language. 1910, 55, 486-493.

DAVIDSON, Samuel G. The principles of language teaching. 1911, 56, 422-430.

BUELL, Edith M. Word pictures as a means of mental development. 1912, 57, 512-518.

ROBINSON, Warren. The bracket device for teaching language. 1913, 58, 249-271.

Language Acquisition (Contd.)

ANNALS OF THE DEAF (Contd.)

DAVIDSON, Samuel G. Mental development through language study. 1914, 59, 113-117.

HOWSON, James W. Teaching language to the deaf. 1914, 59, 214-223.

STRUCK, A. N. The deaf and the dictionary. 1915, 60, 233-238.

GALE, Edward P. More English as it is spoken. 1915, 60, 329-333.

KELLY, Emma. The difficulties of language teaching. 1916, 61, 124-127.

TAYLOR, Harris. Certain accepted elements of a course of study: the five-slate system of language teaching. 1916, 61, 393-404.

BARNES, F. G. The first steps in original composition. 1917, 62, 145-150.

PINTNER, Rudolf, and PATERSON, Donald. A measurement of the language ability of deaf children. 1917, 62, 211-239.

DAVIDSON, Samuel G. Some observations on language methods. 1917, 62, 308-320.

SHERIDAN, Laura C. Teaching the article and related things. 1917, 62, 440-447.

FITZGERALD, Edith. Language building in the primary grades. 1918, 63, 342-353.

WEAVER, James A. Some remarks on the teaching of language. 1918, 63, 407-415.

THOLLON, B. The meaning of words and their value. 1918, 63, 435-440.

BARNES, F. G. The elementary language lesson. 1918, 63, 446-450.

TAYLOR, Nellie M. How I interested my class in calendar work. 1918, 63, 475-478.

STEWART, W. J. Language teaching. 1919, 64, 191-196.

COX, Mary R. The use of language (how it may be improved). 1920, 65, 301-311.

JONES, John W. Language for advanced grades of deaf pupils. 1920, 65, 378-394.

WEAVER, James A. Simplifying the simple. 1921, 66, 147-164.

Language Acquisition (Contd.)

ANNALS OF THE DEAF (Contd.)

THOLLON, B. Classification of the determinatives of the noun. 1921, 66, 261-265.

DEMOTTE, Amelia. Language. 1922, 67, 386-392.

CROKER, Gertrude W. Intermediate language work. 1923, 68, 384-392.

HENDERSON, Myrtle W. Intermediate language. 1925, 70, 311-319.

PEET, Elizabeth. More and better English. 1925, 70, 328-338.

PADDLEFORD, Lillian. Punctuation as a means, not an end. 1926, 71, 208-213.

TOMB, John W. On the intuitive capacity of children to understand spoken language. 1926, 71, 270-273.

PEET, Elizabeth. Straight language for the deaf. 1926, 71, 348-351.

POLLARD, Nannie A. An outline of first-year language work at the Minnesota school. 1926, 71, 399-407.

READ, Utten. Spelling. 1926, 71, 407-419.

ROSE, M. Lilliam. Tell-ask-say. 1927, 72, 415-426.

INGLE, Helen F. Outline for pronoun work. 1927, 72, 427-432.

SENSENIG, Barton. A thousand words our deaf pupils should know when they leave school. 1928, 73 216-221.

HURST, Fannie D. Drill type-errors out by drilling smooth phrasing in. 1928, 73, 221-230.

SHIFLET, Cleta. Drill verbs. 1928, 73, 251-253.

WHITTLESEY, Addie. News. 1928, 73, 257-262.

HURST, Fannie D. Some methods of teaching grammar. 1928, 73, 344-355; 442-458.

DAY, Herbert E. Bridging our educational gap by broader use of English. 1929, 74, 288-291.

STEWART, W. J. Lessons in English. 1929, 74, 486-496; 1930, 75, 115-124; 222-231; 375-389; 1932, 77, 335-342; 1937, 82, 272-279.

HURST, Fannie D. Some work in grammar. 1930, 75, 104-115.

ORMAN, James N. The language sense. 1930, 75, 124-131.

Language Acquisition (Contd.)

ANNALS OF THE DEAF (Contd.)

DAY, Herbert E. Outline of language for deaf children. 1930, 75, 291-292.

GROFF, Marné L. An analysis of first-year vocabularies of the public residential schools for the deaf in the U. S. 1932, 77, 304-314; 1933, 78, 120-131; 219-228; 418-427; 1934, 79, 147-160.

HURST, Fannie D. Composition--a live issue. 1933, 78, 229-248.

MEYER, Max F. Can teaching the deaf profit from philology? 1934, 79, 95-108.

LETZTER, Margaret C. Enriching the vocabulary. 1935, 80, 264-271.

THOMPSON, William H. An analysis of errors in written composition by deaf children. 1936, 81, 95-99.

GROFF, Marné L. The psychology of language with special reference to the deaf. 1936, 81, 113-125.

CROUTER, Alan Y. The infinitive of purpose. 1936, 81, 204-208.

RAWLINGS, Charles G. Review of "logical system of language-teaching and an analysis of the English language." 1938, 83, 6-7.

YELTON, D. C. Language and the deaf. 1938, 83, 114-119.

HURST, Fannie D. Vocabulary building. 1938, 83, 209-217.

CROUTER, Alan Y. "A" and "the". 1938, 83, 323-329.

ORMAN, James N. A verb-type method of language instruction. 1938, 83, 330-337.

ROBINSON, Mary W. Outline of composition work in the intermediate grades of the California school. 1939, 84, 445-448.

MARBUT, Musa. A fundamental vocabulary suggested for deaf children for the first five years in school. 1941, 86, 137-158.

IRION, Theo. W. The place of language in mental development. 1941, 86, 364-373.

CROSBY, Laura L. Suggestions for composition work in advanced classes. 1942, 87, 123-130.

VOELKER, Charles H. The vocabulary to teach deaf children. 1942, 87, 266-273.

MOSSEL, Max N. Words, words everywhere but--. 1943, 88, 258-269.

Language Acquisition (Contd.)

ANNALS OF THE DEAF (Contd.)

LAURITSEN, Wesley. Language teaching--the greatest thing. 1943, 88, 296-299.

AVERY, Elizabeth B. The habitual present. 1944, 89, 147-159.

DIETRICH, Rose I. Goals in language development for the deaf and the hard of hearing. 1945, 90, 121-127.

STEWART, Helen L. A vocabulary project. 1945, 90, 154-163.

QUINN, Josephine. First year's language work. 1946, 91, 177-189.

REAY, Edward W. A comparison between deaf and hearing children in regard to the use of verbs and nouns in compositions describing a short motion picture story. 1946, 91, 453-491.

NELSON, Myrthel S. The evolutionary process of methods of teaching language to the deaf with a survey of the methods now employed. 1949, 94, 230-294; 354-396; 491-511.

FITZGERALD, Margaret H. Vocabulary development for acoustically handicapped children. 1949, 94, 409-449.

_____. Language outline (C.I.D.). 1950, 95, 353-378.

_____. A study of the proceedings of the Convention of American Instructors of the Deaf, 1850-1949: language. 1950, 95, 501-518.

INGVARSSON, Ivar M. Language teaching in schools for the deaf: psychological aspects. 1952, 97, 267-281.

GIANGRECO, Joseph. Developing language through a daily news period. 1954, 99, 380-390.

WALTER, Jean. A study of the written sentence construction of a group of profoundly deaf children. 1955, 100, 235-252.

STREETER, Helen M. A study of the dependent clause in primary reading of the deaf. 1956, 101, 288-297.

BRANDON, Wallace R. Foreign language study and the deaf student's vocabulary. 1957, 102, 312-318.

FUSFELD, Irving S. How the deaf communicate--written language. 1958, 103, 255-263.

THOMAS, Elizabeth S. A system of sentence structure for the development of language for the deaf. 1958, 103, 510-523.

Language Acquisition (Contd.)

ANNALS OF THE DEAF (Contd.)

STRENG, Alice. On improving the teaching of language. 1958, 103, 553-563.

WALTER, Jean. Some further observations on the written sentence construction of profoundly deaf children. 1959, 104, 282-285.

SISTER MARY WALTER. The Fitzgerald Key on wheels. 1959, 104, 366-371.

PATTON, Livingston. Question forms. 1960, 105, 240-248.

SCOUTEN, Edward L. Meeting the problem of literalness in deaf students (college prep classes). 1960, 105, 425-426.

KENT, Margaret S. Language for young deaf children. 1960, 105, 435-436.

TERVOORT, Bernard T. Esoteric symbolism in the communication behavior of young deaf children. 1961, 106, 436-480.

BIRCH, Jack W., and STUCKLESS, E. Ross. Programming instruction in written language for deaf children. 1963, 108, 317-336.

CRAIG, William N., et al. Comparison of two methods of teaching written language to deaf students. 1964, 109, 248-256.

RUSH, Mary Lou. Programmed instruction for "The Language of Directions." 1964, 109, 356-358.

LLOYD, Glenn T. Teaching language to the individual deaf child. 1964, 109, 359-363.

PFAU, Glenn S. Project LIFE pi analysis. 1969, 114, 829-837.

MOORES, Donald F. Psycholinguistics and deafness. 1970, 115, 37-48.

LENNEBERG, Eric H. What is meant by a bilogical approach to language? 1970, 115, 67-72.

GOSS, Richard N. Language used by mothers of deaf children and mothers of hearing children. 1970, 115, 93-96.

ALTERMAN, Arthur I. Language and the education of children with early profound deafness. 1970, 115, 514-521.

MARSHALL, William A. Contextual constraint on deaf and hearing children. 1970, 115, 682-689.

Language Acquisition (Contd.)

ANNALS OF THE DEAF (Contd.)

OLSON, Jack R. A "naturalistic" approach to teaching oral and written communication. 1970, 115, 690-692.

WINKELMAN, Nancy L. The news story can help students learn to write. 1971, 116, 20-24.

EACHUS, Todd. Modification of sentence writing by deaf children. 1971, 116, 29-43.

KLOPPING, Henry W. E. Language understanding of deaf students under three auditory-visual stimulus conditions. 1972, 117, 389-396.

GRISWOLD, L. Earl, and COMMINGS, Janet. The expressive vocabulary of preschool deaf children. 1974, 119, 16-28.

IVEY, Lillian P., and TEEL, Jerry R. Tri-sensory language stimulation with the TAVF unit. 1974, 119, 318-320.

GREEN, Walter B. The development of semantic differential scales for deaf children. 1974, 119, 361-364.

ERBER, Norman P., and CRAMER, Kathryn D. Vibrotactile recognition of sentences. 1974, 119, 716-720.

GOLDBERG, J. Philip, and BORDMAN, Marcia B. The ESL approach to teaching English to hearing impaired students. 1975, 120, 22-27.

DALGLEISH, Barrie. Communication preference and the social conditions of language learning in the deaf. 1975, 120, 70-77.

SCROGGS, Carolyn Lee. The effects of expansions on the communication rate of hearing impaired students. 1975, 120, 350-359.

BRENNAN, Mary. Can deaf children acquire language? 1975, 120, 463-479.

COLLINS-AHLGREN, Marianne. Language development of two deaf children. 1975, 120, 524-539.

HARDY-BECK, Pamela. Assessment and instruction: don't push the hard-of-hearing child into the pit! 1975, 120, 556-557.

KRAMER, Aaron, and BUCK, Lucien A. Poetic creativity in deaf children. 1976, 121, 31-37.

LAYZER, Arthur. Computer animated and textured presentation of language for the deaf. 1976, 121, 38-43.

Language Acquisition (Contd.)

ANNALS OF THE DEAF (Contd.)

SHEPARD, Charlotte H. Teaching language to mentally retarded deaf children: a review of the literature and a description of one classroom program. 1976, 121, 366-369.

LUTERMAN, David M. A comparison of language skills of hearing impaired children trained in a visual/oral method and an auditory/oral method. 1976, 121, 389-393.

HOEMANN, Harry W., ANDREWS, Carol E., FLORIAN, Vicki A., HOEMANN, Shirley A., and JENSEMA, Carl J. The spelling proficiency of deaf children. 1976, 121, 489-493.

GAWLIK, Rev. Rudolph, MCALEER, Marlene, OZER, Mark N. Language for adaptive interaction. 1976, 121, 556-559.

Mainstreaming/Integration

THE VOLTA REVIEW

BOOTH, Frank W. A roster of former pupils of schools for the deaf now in schools for the hearing. 1905, 7, 275-279.

REMNITZ, Annabel. Education in a hearing high school. 1955, 57, 117-119.

MCINTIRE, Wayne (panel chairman). A discussion of children with severe hearing impairments in schools with hearing children. 1957, 59, 53-63; 84-85.

VANWYK, Mary K. Integration? Yes, if. . . . 1959, 61, 59-62.

POITRAS, Bonnie. The case for the deaf child in the regular school. 1961, 63, 16-17; 43.

MOTTO, Joseph, and WAWRZASZEK, Frank J. Integration of the hearing handicapped: evaluation of the current status. 1963, 65, 124-129; 160.

FLEGEL, Elynor. Services for the hearing handicapped in a special school district. 1964, 66, 253-257.

Mainstreaming/Integration (Contd.)

THE VOLTA REVIEW (Contd.)

MILLER, Anne S. Academic preparation to insure adjustment into classes with hearing students. 1964, 66, 414-425.

SCHWARTZ, Marcia G. A deaf child in my hearing class. 1964, 66, 627-630.

COHEN, Oscar P. An integrated summer recreation program. 1969, 71, 233-237.

GOLDIN, George J., et al. Some attitudes of deaf high school students toward attendance at college with normally hearing students. 1969, 71, 408-414.

SALEM, James M. Deaf students in a "hearing" college. 1967, 69, 36-40. Follow-up study, 1969, 71, 435-436.

NORTHCOTT, Winifred N. An experimental summer school: impetus for successful integration. 1970, 72, 498-507.

SALEM, James M. Partial integration at the high school level. 1971, 73, 42-46.

MECHAM, Steven R., and VANDYKE, Robert C. Pushing back the walls between hearing and hearing impaired children. 1971, 73, 359-364.

SCHEELINE, Alice. Integrating deaf children into public school. 1971, 73, 370-373.

GARRETT, Constance and STOVALL, Esther M. A parent's view on integration. 1972, 74, 338-344.

BITTER, Grant B. and MEARS, Edwin G. Facilitating the integration of hearing impaired children into regular public school classes. 1973, 75, 13-22.

LECKIE, Doris J. Creating a receptive climate in the mainstream program. 1973, 75, 23-27.

OWSLEY, Peter J. Can a residential school program students into public schools? 1973, 75, 28-31.

NORTHCOTT, Winifred H. Reading list on integration. 1973, 75, 33-35.

FRICK, Elizabeth. Adjusting to integration: some difficulties hearing impaired children have in public schools. 1973, 75, 36-46.

Mainstreaming/Integration (Contd.)

THE VOLTA REVIEW (Contd.)

BOWMAN, Elizabeth. A resource room program for hearing impaired students. 1973, 75, 208-213.

_____. Hearing impaired graduates of regular schools (1971-1972 survey). 1973, 75, 232-255.

LAYMAN, Ellen. Children who hear aid the hearing impaired. 1974, 76, 36-41.

CROFT, John C. A look at the future for a hearing impaired child of today. 1974, 76, 115-122.

HEDGECOCK, Dorothy. Facilitating integration at the junior high level. 1974, 76, 182-188.

RISTER, Anne. Deaf children in mainstream education. 1975, 77, 279-290.

FALLIS, John R. The key to integrated learning for children who are hearing impaired. 1975, 77, 363-367.

PORTER, Geraldine. The missing vital dimension in successful integration. 1975, 77, 416-422.

KINDRED, Elizabeth M. Integration at the secondary school level. 1976, 78, 35-43.

ANNALS OF THE DEAF

WORTHINGTON, Anna M. Psychological implications of integration of deaf children with hearing children. 1958, 103, 467-472.

O'CONNOR, Clarence D. The integration of the deaf in schools for the normally hearing. 1961, 106, 229-232.

CRAIG, William N., and SALEM, James M. Partial integration of deaf with hearing students: residential school prospectives. 1975, 120, 28-36.

BRILL, Richard G. Mainstreaming: format or quality? 1975, 120, 377-381.

BIKLEN, Douglas P. Deaf children vs. the board of education. 1975, 120, 382-386.

Mainstreaming/Integration (Contd.)

ANNALS OF THE DEAF (Contd.)

MACKLIN, Fay. Mainstreaming: the cost issue. 1976, 121, 364-365.

DESALLE, Jean Marie, and PTASNIK, Joseph. Some problems and solutions: high school mainstreaming of the hearing impaired. 1976, 121, 533-536.

Media/Visual Aids

THE VOLTA REVIEW

NITCHIE, Edward B. Moving pictures applied to lip-reading. 1913, 15, 117-125.

ALCORN, Alice. Visual education as an aid to geography. 1926, 28, 707-708.

LARVE, Sarah J. Correlating motion pictures with classroom work. 1927, 29, 253-254.

HESTER, M. S. The use of educational films. 1932, 34, 51-55.

SCOTT, Elizabeth V. The use of slides in the primary classes. 1932, 34, 56-58.

BURDGE, Alice V. The value and administration of visual education. 1932, 34, 496-502.

HESTER, M. S. A program of visual education for a residential school. 1932, 34, 503-506.

DEANNARD, Elizabeth. The sand table. 1933, 35, 125-126.

FINN, Betsy A. Pictures in lower intermediate grades. 1933, 35, 367-369.

KENNEDY, Lydia B. Pictures in the primary grades. 1933, 35, 376-377.

HEIDER, Grace M. and Fritz. Motion pictures in classroom work. 1935, 37, 71-75.

Media/Visual Aids (Contd.)

THE VOLTA REVIEW (Contd.)

KENNARD, Marie S. Pictures used with drill verbs. 1935, 37, 157; 186-187.

HUDGINS, Clarence V. Visual aids in the correction of speech. 1935, 37, 637-643; 703-704.

DAVENPORT, Virginia H. Cross-word puzzle. 1936, 38, 641-642; 679.

MACKIN, Helen. Hand work helps language work. 1938, 40, 761-762.

NELSON, Wilma I., et al. The use of visual aids in teaching. 1939, 41, 499-502; 534; 566-568; 600; 631-633; 668-669.

MONTAGUE, Harriet. Non-reading aid project in Wisconsin. 1941, 43, 15-17; 70.

NELSON, Wilma I. Advancing the use of visual aids. 1942, 44, 11-12; 60.

PURDY, Martha E. An experiment in visual education with the deaf. 1943, 45, 201; 248-249.

UTLEY, Jean, et al. Lip reading and motion pictures. Factors involved in the teaching and testing of lip reading ability through the use of motion pictures. 1946, 48, 657-660.

MASON, Marie K. Personal experience in teaching lip reading through motion pictures. 1946, 48, 661-663.

DOMMISSE, Elsa J. Visual material for language teaching. 1947, 49, 84-86.

ROMERO, Emerson. Sound films for the deaf. 1948, 50, 259-260; 288-290.

SIGURDSON, Haldora K. Films for speech and hearing instruction. 1949, 51, 224-226; 240-242.

CAVANAGH, Anita. A new audio-visual aid for speech. 1951, 53, 12-13; 40-42.

LANE, Helen S. Television for the deaf. 1951, 53, 345; 392.

MCLAUGHLIN, Marjorie. Uses of the flannelgraph. 1952, 54, 317; 326-328.

OSTERN, Beatrice. Use of movie films in a class of the deaf. 1953, 55, 247; 276.

Media/Visual Aids (Contd.)

THE VOLTA REVIEW (Contd.)

MCLEOD, Frances. A pictionary. 1955, 57, 59-60.

MOORE, Lucelia. Television as a medium for teaching speechreading and speech. 1955, 57, 263-264.

VAN WYK, Mary K. A new visual aid trainer. 1955, 57, 347-348.

CORY, Patricia B. Materials center. 1956, 58, 15-19.

_____. Films and filmstrips pertaining to deafness. 1956, 58, 158-160.

KRAFT, Dorothy G. Presentation of visual aids materials to the upper grades. 1956, 58, 247-250; 255.

DRENNEN, Genevieve. Make it pretty. 1956, 58, 337-340.

CYPREANSEN, Lucile, and MCBRIDE, Jack. Lipreading lessons on television. 1956, 58, 346-348.

CORY, Patricia B. Filmstrips for deaf children. 1957, 59, 451-454; 1961, 63, 299; 1962, 64, 507-508.

OLSON, Christine. Using the opaque projector. 1958, 60, 267-268.

THORNTON, Joyce. Pictures make words. 1959, 61, 18; 43.

LARR, Alfred. Speechreading through closed circuit television. 1959, 61, 19-21.

CORY, Patricia B. Films and filmstrips. 1959, 61, 71.

FALCONER, George A. Teaching machines for the deaf. 1960, 62, 59-62; 76.

COLE, Roy. Television for deaf children. 1960, 62, 256-259; 281.

OYER, Herbert J. Teaching lipreading by television. 1961, 63, 131-132; 141.

GREY, Howard A., et al. Cinefluorography as an aid to more intelligible speech. 1961, 63, 323-327; 356.

_____. Television for deaf children in Chicago. 1962, 64, 30.

_____. Films on hearing and deafness. 1962, 64, 77-83; 104.

CRANE, Norman, and EVANS, Betty. The talking dictionary. 1962, 64, 125-127.

Media/Visual Aids (Contd.)

THE VOLTA REVIEW (Contd.)

PETERSON, Gordon E. Technological frontiers in communication. 1962, 64, 369-374.

FALCONER, George A. Teaching machines for teaching reading. 1962, 64, 389-392.

DAVID, Edward E., Jr. Speech in the computer age. 1962, 64, 394-397.

SCHOWE, Ben M., Jr. Projecting books as an aid to teaching reading. 1962, 64, 421-422.

GOUGH, John A. Captioned films for the deaf: the new program. 1963, 65, 24-25; 50.

GOUGH, John A. Visual aid back-up service for teachers of the deaf. 1964, 66, 548-551.

DIEDRICH, William M. Use of videotape in teaching clinical skills. 1966, 68, 644-647.

OLSHIN, George M. The emergence of a new special education resource: the IMC. 1968, 70, 309-313.

RATHE, Gustave H., Jr. Computer-assisted instruction: promising new tool for teaching deaf students. 1968, 70, 447-452.

STEPP, Robert E. Educational media and deaf education: the emerging literature. 1968, 70, 465-474.

WYMAN, Raymond. A visual response system for teacher-group interaction in the education of deaf children. 1969, 71, 155-160.

CUNNINGHAM, Dean. Testing modified transparencies for teaching the deaf with overhead projectors. 1969, 71, 174-181.

ANDERSON, Norman O., and LAIRD, Roderick D. Use of multimedia at Wyoming School for the Deaf. 1969, 71, 420-425.

ALTSCHULER, David. Use of video-tape in programs for the deaf. 1970, 72, 102-106.

BOLESTA, Mrs. Burl. Multimedia in the preschool. 1970, 72, 175-179.

PFAU, Glenn S. The application of programmed instruction principles to classroom instruction. 1970, 72, 340-348.

Media/Visual Aids (Contd.)

THE VOLTA REVIEW (Contd.)

PFAU, Glenn S. Reinforcement and learning--some considerations with programmed instruction and the deaf child. 1970, 72, 408-411.

WITHROW, Frank B. Applications of technology to communication. 1976, 78, 102-106 (monograph).

ANNALS OF THE DEAF

MCALONEY, Thomas S. The value of pictures in teaching the deaf. 1893, 38, 196-203.

EARLE, Carrie W. The use of pictures in the primary grades. 1896, 41, 357-370.

KIESEL, Theodore A. Picture teaching. 1902, 47, 403-439.

CARPENTER, Lula E. Teaching from objects. 1903, 48, 424-435.

WALKER, E. W. Instruction by means of pictures. 1906, 51, 276-280.

ROSS, Louise. Vitalizing object work for beginning classes. 1928, 73, 248-249.

SMITH, James L. Visual education by use of the blackboard. 1933, 78, 257-262.

PETERSON, Edwin G. Testing deaf children with Kohs block designs. 1936, 81, 242-254.

GAY, Ruth C. A doll house unit of work. 1938, 83, 425-426.

VERMILLION, Frances F. Visual aids in arithmetic. 1940, 85, 487-493.

MCCLURE, William J. Visual education and the deaf. 1941, 86, 166-180.

BOATNER, Edmund B. Captioned films for the deaf. 1951, 96, 346-352.

Media/Visual Aids (Contd.)

ANNALS OF THE DEAF (Contd.)

BOWER, Dolores. Comics--a meaningful teaching experience in the language arts. 1960, 105, 230-231.

FALCONER, George A. A mechanical device for teaching sight vocabulary to young deaf children. 1961, 106, 251-257.

FESSANT, John M. Application of programmed learning for deaf children to industrial arts. 1963, 108, 241-244.

_____. Introduction to symposium on research and utilization of educational media for teaching the deaf. 1966, 111, 599-602.

HEINICH, Robert. Application of systems concepts to instruction. 1966, 111, 603-616.

KENT, Alice A. Synthesizing language arts skills with the overhead projector. 1966, 111, 617-621.

DIAMOND, Robert M. A rationale for decision: selecting the right tool for the job. 1966, 111, 648-656.

POSTLETHWAIT, Sam. A multi-faceted approach to teaching. 1966, 111, 657-660.

SCHMITT, Robert J. A multi-media approach in the classroom for the deaf. 1966, 111, 661-667.

KOPP, Harriet G. Applications of systems concept to teaching the deaf. 1966, 111, 668-677.

GOUGH, John A., et al. Report from captioned films for the deaf. 1967, 112, 642-649.

WHITENACK, Carolyn I. The instructional materials center: a changing concept. 1967, 112, 650-654.

MCMAHAN, Marie. Educational media center--the library's new look. 1967, 112, 655-671.

FARIS, Gene. Quantitative personnel, materials, and equipment standards for audiovisual programs. 1967, 112, 672-679.

JACKSON, William D. Media production facilities in schools for the deaf. 1967, 112, 680-687.

Media/Visual Aids (Contd.)

ANNALS OF THE DEAF (Contd.)

SCHOWE, Ben M., Jr. A small school instructional materials center: its diffusion of innovations for learning. 1967, 112, 693-699.

CORY, Patricia. Report on library programs in schools for the deaf. 1967, 112, 701-711.

DARLING, Richard L. Implementing the media program in schools for the deaf. 1967, 112, 712-718.

WYMAN, Raymond. Media personnel at schools for the deaf. 1967, 112, 719-723.

MEIERHENRY, Wesley C. The purpose of educational media in the learning process. 1967, 112, 728-733.

PROPP, George. Symposium discussion summary. 1967, 112, 734-743.

RISBERG, Arne. Visual aids for speech correction. 1968, 113, 178-194.

STARK, Rachel E. Preliminary work with the new Bell Telephone visible speech translator. 1968, 113, 205-214.

PRONOVOST, Wilbert, et al. The voice visualizer. 1968, 113, 230-238.

PHILLIPS, Nathan D., et al. Teaching of intonation to the deaf by visual pattern matching. 1968, 113, 239-246.

PICKETT, J. M., and CONSTAM, A. A visual speech trainer with simplified indication of vowel spectrum. 1968, 113, 253-258.

KRINGLEBOTN, M. Experiments with some visual and vibrotactile aids for the deaf. 1968, 113, 311-317.

VOSS, Don, et al. Project design. 1968, 113, 1021-1029.

PERRIN, Donald G. Ten thousand hours. 1968, 113, 1106-1114.

GOUGH, John A. Report from captioned films for the deaf. 1968, 113, 1117-1122.

PROPP, George. Symposium discussion summary. 1968, 113, 1124-1132.

NORWOOD, Malcolm J. The second decade. 1969, 114, 824-828.

POSTLETHWAIT, Sam. Mediated self instruction. 1969, 114, 874-879.

Media/Visual Aids (Contd.)

ANNALS OF THE DEAF (Contd.)

RATHE, Gustave H., Jr. Computer-assisted instruction and its potential for teaching deaf students. 1969, 114, 880-883.

RATHE, Gustave H., Jr. Computer-assisted instruction--exciting new tool for teaching the deaf. 1969, 114, 884-888.

PERRIN, Donald G. The role of media in individualized instruction for teaching the deaf. 1969, 114, 912-919.

PROPP, George. Symposium discussion summary. 1969, 114, 920-930.

FERGUSON, Donald G. Teacher assessment of Project Hurdle. 1969, 114, 946-961.

JACKSON, William D. Designing a prototype television studio-laboratory. 1970, 115, 558-561.

PFAU, Glenn S. Programmed movies--a supplemental medium for language development. 1970, 115, 569-572.

OFIESH, Gabriel. The potential of television for teaching the deaf. 1970, 115, 577-586.

CALLACE, Charles. Basic principles for instructional television. 1970, 115, 587-591.

ANDERSON, Deyrol. Breaking the television time-lock. 1970, 115, 592-596

MCINTIRE, William. Electronic video recording. 1970, 115, 597-600.

PALMER, Edward L. Television's neglected strengths. 1970, 115, 601-604.

TETTEMER, Clair. The slant track mushroom. 1970, 115, 605-610.

JACKSON, William D. 1970 survey of instructional television in programs for the deaf. 1970, 115, 615-618.

PROPP, George. Symposium discussion summary. 1970, 115, 632-640.

SUMMERS, Hubert, et al. Programmed instruction at the SWRMCD--its impact. 1971, 116, 449-455.

GARNER, Waunita L., and ZERRUP, Charles E., Jr. Evaluating programmed learning materials. 1971, 116, 456-464.

LOWELL, Edgar L. Is there a middle ground? 1971, 116, 473-475.

MCCARR, James E. Programmed instruction in a school curriculum. 1971, 116, 476-479.

Media/Visual Aids (Contd.)

ANNALS OF THE DEAF (Contd.)

MURPHY, Harry. Activities in programmed instruction at the Southwest School for the Deaf. 1971, <u>116</u>, 480-483.

PIPE, Peter. New directions in programmed learning. 1971, <u>116</u>, 485-488.

SUPPES, Patrick. Computer assisted instruction for deaf students. 1971, <u>116</u>, 500-508.

PERSSELIN, Leo E. Electronic assembly programmed learning system for the deaf. 1971, <u>116</u>, 515-525.

TORR, Donald. A graduate course in educational technology. 1971, <u>116</u>, 509-514.

_____. Symposium on research and utilization of educational media for teaching the deaf. 1972, <u>117</u>, 473-570.

FITCH, James L. A program to improve visual perception skills of preschool deaf children. 1973, <u>118</u>, 429-432.

CALDWELL, Doris Cooper. Use of graded captions with instructional television for deaf learners. 1973, <u>118</u>, 500-507.

LAURITSEN, R., and CUSTER, David. Careers. . . a multi-variate approach. 1973, <u>118</u>, 541-548.

BOX, Mattie S. Total mediation: toward creative human experience for the deaf student. 1973, <u>118</u>, 551-557.

FONVILLE, Wilson. Making and using self teaching movies in the occupational education classroom. 1973, <u>118</u>, 561-566.

CLARCQ, Jack, JOHNSON, Donald, and SPIEGLE, James. Career development and media utilization at the National Technical Institute for the Deaf. 1973, <u>118</u>, 607-616.

NORWOOD, Malcolm J. Review of media services and captioned films. 1974, <u>119</u>, 460-464.

MEIERHENRY, Wesley C. Developments in educational media--the past and for the future. 1974, <u>119</u>, 466-471.

DRACKLEY, Bruce. Wisconsin School for the Deaf Media Tornado. 1974, <u>119</u>, 485-487.

LAIRD, Roderick. The Wyoming picture '74: development and use of a coordinated media system in a small school setting. 1974, <u>119</u>, 488-499.

Media/Visual Aids (Contd.)

ANNALS OF THE DEAF (Contd.)

OLSON, LeAnn. A decade of success with media for pre-school deaf children. 1974, 119, 500-502.

GOLDBERG, Leonard. The applications of educational media and technology at the Boston School for the Deaf. 1974, 119, 503-509.

PECK, William. Growth and development of Oregon's media program. 1974, 119, 510-515.

WAUGH, Michael, and PARSONS, Richard. In the eyes of a child: mediated learning experiences. 1974, 119, 516-524.

POSTLETHWAIT, Sam. Minicourses--a concern for individualization of content. 1974, 119, 525-532.

WYMAN, Raymond. The ubiquitous overhead. 1974, 119, 533-536.

JACKSON, William, and PERKINS, Roger. Television for deaf learners: a utilization quandry. 1974, 119, 537-548.

PFAU, Glenn. Project LIFE a decade later: some reflections and projections. 1974, 119, 549-553.

LAGOW, Robert, and KELLY, Ronald. The Midwest Regional Media Center for the Deaf: eight years of media service. 1974, 119, 554-564.

BURROUGHS, Judy. Media in a systems approach to individualizing instruction. 1974, 119, 565-571.

NEWBY, Robert. Language and reading: a visual structure. 1974, 119, 572-577.

STARK, Bill. The decade that was birth and growth of media at the Illinois School for the Deaf. 1974, 119, 578-583.

NAZZARO, Kristine. The flexibility of media in the open classroom. 1974, 119, 584-587.

BOURNE, Janet. Let's see it one more time. 1974, 119, 588-591.

MOORE, Omar Khayyam. The inclusion of the deaf within communication networks. 1974, 119, 597-601.

RAY, Henry. Media--a decade of change and progress. 1974, 119, 602-604.

WITHROW, Frank. Educational technology and the future. 1974, 119, 605-607.

Media/Visual Aids (Contd.)

ANNALS OF THE DEAF (Contd.)

ASHCROFT, Sam. Multiple choice: criterion test of special education. 1974, 119, 608-611.

STEPP, Robert E. A summary of progress. 1974, 119, 612-618.

NORWOOD, Malcolm J. Future trends. 1974, 119, 619-623.

HESTER, Marshall. "Update '74: a decade of progress"--conference summary. 1974, 119, 624-625.

GOLDFEDER, Cheryl, and GOLDFEDER, Jim. Television: a teaching tool for deaf students. 1975, 120, 406-407.

SHUEY, Herbert E. Video tapes in the classroom. 1976, 121, 370-372.

Multiply Handicapped
(see also Deaf-Blind)

THE VOLTA REVIEW

FOLEY, Julia A. Backward children. 1900, 2, 137-145; 231-237; 367-380.

BOOTH, Frank W. Feeble-minded and backward children. 1900, 2, 197-202.

BRECKINRIDGE, Mary S. James: an unusual pupil. 1903, 5, 228-230.

YALE, Caroline A. A plea for the instruction and after-school care of the feeble-minded deaf. 1917, 19, 578-581.

PENCE, Helen W. The retarded child--his education. 1927, 29, 190-192.

CLARK, Alice E. Deaf children with multiple handicaps. 1946, 48, 393-395; 428-430.

BANGS, Jack L. Preschool language education for the brain-damaged child. 1957, 59, 17-19; 39.

COSTELLO, Patrice. Where does Mike belong? 1960, 62, 66-67; 91.

Multiply Handicapped (Contd.)

THE VOLTA REVIEW (Contd.)

SISTER M. PAULINE. The multiply-handicapped deaf child. 1960, 62, 350-354.

SHERE, Marie O. The cerebral palsied child with a hearing loss. 1960, 62, 438-441.

SORTINI, Adam J. Hearing evaluation of brain-damaged children. 1960, 62, 536-540.

SORTINI, Adam J. Rehabilitation of brain-damaged children. 1961, 63, 20-23; 42.

NELSON, M., and SIBILIO, J. P. Audiologic aspects of a deaf-retarded population. 1962, 64, 426-427.

DUBARD, Etoile. A "deaf" child who did not learn. 1962, 64, 589-592.

LESHIN, George J., and STAHLECKER, Lotar V. Academic expectancies of slow-learning deaf children. 1962, 64, 599-602.

WEIR, Robert C. Impact of the multiple handicapped deaf on special education. 1963, 65, 287-289; 325.

WARREN, Sue A., and KRAUS, Matthew J., Jr. Deaf children, mental retardation and academic expectancies. 1963, 65, 351-352; 383.

LACROSSE, Edward L., and BIDLAKE, Harry. A method to test the hearing of mentally retarded children. 1964, 66, 27-30.

SELLIN, Donald F. The mentally retarded, hearing-handicapped learner: implications for teacher education. 1964, 66, 258-261.

MONAGHAN, Alice. Educational placement for the multiply handicapped hearing impaired child. 1964, 66, 383-387.

LANGDON, Marcia A. The multiply handicapped in a working world. 1964, 66, 504-507.

ANDERSON, Robert M. Hearing impairment and mental retardation: a selected bibliography. 1965, 67, 425-432.

WITHROW, Frank B. Acquisition of language by deaf children with other disabilities. 1966, 68, 106-115.

SCAGLIOTTA, Edward G. Home language training program for dysacusic and aphasic children. 1966, 68, 553-559.

Multiply Handicapped (Contd.)

THE VOLTA REVIEW (Contd.)

COSTELLO, Patrice M. The dead end kid. 1966, 68, 639-643.

VERNON, McCay. Characteristics associated with post-rubella deaf children: psychological, educational, and physical. 1967, 69, 176-185.

RAPIN, I., et al. The Purdue pegboard as a screening test for brain damage and mental retardation in nonverbal children. 1967, 69, 635-638.

HARLOW, Joyce L. Mentally retarded or hearing impaired? 1967, 69, 664-667.

SUCHMAN, Rosslyn G. Visual impairment among deaf children--frequency and educational consequences. 1968, 70, 31-37.

TAYLOR, Annette P., and POLLOCK, Barbara E. A structured program of learning for moderately retarded deaf adults. 1968, 70, 114-117.

MASLAND, Richard L. Rubella can rob children of their hearing. 1968, 70, 304-307.

THOMPSON, Richard E. Who are the multiply handicapped deaf children? 1968, 70, 569-574.

MITRA, Sudhansu B. Educational provisions for mentally retarded deaf students in residential institutions for the retarded. 1970, 72, 225-236.

JABLONS, Beverly. A public school program for multiply handicapped deaf children. 1970, 72, 552-559.

BUNCH, Gary O. An academic-vocational program for multiply-handicapped deaf students. 1971, 73, 417-425.

VOCKELL, Karen, VOCKELL, Edward, and MATTICK, Pamm. Language for mentally retarded deaf children: Project LIFE. 1973, 75, 431-439.

TWEEDIE, David. Behavioral change in a deaf-blind multihandicapped child. 1974, 76, 213-218.

Multiply Handicapped (Contd.)

ANNALS OF THE DEAF

COBB, Jennie L. Teaching the abnormal deaf child. 1914, <u>59</u>, 233-238.

GRUVER, E. A. The subnormal deaf. 1919, <u>64</u>, 298-305.

LARUE, Mary S. A plan for retarded deaf children. 1937, <u>82</u>, 445-449.

MACPHERSON, James R. The status of the deaf and/or hard of hearing mentally deficient in the United States. 1952, <u>97</u>, 375-386.

PORTER, Van C. The cerebral-palsied deaf pupil. 1957, <u>102</u>, 359-363.

DOCTOR, Powrie V. Multiple handicaps in the field of rehabilitation. 1958, <u>103</u>, 409-413.

MYKLEBUST, Helmer R. The deaf child with other handicaps. 1958, <u>103</u>, 496-509.

VERNON, McCay. The brain injured (neurologically impaired) deaf child: a discussion of the significance of the problem, its symptoms and causes in deaf children. 1961, <u>106</u>, 239-250.

ANDERSON, Robert M., and STEVENS, G. D. Deafness and mental retardation in children: the problem. 1969, <u>114</u>, 15-22.

LENNAN, Robert K. Use of programmed instruction with emotionally disturbed deaf boys. 1969, <u>114</u>, 906-911.

ANDERSON, Robert M., and STEVENS, G. D. Policies and procedures for admission of mentally retarded deaf children to residential schools for the deaf. 1970, <u>115</u>, 30-36.

HICKS, Doin E. Comparison profiles of rubella and non-rubella deaf children. 1970, <u>115</u>, 86-92.

LENNAN, Robert K. Report on a program for emotionally disturbed deaf boys. 1970, <u>115</u>, 469-480.

STEWART, Larry G. Problems of severely handicapped deaf, implications for educational programs. 1971, <u>116</u>, 362-368.

MITRA, Sudhansu B. Guidelines for hospitalized retarded-deaf children. 1971, <u>116</u>, 385-388.

LENNAN, Robert K. The deaf multi-handicapped unit at the California School for the Deaf, Riverside. 1973, <u>118</u>, 439-445.

Multiply Handicapped (Contd.)

ANNALS OF THE DEAF (Contd.)

NAIMAN, Doris, SCHEIN, Jerome D., and STEWART, Larry. New vistas for emotionally disturbed deaf children. 1973, 118, 480-487.

STEWART, Larry B. We have met the enemy and he is us. 1974, 119, 706-715.

JENSEMA, Carl. A note on the achievement test scores of multiply handicapped hearing impaired children. 1975, 120, 37-39.

BRANNON, A. Clark, SIGELMAN, Carol, and BENSBERG, Gerard. The hearing impaired in state institutions for the retarded: I. prevalence, characteristics, and diagnosis. 1975, 120, 408-416.

BRANNON, A. Clark, SIGELMAN, Carol, and BENSBERG, Gerard. The hearing impaired in state institutions for the retarded: II. services and programs. 1975, 120, 502-508.

Parent-Child

THE VOLTA REVIEW

GUSOW, F. The family as co-worker in the education of deaf children. 1900, 2, 242-247.

WHITE, Stella K. The home instruction of a little deaf child. 1901, 3, 418-427.

ANDERSON, Mrs. J. Scott. What home training is to the deaf baby. 1910, 12, 436-442.

MOORE, Mrs. Sidney M. Suggestions to mothers of little deaf children. 1912, 14, 1-6.

SAWYER, Mrs. S. E. What an heroic mother accomplished. 1912, 14, 193-198.

ROORDA, P. The deaf child in the family. 1912, 13, 586-590.

FULLER, Sarah. Home training in the development of speech. 1912, 14, 701-709.

Parent-Child (Contd.)

THE VOLTA REVIEW (Contd.)

SMITH, Muriel A. The stammering child in his home. 1913, 15, 69-72.

WORCESTER, Eleanor B. To mothers of little deaf children. 1914, 16, 335-338; 499-502; 1915, 17, 207-212; 1925, 27, 156-165; 217-220; 276-281.

──────────. The over-specialization of parents. 1914, 16, 711-716.

BELL, Alexander G. Suggestions concerning the formation of a local association of parents of deaf children. 1914, 16, 750-751.

JELKS, Mrs. F. W. Teach your deaf baby to talk. 1914, 16, 773-775.

──────────. Helpful suggestions to parents of deaf children. 1914, 16, 777-779.

SANDERS, Mrs. George T. Instructors of parents of deaf children. 1914, 16, 812-814.

ANDREWS, Harriet U. A deaf boy who is being rightly trained. 1915, 17, 165-171.

CAYLEY, Stephanie. A mother to other mothers. 1915, 17, 341-344.

ROBERTS, Emma. Helpful suggestions for the mother of a deaf child. 1915, 17, 445-450.

ANDREWS, Harriet U. Home training for deaf children. 1917, 19, 145-174.

BICKLER, Mary H. How a deaf child was taught speech-reading and speech. 1917, 19, 305-313; 373-379; 426-431; 497-500; 605-610.

REED, Katharine F. How to approach the parents of the deaf. 1917, 19, 586-590.

HARMAN, Augusta. Helpful suggestions for mothers of deaf children. 1917, 19, 650-653.

──────────. A mother of two: training deaf children. 1918, 20, 85-87.

BARTLETT, Bertha L. How a mother taught herself to train her deaf child. 1918, 20, 609-614; 671-674; 733-738; 1919, 21, 41-48; 1921, 23, 193-210.

Parent-Child (Contd.)

THE VOLTA REVIEW (Contd.)

ANDREWS, Harriet U. The diary of a deaf child's mother. 1918, 20, 614-619; 687-691; 739-743; 1919, 21, 54-59; 78-82; 184-187; 1921, 23, 112-137.

HENDERSON, Myrtle L. Problems of the mother of the young deaf child. 1918, 20, 619-624; 777-781; 1919, 21, 20-23; 133-140; 365-378; 417-422; 496-501.

FAY, Helen. How the parents can help. 1922, 24, 246-249.

STEFFEY, Mary E. Proxy ears for mother. 1925, 27, 682-686.

HOOPER, Mrs. J. C. A mother teaches her deaf child. 1929, 31, 345-346.

O'DONNELL, Elizabeth K. Parent co-operation. 1932, 34, 152-153.

EVANS, Mildred. What you can teach your deaf child at home this summer. 1932, 34, 293-299.

EVANS, Mildred. Self-help for your deaf child in vacation days. 1932, 34, 342-351; 375-376.

WRIGHT, John D. What parents can do for their deaf children in and out of school. 1932, 34, 467-470.

SIMON, Adele. Responsibility for the speech of our children. 1932, 34, 470-473.

MCCLELLAN, Grace A. A talk with parents of deaf children. 1933, 35, 299-300; 316.

WINSTON, Matie E. What the parent can do for the preschool child. 1933, 35, 411-413.

ENGLISH, Sandra. What parents can do about it: an open letter to mothers of hard of hearing children. 1938, 40, 351-352; 374.

HALL, Grace D. A teacher of deaf children speaks to parents of deaf children. 1939, 41, 495-498; 533-534.

GODA, Sidney. Parents as teachers: how to help your school-age hard of hearing child communicate better. 1941, 53, 350-352; 382.

WATTS, Jo D. A preschool program for parents. 1942, 44, 329-330; 368.

Parent-Child (Contd.)

THE VOLTA REVIEW (Contd.)

_____. To the parents of little deaf children: suggestions offered by the Lexington School for the Deaf. 1944, 46, 69-71; 110-112.

ROONEY, Alice G. Parent education: emphasis on the preschool. 1946, 48, 759-761; 802-803.

LEVINE, Edna S. Psychological sidelights. 1947, 49, 123-124; 154-156; 175-176; 200; 219; 246-248.

AVERY, Charlotte B. A suggested reading list for parents. 1948, 50, 355-356; 376-378.

ROONEY, Alice G. Parents go to school. 1948, 50, 517-518; 552-554.

LASSMAN, Grace, and MONTAGUE, Harriet. The deaf baby. 1949, 51, 325-328; 372-374.

O'CONNOR, Clarence D. Sources of help for parents. 1950, 52, 397-398; 438.

NICHOLAS, Georgia C. Sincerely yours, a housemother. 1950, 52, 494-495.

WHILDIN, Olive A. The parent, the school, and the community. 1950, 52, 503-504; 522-524.

KLIENFELD, L. What are the chances of having another deaf child? 1952, 54, 107; 136-137.

STONER, Marguerite (panel moderator). Parent participation. 1953, 55, 78-90.

CURRY, Lorre. Home-school relationships. 1954, 56, 24-27.

WORK, Robert. Working with your young deaf child. 1954, 56, 114-117.

VORCE, Eleanor. Your child is deaf--advice for parents. 1954, 56, 201-204.

REISS, Mrs. K. The deaf child's place in the hearing family. 1955, 57, 148.

SCHEELINE, Mrs. Isaiah. Planning for the deaf child's first school days away from home. 1955, 57, 211-212.

HANSEN, M. R. A letter to my daughter. 1956, 58, 69-72.

Parent-Child (Contd.)

THE VOLTA REVIEW (Contd.)

SMITH, Alathena J. Guidance at the John Tracy Clinic. 1956, 58, 301-304.

COLE, Robert H., et al. The parents speak in open forum. 1956, 58, 351-361.

ROTTER, Paul. Human relations in parent education. 1957, 59, 20-24.

FELLENDORF, Mr. and Mrs. George W. What parents can do for their deaf child. 1957, 59, 149-156.

VAN WYK, Mary K. Home help with speech. 1957, 59, 207-208; 227.

ROTTER, Paul. A guide for educating parents of deaf children. 1958, 60, 28-32.

PAGENSTECHER, Adelyn. What parents can do. 1958, 60, 201-202.

ROTTER, Paul. Relationship between the educator and parents of deaf children. 1958, 60, 370-371.

BREUNIG, H. Latham. Parents and the specialists. 1958, 60, 372-373.

JACOBY, Beatrice. The relationship of the speech and hearing center to the parent of the deaf child. 1958, 60, 373-374.

HANEY, Mary R. Teach your child the language of games. 1959, 61, 212-213.

LEHMANN, Mrs. Floyd, and BUCHAN, Mrs. John. How the teacher of a deaf child can help the parents. 1959, 61, 283; 289.

WALCHER, Helen. Parents are our greatest helpers. 1959, 61, 325-326.

SORTINI, Adam J. To the parent of a hearing handicapped child. 1960, 62, 26-28; 46.

FELLENDORF, George W. Factors affecting parents' decisions. 1960, 62, 341-345.

HARRIS, Norma. A pilot study of parental attitudes. 1960, 62, 355-361.

OSTERN, Beatrice. Home help with reading. 1960, 62, 494-496.

WOODWARD, Helen. Read with your children. 1960, 62, 517-519.

Parent-Child (Contd.)

THE VOLTA REVIEW (Contd.)

GIANGRECO, C. Joseph. Parent counseling--a must. 1960, 62, 543-545.

ROTTER, Paul. The parents' role in encouraging speech growth. 1961, 63, 12-15; 46.

YORTY, Jeane B. Parents, let's relax! 1961, 63, 30-33; 39.

SIMON, Arthur B. Helping your deaf child grow up--let him experiment and explore. 1961, 63, 35-39.

MANNEN, Grace. Enriching the language of the older deaf child: the parent's part. 1961, 63, 224-227.

CRUM, Carole. The normality of deaf children. 1961, 63, 231-232; 249.

SHIPPY, Ardell. How an active parent group can strengthen a school program. 1961, 63, 297-298.

ZANDER, Alvin. How we can work together. 1962, 64, 30-33.

WILLIAMS, Boyce R. Your deaf child's job prospects. 1962, 64, 246-248; 273.

LANE, Helen S. Two years of progress. 1962, 64, 446-448.

TATMAN, Mrs. Donald. Let's talk about talk. 1962, 64, 449-452.

ANDERSON, William A. That the deaf may speak. 1962, 64, 456-458.

JOHNSON, Jeanette N. Association services. 1962, 64, 458-460.

NORTHCOTT, Winifred N. To and for parents. 1962, 64, 603-605.

REINEKE, Mary E. You are blessed among mothers. 1963, 65, 190-192.

LANE, Helen S. Parent-teacher cooperation in the communication of the deaf child. 1963, 65, 595-598.

HARRIS, Grace M. For parents of very young deaf children. 1964, 66, 19-26; 70-77.

MILLER, June. Institute for parents and their deaf children. 1964, 66, 185-197.

RALSTON, Patricia and Frances. A mother and her deaf daughter compare notes. 1964, 66, 209-212.

Parent-Child (Contd.)

THE VOLTA REVIEW (Contd.)

FIELD, Lois G. Johnny is a "window of the home." 1964, 66, 508-510.

FUNK, Stanton C. The parents' role in educational planning. 1964, 66, 517-520.

SIMON, Mrs. Richard. A parent speaks. 1964, 66, 570-573.

POLLACK, Doreen C., and DOWNS, Marion P. A parent's guide to hearing aids for young children. 1964, 66, 745-749.

QUICK, Marian. Parents' responsibility in their deaf child's social adjustment. 1965, 67, 152-154.

REINEKE, Mary E. Junior high--a cooperative adventure. 1966, 68, 284-288.

BURKE, Douglas. Parental roles in job placement of deaf adolescents. 1967, 69, 253-256.

NORTHCOTT, Winifred N. Preparing your child for his first year away from home. 1967, 69, 391-393.

LUTERMAN, David M. A parent-oriented nursery program for preschool deaf children. 1967, 69, 515-520.

HORTON, Kathryn B. Home demonstration teaching for parents of very young deaf children. 1968, 70, 97-101.

FRENCH, Sophie. To parents of young deaf children: some suggestions for child management. 1968, 70, 253-257.

LING, Agnes H. Advice for parents of young deaf children: how to begin. 1968, 70, 316-319.

HARRIS, Norma. To parents of young deaf children, an open letter II. 1969, 71, 19-22.

FELLENDORF, George W., and HARROW, Icie. Parent counseling, 1961-1968. 1970, 72, 51-57.

WILLIAMS, Mrs. Pat. The fears we face. 1970, 72, 303-309.

MCAREE, Ruth. What price parenthood? 1970, 72, 431-437.

COLE, Nell. Hear the wind blow. 1971, 73, 36-41.

LUTERMAN, David M. A parent-oriented nursery program for preschool deaf children--a follow-up study. 1971, 73, 106-112.

Parent-Child (Contd.)

THE VOLTA REVIEW (Contd.)

KATZ, David L. A home-made curriculum. 1971, <u>73</u>, 173-277.

GERMAIN, Lois. Older deaf students' advice to parents of young deaf children. 1971, <u>73</u>, 497-502.

SCHWARTZBERG, Joanne G. When a hearing impaired child must go to the hospital. 1972, <u>74</u>, 30-37.

OWRID, H. L. Education and communication. 1972, <u>74</u>, 225-234.

REYNOLDS, James A. and Ligia R. A parents' approach to language: the daily journal. 1972, <u>74</u>, 345-351.

ROLLINS, Joan C. "I heard that!" Auditory training at home. 1972, <u>74</u>, 426-435.

BERGLUND, Jean B. Family education in Alaska. 1973, <u>75</u>, 97-102.

WILKIE, Jane. My baby's deaf! 1973, <u>75</u>, 103-108.

ANDERSON, Norman O., and GUSTAFSON, Monty C. F. A co-parent program for hearing impaired children. 1973, <u>75</u>, 161-173.

LIVERIDGE, Ellen B., and GRANA, Gregory M. A hearing impaired child in the family: the parent's perspective. 1973, <u>75</u>, 174-184.

SHEPHERD, Bruce D. Parent potential. 1973, <u>75</u>, 220-224.

LUTERMAN, David. On parent education. 1973, <u>75</u>, 504-508.

NARDINE, Frank E. Parents as a teaching resource. 1974, <u>76</u>, 172-177.

ROSSETT, Allison. Special strategies for a special problem improving communication between hearing impaired adolescents and their parents. 1974, <u>76</u>, 231-238.

BERRETT, Richard D., and KELLEY, Randall. Discipline and the hearing impaired child. 1975, <u>77</u>, 117-124.

SCHWARTZBERG, Joanne G., M.D. Parent Effectiveness: Helping your child achieve better language at home. 1975, <u>77</u>, 296-302.

MCELROY, Dierdre, and BERNSTEIN, H. William. The role of parents in developing self-esteem in a hearing impaired child. 1976, <u>78</u>, 219-223.

BITTER, Grant B. Family impact: fallacies, feuds, and fundamentals. 1976, <u>78</u>, 312-317.

Parent-Child (Contd.)

ANNALS OF THE DEAF

PETTENGILL, B. D. Home education for deaf-mutes. 1874, 19, 1-10.

HIRSCH, D. Advice to parents, guardians, and teachers concerning the education of deaf-mutes. 1877, 22, 93-103.

STERN, Rose G. The problem of the training of a deaf child as viewed by a mother. 1918, 63, 151-189; 250-278.

WRIGHT, John D. Suggestions from a correspondence course for parent-teachers of deaf children. 1921, 66, 462-475; 1922, 67, 144-154; 241-252.

FULLER, Sarah. To the mothers of very young deaf children. 1930, 75, 363-375.

ADAMS, Mabel E., et al. What parents want for their deaf children. 1931, 76, 264-275.

ANDERSON, Tom L. Parental co-operation. 1937, 82, 244-248.

JESSEMAN, V. C. Ways in which the home should cooperate with the school. 1943, 88, 1-7.

HEDGECOCK, LeRoy D. Counselling the parents of acoustically handicapped children. 1952, 97, 329-339.

MONTAGUE, Harriet. Parents of deaf children. 1953, 98, 358-361.

MAGNER, Marjorie E. Parents can help deaf children to acquire ability in speechreading. 1960, 105, 431-433.

VORCE, Eleanor R. You, your child and the language. 1960, 105, 437-441.

GOUGH, John A. Use of pictures in teaching young deaf children at home. 1960, 105, 442-445.

FULLER, Carl W. Your child, maturity, and you: a talk with parents. 1962, 107, 320-328.

HERSCH, L. Brian, and AMON, Carol. A child has a hearing loss: reporting the diagnosis of handicaps in children and its impact on parents. 1975, 120, 568-571.

Psychoeducational Testing

THE VOLTA REVIEW

KITSON, H. D. Psychological tests for lip-reading ability. 1915, 17, 471-476.

PINTNER, Rudolf, and PATERSON, Donald. Psychological tests of deaf children. 1917, 19, 661-667.

PINTNER, Rudolf, and PATERSON, Donald. Some conclusions from psychological tests of the deaf. 1918, 20, 10-14.

BOSHLER, Irene E. Mental tests. 1918, 20, 193-195.

NEWLEE, Clara E. Report of learning tests with deaf children. 1919, 21, 216-223.

PINTNER, Rudolf. Deductions from tests of mentality in schools for the deaf in comparison with schools for the hearing. 1920, 22, 197-207.

GRAVES, Frank P. The use and abuse of intelligence tests. 1925, 27, 73-75.

WOODS, Elizabeth L. Standard tests in the Los Angeles School for the Deaf. 1926, 28, 600-604.

ANDREWS, Harriet U. Thought test exercise. 1927, 29, 452-454.

SCHICK, H. F. A performance test for children of school age. 1934, 36, 657-658; 694-695.

BISHOP, Helen M. Performance scale tests applied to deaf and hard of hearing children. 1936, 38, 447; 484-485.

BENDER, James F. Seven simple tests of motor coordination. 1944, 46, 267; 310.

BLUETT, Charles G. Tests and follow-up of deaf graduates. 1944, 46, 617-622; 662; 686-689; 772; 1945, 47, 12-16; 82-85; 106-108.

HISKEY, M. S. Determining mental competence levels of children with impaired hearing. 1950, 52, 349-351; 388-390; 406-408; 430-432.

BILGER, Robert. Limitations on the use of intelligence scales to estimate the mental ages of children. 1958, 60, 321-325.

LARR, Alfred L., and CAIN, Earl R. Measurement of native learning abilities of deaf children. 1959, 61, 160-162.

Psychoeducational Testing (Contd.)

THE VOLTA REVIEW (Contd.)

GOETZINGER, Cornelius P., et al. Non-language IQ tests used with deaf children. 1967, 69, 500-506.

LEVINE, Edna S. Mental assessment of the deaf child. 1971, 73, 80-96.

LEVINE, Edna S. Psychological tests and practices with the deaf: a survey of the state of the art. 1974, 76, 298-319.

ANNALS OF THE DEAF

PINTNER, Rudolf, and PATERSON, Donald. Mental tests. 1915, 60, 297-300.

PINTNER, Rudolf, and PATERSON, Donald. The Binet scale and the deaf child. 1915, 60, 301-311.

PINTNER, Rudolf, and PATERSON, Donald. The form-board ability of young deaf and hearing children. 1916, 61, 184-189.

PINTNER, Rudolf, and PATERSON, Donald. A class test with deaf children. 1916, 61, 264-275.

PINTNER, Rudolf, and PATERSON, Donald G. The ability of deaf and hearing children to follow printed directions. 1917, 62, 448-472.

PINTNER, Rudolf. The value of mental tests in the classification of pupils. 1918, 63, 196-204.

PINTNER, Rudolf. Deductions from tests of mentality in schools for the deaf. 1920, 65, 278-300.

PINTNER, Rudolf, and REAMER, Jeannette. A mental and educational survey of schools for the deaf. 1920, 65, 451-472.

PINTNER, Rudolf, and REAMER, Jeannette. Problems raised by the survey of schools for the deaf. 1921, 66, 8-28.

PINTNER, Rudolf, and REAMER, Jeannette. Individual differences measured by psychological tests. 1921, 66, 168-181.

DAY, Herbert A. A classification test given to the students of Gallaudet College. 1921, 66, 409-424.

Psychoeducational Testing (Contd.)

ANNALS OF THE DEAF (Contd.)

PINTNER, Rudolf. The survey of schools for the deaf: psychological survey. 1927, 72, 377-414.

PETERSON, Edwin G. Intelligence of deaf children as measured by drawings. 1930, 75, 273-290.

SHIRLEY, Mary, and GOODENOUGH, F. L. A survey of intelligence of deaf children in Minnesota schools. 1932, 77, 238-247.

LYON, V. W. Personality tests with the deaf. 1934, 79, 1-4.

PINTNER, Rudolf, and BRUNSCHWIG, L. An adjustment inventory for use in schools for the deaf. 1937, 82, 152-167.

PINTNER, Rudolf. Latest phases of psychological testing with the deaf. 1937, 82, 327-337.

SPRINGER, N. Norton. A comparative study of the intelligence of a group of deaf and hearing children. 1938, 83, 138-152.

ZECKEL, Adolf. A comparative intelligence test of groups of children born deaf and of good hearing, by means of the Porteus test. 1939, 84, 114-123.

SCHICK, Helen, et al. A performance test for school-age deaf children. 1941, 86, 441-447.

LAVOS, George. The reliability of an educational achievement test administered to the deaf. 1944, 89, 226-232.

KLINE, Thomas K. A study of the free association test with deaf children. 1945, 90, 237-257.

JOHNSON, E. H. The effect of academic level on scores from the Chicago non-verbal examination for primary pupils. 1947, 92, 227-233.

MCPHERSON, Jane G., and LANE, Helen S. A comparison of deaf and hearing on the Hiskey test and on performance scales. 1948, 93, 178-184.

KIRK, Samuel A., and PERRY, June. A comparative study of the Ontario and Nebraska tests for the deaf. 1948, 93, 315-323.

OLÉRON, Pierre. A study of the intelligence of the deaf. 1950, 95, 179-195.

LAVOS, George. The Chicago non-verbal examination. 1950, 95, 379-386.

Psychoeducational Testing (Contd.)

ANNALS OF THE DEAF (Contd.)

BIRCH, Jane R. and Jack W. The Leiter international performance scale as an aid in the psychological study of deaf children. 1951, 96, 502-511.

DUTOIT, J. M. Measuring the intelligence of deaf children. 1954, 99, 237-251.

LAVOS, George. Interrelationships among three tests of non-language intelligence administered to the deaf. 1954, 99, 303-313.

HICKEY, Marshall S. A study of the intelligence of deaf and hearing children. 1956, 101, 329-339.

STUNKEL, E. The performance of deaf and hearing college students on verbal and non-verbal intelligence tests. 1957, 102, 342-355.

GOETZINGER, C. P., and ROUSEY, K. L. A study of the Wechsler performance scale (form) II and the Knox cube test with deaf adolescents. 1957, 102, 388-398.

MIRA, Mary P. The use of the Arthur adaptation of the Leiter international performance scale and the Nebraska test of learning aptitude with preschool deaf children. 1962, 107, 224-228.

WRIGHTSTONE, J. W., et al. Developing reading test norms for deaf children. 1963, 108, 311-316.

FARRANT, Roland H. The intellective abilities of deaf and hearing children compared by factor analyses. 1964, 109, 306-325.

FURTH, Hans G. A comparison of reading test norms of deaf and hearing children. 1966, 111, 461-462.

GOETZINGER, C. P., et al. A study of the S. O. Rorschach with deaf and hearing adolescents. 1966, 111, 510-522.

GIANGRECO, C. Joseph. The Hiskey-Nebraska test of learning aptitude (revised) compared to several achievement tests. 1966, 111, 566-577.

VEGELY, Ann B., and ELLIOTT, Lois L. Applicability of a standard personality test to a hearing-impaired population. 1968, 113, 858-868.

KEARNEY, Jacqueline E. A new performance scale of cognitive capacity for use with deaf subjects. 1969, 114, 2-14.

Psychoeducational Testing

ANNALS OF THE DEAF (Contd.)

GOETZINGER, Madelon R., and HOUCHINS, Rollie R. Colored raven's progressive matrices with deaf and hearing subjects. 1969, 114, 95-101.

BORNSTEIN, Harry. Some effects of verbal load on achievement tests. 1971, 116, 44-48.

VEGELY, Ann B. Performance of hearing-impaired children on a nonverbal personality test. 1971, 116, 427-433.

BORNSTEIN, Harry, and KANNAFELL, Barbara. More on the effects of verbal load on achievement tests. 1971, 116, 575-579.

VONDERHAAR, William F., and CHAMBERS, Jean F. An examination of deaf students' Wechsler performance subtest scores. 1975, 120, 540-544.

LINDSEY, Dianne, and O'NEAL, Janet. Static and dynamic balance skills of eight year old deaf and hearing children. 1976, 121, 49-55.

MURPHY, Harry J. Comparative studies of academic achievement between hearing impaired and non-hearing students at California State University, Northridge. 1976, 121, 305-311.

Psychology

THE VOLTA REVIEW

BOYD, Hypatia. University experience. 1900, 2, 127-136.

FINNEY, Mariette E., and WAY, Daisy M. The deaf and their social relations. 1901, 3, 11-23.

BALIS, Sylvia C. The deaf and their social relations with the hearing. 1901, 3, 141-144.

JENKINS, Weston. Training for practical life. 1901, 3, 199-203.

Psychology (Contd.)

THE VOLTA REVIEW (Contd.)

BOYD, Hypatia. The deaf and their social relations with the hearing. 1901, 3, 227-235.

DANGER, O. The education of the deaf for life in human society. 1904, 6, 101-108.

STEVENSON, Margaret J. Discipline. 1904, 6, 222-224.

HANSEN, Anders. The basis of the Binet-Simon inquiry. 1910, 12, 190-193.

NITCHIE, Edward B. The association of deaf and hearing. 1911, 13, 149-152.

STORY, Arthur J. The intelligence of the deaf child. 1911, 13, 349-352.

LOWRY, C. D. Physiology and psychology of the deaf child. 1911, 13, 386-391.

NITCHIE, Edward B. Some assets of deafness. 1913, 15, 204-206.

MARTINEAU, Harriet. Letter to the deaf. 1913, 15, 219-227.

ANDREWS, Harriet U. Building a bridge to the child. 1913, 15, 357-360.

NITCHIE, Edward B. To be or not to be. 1914, 16, 53-55.

SMITH, Rena A. The veil of silence. 1914, 16, 198-207.

FERRERI, Giulio. Notes on pedagogy and psychology in regard to the deaf. 1914, 16, 233-239; 365-368; 467-471; 523-527; 719-721.

ANDREWS, Harriet U. Misdirected energies. 1914, 16, 240-244.

PIERCE, Jerry A. The privilege of being deaf. 1914, 16, 351-354.

MORGENSTERN, Louise I. The philosophy of self-culture. 1915, 17, 171-174.

PIERCE, Jerry A. Human tragedies. 1915, 17, 483-485.

HAYS, Harold. How can we meet the problem of the deaf. 1916, 18, 506-510.

DELANY, Elizabeth G. Cheer: a symposium. 1917, 19, 621-622.

ADRAIN, E. D., and YEALLAND, L. R. The treatment of some common war neuroses. 1917, 19, 680-682.

Psychology (Contd.)

THE VOLTA REVIEW (Contd.)

KENNEDY, Mildred. How to bear and forbear deafness. 1917, 19, 692-695; 1918, 20, 19-22; 107-110.

HURST, et al. Hysterical deafness in soldiers. 1917, 19, 686-691.

FERRALL, John A. Smiling the clouds away. 1918, 20, 149-152.

_____. Hysterical deafness in soldiers. 1918, 20, 173-175.

FERRALL, John A. If I were deaf--. 1918, 20, 647-650.

FERRALL, John A. A bottle of tonic. 1919, 21, 503-505.

SYLVESTER, Elfrieda M. Fourteen. 1919, 21, 517-522.

STOREY, John D. The psychology of deafened people from a layman's point of view. 1920, 22, 268-271.

TOMPKINS, Ernest. Is stammering emotional? 1920, 22, 752-754.

ROE, W. Carey. Some observations on the psychology of the deaf child. 1921, 23, 52-59.

FERRALL, John A. Please pass the butter! 1922, 24, 297-300.

MENNINGER, K. A. The mental effects of deafness. 1923, 25, 439-445.

NEVINSON, Elizabeth. "Beg pardon?" 1925, 27, 84-88.

STEFFEY, Mary E. The hollow cross of deafness. 1925, 27, 138-142.

FERRALL, John A. Sound. . . and nothing else. 1925, 27, 145-148.

ROSS, Ellen B. Beating a handicap. 1925, 27, 181-184.

_____. The feathering of the ugly duckling. 1925, 27, 508-512.

CALKINS, Ernest E. The lives of the deafened. 1926, 28, 7-11; 114-117.

SIEVERS, A. D. The function of the psychiatrist in the school. 1928, 30, 561-566.

WEIL, Clara S. Society versus solitude. 1929, 31, 205-206.

TONLEY, Lucia S. Ten strangers. 1929, 31, 207-208.

Psychology (Contd.)

THE VOLTA REVIEW (Contd.)

ALLISON, Margaret G. Mental hygiene as applied to work with the deafened from the psychiatric social worker's point of view. 1929, 31, 646-649.

EFFLER, Louis R. Lost and found. 1930, 32, 115-118.

WASHBURNE, C. Educational significance of individual differences. 1930, 32, 459-469.

STILLSON, S. V. The teacher and the problem child. 1930, 32, 501-505.

_____. Do deaf children grasp abstractions readily? 1931, 33, 75-78.

TIMBERLAKE, Josephine B. A plea for the abolition of prejudice. 1931, 33, 200-202.

FROHN, W. Experiments on the thinking of the deaf. 1931, 33, 313-315; 324-325.

FRANZ, Shepherd I. Psychological problems of the deaf. 1932, 34, 545-546.

HEIDER, Grace M. A psychological study of the effects of deafness. 1933, 35, 117-119.

GIBIAN, Rose. Social work in a school for deaf children. 1933, 35, 285-287.

SAUNDERS, Nida. Personality problems. 1934, 36, 9-11.

RAUBICHECK, Letitia. Psychology of multilingualism. 1934, 36, 17-20; 57.

WHILDIN, Olive. By-products of the lip-reading class. 1934, 36, 159-161; 181.

VINSON, M. R. Retardation problems. 1934, 36, 206; 246.

MOORE, Lucile M. A comparison of deaf and hearing children. 1934, 36, 325; 372-373.

GRATZ, Leola A. The deaf child's contact with hearing children. 1934, 36, 326-327; 379.

QUINN, Josephine. A comparison of deaf and hearing children. 1934, 36, 381; 311-312; 325; 372-373.

Psychology (Contd.)

THE VOLTA REVIEW (Contd.)

DEMOTTE, Amelia. Mental hygiene of the deaf child. 1935, 37, 224-225; 260-261.

MILLER, E. O. Studying the psychology of the deaf. 1935, 37, 738; 780-781.

GAY, Ruth. Mental hygiene clinics in schools for the deaf. 1935, 37, 741; 781-782.

WATSON, Charles W. Subnormality or late enrollment? 1936, 38, 448-449; 480.

HARKNESS, Margaret. Deaf children do have imagination. 1936, 38, 567-569.

ARNOLD, Allie. Personality and discipline. 1936, 38, 582-583; 611.

LANE, Helen S. Personality adjustments of adolescents. 1937, 39, 166; 186.

HEDLEY, Arthur. The futility of fear. 1937, 39, 167; 184-185.

CRAWFORD, M. T., and NACE, J. C. A program of social guidance. 1939, 41, 156-157.

COGSWELL, Elaine Ward. The psychic side of deafness. 1939, 41, 285-287.

HEIDER, Grace M. and Fritz. The thinking of the young deaf child as shown in sorting experiments. 1941, 43, 111-113; 146.

HEIDER, Grace M. and Fritz. Phonetic symbolism of deaf children. 1941, 43, 165-168; 233-236.

KNIGHT, Maude H. Emotions of the young deaf child. 1942, 44, 69-72; 122-124.

LEIGH, Jean W. Emotional stability for the deaf child. 1942, 44, 685-688; 724.

VALENTINE, Cristina. How to be happy in a hearing world. 1943, 45, 76-80; 120-122.

BERRYMAN, Florence S. Social technique for the submerged tenth. 1944, 46, 401-404; 426.

KIMBER, W. J. Some psychology for the deafened. 1946, 48, 522-523.

LEVINE, Edna S. The work of the school psychologist. 1946, 48, 728-734.

Psychology (Contd.)

THE VOLTA REVIEW (Contd.)

MYKLEBUST, Helmer R. Clinical diagnosis and classification of children with impaired hearing. 1946, 48, 738-742.

LEVINE, Edna S. Psychological sidelights. 1948, 50, 5-6; 40-44; 152-154; 194-196; 309-310; 330-334.

MYKLEBUST, Helmer R. Clinical psychology and children with impaired hearing. 1948, 50, 55-56; 90-92.

COLLINS, Virginia E. The important thing is attitude. 1949, 51, 121-122.

LEVINE, Edna S. Can we speed up the slow child? 1949, 51, 269-270; 316-318.

DICKINSON, Myrle E. Hearing is believing. 1949, 51, 562-563; 586-588.

GOLDBERG, Rose E. Laugh at your ears. 1950, 52, 458-459; 472-474.

STEWART, P. I am one of the lucky ones. 1953, 55, 41-42; 50.

BROWN, Ruth. Adjusting to the normally hearing. 1954, 56, 11-13.

ARMSTRONG, Lola M. You can learn to live without them. 1954, 56, 29-30.

SIGURDSON, H. K. Changing attitudes. 1954, 56, 118-119.

LEVINE, Edna S. Adolescence--what is it? 1954, 56, 257-259.

MAYER, Jonas H. My deafness. 1954, 56, 440-442.

BOPST, E. G. Face it! 1955, 57, 343-346; 371.

BLISH, Stanford C. An educational and vocational counseling program for deaf students. 1955, 57, 385-389.

STIX, E. F. Life in a hearing world. 1955, 57, 438-440.

GESELL, Arnold. The psychological development of normal and deaf children in their preschool years. 1956, 58, 117-120.

PRATT, George T. Community relations. 1958, 60, 75-76.

TEMPLIN, Mildred C. Relation of speech and language development to intelligence and socio-economic status. 1958, 60, 331-334.

SLANKARD, Harriet. Teaching the deaf child to think. 1958, 60, 523-527.

Psychology (Contd.)

THE VOLTA REVIEW (Contd.)

VAN WYK, Mary K. Integration--a look at the total picture. 1960, 62, 69-70; 82.

MURPHY, A. T., et al. Acceptance, rejection and the hearing handicapped. 1960, 62, 208-211.

PUGH, Bessie. Developing the deaf child's power of reasoning. 1960, 62, 334-340.

THOMPSON, Richard. Adjustment in high school with normal hearing contemporaries. 1960, 62, 414-417.

QUICK, Marian. Role of the administrator in the guidance program. 1960, 62, 418-420.

CARR, Josephine. The teacher's role in promoting mental health. 1961, 63, 65-69; 89.

CRUM, Carole. The normality of deaf children. 1961, 63, 231-232; 249.

WILSON, D. K. The hearing team. 1962, 64, 22-25.

MYKLEBUST, Helmer R. Diagnosis, learning and guidance. 1962, 64, 363-369.

OWSLEY, P. J. A study of intelligence and achievement among children exhibiting symptoms of the Waardenburg syndrome. 1962, 64, 429-431.

TATMAN, Mrs. Donald. Let's talk about talk. 1962, 64, 449-452.

LAVOS, George. W.I.S.C. psychometric patterns among deaf children. 1962, 64, 547-552.

DUBARD, Etoile. A "deaf" child who did not learn. 1962, 64, 589-592.

EWING, Ethel C. Some psychological variables in the training of young deaf children. 1963, 65, 68-73.

LEVINE, Edna S. Studies in psychological evaluation of the deaf. 1963, 65, 496-512.

EDGAR, Lucille S. Determination in the face of prejudice. 1964, 66, 31-34.

MORKOVIN, Boris V. Thought patterns of deaf children: what does this imply for the classroom teacher? 1964, 66, 491-494.

Psychology (Contd.)

THE VOLTA REVIEW (Contd.)

THOMPSON, Richard. Counseling and the deaf student. 1964, 66, 511-513.

WEISBORD, Marvin R. Do you understand the language of behavior? 1964, 66, 610-614.

LIEBMAN, Jeffrey. Reflections of a Presidential scholar. 1964, 66, 683-686.

OSLER, Sonia F. The nature of intelligence. 1965, 67, 285-291; 319.

SHONTZ, Franklin C. Reactions to crisis. 1965, 67, 364-370.

LISENSKY, Robert P. The family and the deaf child. 1966, 68, 673-678.

MURPHY, Kevin P. Deafness and mental health. 1966, 68, 696-700.

SCHLESINGER, Hilde S. A child first. 1969, 71, 545-551.

SUFFRIDGE, Kathleen Hera. Prelinguistic imagery cognition: an individual experience. 1973, 75, 82-87.

GELLENS, Suzanne. Behavior modification: a classroom technique. 1973, 75, 114-125.

BLATCHFORD, Claire H. Hearing in deafness. 1974, 76, 208-212.

GERWICK, Susan, and YSAELDYKE, James E. Limitations of current psychological practices for the intellectual assessment of the hearing impaired: a response to the Levine study. 1975, 77, 243-248.

BLATCHFORD, Claire. Shared thoughts about a hearing loss. 1976, 78, 152-154.

LEVINE, Edna S. Psychological contributions. 1976, 78, 23-33 (monograph).

LEVINE, Edna S. Psycho-cultural determinants in personality development. 1976, 78, 258-267.

Psychology (Contd.)

ANNALS OF THE DEAF

RAY, Luzerne. Thoughts of the deaf and dumb before instruction. 1847, 1, 149-157.

JACOBS, J. A. Importance of teaching deaf-mutes self-reliance. 1858, 10, 161-163.

EDDY, L. The relations of deaf-mutes to the hearing world. 1878, 23, 226-231.

JENKINS, William G. Memory in the education of the deaf. 1892, 37, 85-93.

JAMES, William. Thought before language: deaf-mutes' recollections. 1893, 38, 135-145.

CARDWELL, W. A. Understanding versus expression. 1902, 47, 11-19.

KING, Gordon. A case of hysterical deaf-mutism. 1903, 48, 44-55.

STEINKE, Elsie M. How best to fit the deaf for a useful and active life. 1905, 50, 300-304.

SCHNEIDER, Matthias. The thought and language of the deaf-mute: an inquiry concerning the true foundation of deaf-mute instruction. 1908, 53, 483-492; 1909, 54, 173-190; 254-263; 327-338; 402-412; 1910, 55, 164-172; 474-486; 1911, 56, 1-17.

STONE, Elizabeth A. Hints on discipline. 1910, 55, 177-182.

GALLAUDET, Edward M. The mental development of the deaf child. 1910, 55, 342-349.

PUTNAM, G. H. The use of the imagination in the instruction of the deaf. 1912, 57, 229-241.

LOWRY, Charles D. The physiology and psychology of the deaf child. 1912, 57, 241-253.

WALKER, E. W. The possibilities and limitations of the deaf mind. 1912, 57, 474-483.

LONG, T. Schuyler. The exceptional child. 1917, 62, 154-164.

SMITH, James L. Attention. 1917, 62, 188-198.

STEVENS, H. C. The encouragement of individual ideas. 1918, 63, 279-285.

PINTNER, Rudolf, and OSBORN, Dorothy. The mentality of families of the congenitally deaf. 1919, 64, 96-134.

Psychology (Contd.)

ANNALS OF THE DEAF (Contd.)

SMITH, James L. Training in reasoning and judgment and in the formation and expression of correct opinions. 1919, 64, 166-174.

SHERIDAN, Laura C. The art of living smoothly with one's fellows. 1919, 64, 174-181.

LONG, T. Schuyler. Laggards. 1919, 64, 208-213.

COBB, Jennie L. Psychology in the schoolroom. 1921, 66, 186-190.

COLEMAN, G. D. The efficiency of touch and smell. 1922, 67, 301-325.

WILLIAMS, T. J. Extraordinary development of the tactile and olfactory senses. 1922, 67, 418-432.

READ, Elmer D. Mental reactions of deafness. 1925, 70, 246-253.

ELY, Grace D. Do we think in language. 1926, 71, 205-207.

GARDNER, I. B. Psychology of intermediate grades. 1927, 72, 181-185.

SKYBERG, Victor O. Deafness as a social problem--the physical side. 1929, 74, 106-113.

MILLER, Linda K. Some differences between the psychology of a young deaf child and that of a hearing child. 1930, 75, 212-215.

MOORE, H. T. Teaching pupils how to study. 1932, 77, 248-252.

FLORENCE, Geneva. Institution life--its influence on personality. 1932, 77, 284-288.

HOFMARKSRICHTER, R. Do the deaf see more than those with all their senses? 1933, 78, 113-116.

HOGSTEATER, H. T. The "institution mind"-- and possible means of its correction. 1934, 79, 231-237.

BRILL, Tobias. Mental hygiene and the deaf. 1934, 79, 279-285.

VETIDZ, G. W. The relative value of sight and hearing. 1937, 82, 141-151.

HUNT, J. F. Abstracts of articles concerned with the educational psychology of the deaf. 1937, 82, 176-188.

KIRK, Samuel A. Behavior problem tendencies in deaf and hard-of-hearing children. 1938, 83, 131-137.

Psychology (Contd.)

ANNALS OF THE DEAF (Contd.)

GAY, Ruth C. A case study of word deafness. 1938, 83, 169-176.

SPRINGER, N. Norton. A comparative study of the behavior traits of deaf and hearing children of N.Y.C. 1938, 83, 255-273.

WARFIELD, Ethel B. Problems of deafness. 1938, 83, 300-305.

BRIDGMAN, Olga. The estimation of mental ability in deaf children. 1939, 84, 337-349.

ABERNATHY, E. R. Some social aspects of deafness. 1940, 85, 433-445.

CUTLER, Elizabeth M. Summary of psychological experiments with the deaf. 1941, 86, 181-192.

DRENNAN, George L. The psychology of deafness in children. 1941, 86, 393-404.

PETERS, E. F. Guidance for exceptional children. 1942, 87, 1-7.

BURCHARD, Edward M., and MYKLEBUST, Helmer R. A comparison of congenital and adventitious deafness with respect to its effect on intelligence, personality, and social maturity. 1942, 87, 140-154; 241-251; 342-360.

ZECKEL, Adolf. Research possibilities with the deaf. 1942, 87, 173-191.

O'CONNOR, Clarence D., and SIMON, E. A preliminary survey into the problems of adjustment among pupils of the Lexington School for the Deaf. 1942, 87, 224-240.

SMALTZ, Warren M. The probability that deafness can affect personality. 1945, 90, 330-339.

LEVINE, Edna S. The psychological service program of the Lexington School for the Deaf. 1948, 93, 149-164.

SCHUNHOFF, Hugo F. Conference on the moral, social and religious welfare of the deaf. 1951, 96, 414-419.

TEMPLIN, Mildred C. Personal references and illustrations used in explaining physical casualty. 1951, 96, 482-493.

ORMAN, James N., and BRILL, Richard G. An experiment in the training of deaf children in memory for sentences. 1953, 98, 270-279.

Psychology (Contd.)

ANNALS OF THE DEAF (Contd.)

OLÉRON, Pierre. Conceptual thinking of the deaf. 1953, 98, 304-310.

GLOWATSKY, Edward. Verbal element in the intelligence scores of congenitally deaf and hard of hearing children. 1953, 98, 328-335.

MYKLEBUST, Helmer R. Towards a new understanding of the deaf child. 1953, 98, 345-357.

SHINPAUGH, Joe R. Follow-up and adjustment problems of the acoustically handicapped and techniques of solution. 1956, 101, 298-307.

BIRCH, Jane R. and Jack W. Predicting school achievement in young deaf children. 1956, 101, 348-352.

BUTLER, Stahl. Formative influences on the deaf child and young adult. 1958, 103, 312-316.

ALTSHULER, K. Z., and RAINER, J. D. Institute on Personal, Social and Vocational Adjustment to Total Deafness: Psychiatric Aspects. 1958, 103, 317-323.

LEVINE, Edna S. Psychological aspects and problems of early profound deafness. 1958, 103, 324-347.

LEVINE, Edna S., and SAFIAN, M. Z. Psychological evaluation in vocational adjustment. 1958, 103, 348-364.

PHILLIPS, Richard M. Experiences in the community. 1958, 103, 382-388.

LEVINE, Edna S. Psychiatric-preventive and sociogenetic study of the adjustive capacities, optimum work potentials and total family problems of literate deaf adolescents and adults. 1960, 105, 272-274.

MYKLEBUST, Helmer R. The psychological effects of deafness. 1960, 105, 372-385.

MYKLEBUST, Helmer R., NEYHUS, Arthur, and MULHOLLAND, A. M. Guidance and counseling for the deaf. 1962, 107, 370-415.

BIRCH, Jane R. and Jack W., and STUCKLESS, E. Ross. An eleven year study of predicting school achievement in young deaf children. 1963, 108, 236-240.

Psychology (Contd.)

ANNALS OF THE DEAF (Contd.)

GOETZINGER, C. P., and HUBER, T. G. A study of immediate and delayed visual retention with deaf and hearing adolescents. 1964, 109, 297-305.

BOYD, John. Comparison of motor behavior in deaf and hearing boys. 1967, 112, 598-605.

BLAKE, Kathryn A., et al. Effects of induction and deduction on deaf and hearing individuals' attainment of first-order concepts. 1967, 112, 606-613.

OSBORNE, J. Grayson, and WAGEMAN, Robert M. Some operant conditioning techniques and their use in schools for the deaf. 1969, 114, 741-753.

ESPESETH, V. K. An investigation of visual-sequential memory in deaf children. 1969, 114, 786-789.

SALZINGER, Kurt. Behavior theory and problems of the deaf. 1970, 115, 459-468.

CLAYTON, Lynette, and ROBINSON, Luther D. Psychodrama with deaf people. 1971, 116, 415-419.

KRIPPNER, Stanley, and EASTON, Harry. Deafness: an existential interpretation. 1972, 117, 440-445.

HERSCH, L. Brian, and SOLOMON, M. A. A comprehensive approach to understanding deafness. 1973, 118, 34-36.

DOWLING, R. M., and FURTH, H. G. Expressive symbolic representation in deaf and hearing subjects. 1973, 118, 433-438.

WEBSTER, L. Michael, and GREEN, Walter B. Behavior modification in the deaf classroom: current applications and suggested alternatives. 1973, 118, 511-518.

ROBINSON, Luther D., and WEATHERS, Alethia D. Family therapy of deaf parents and hearing children: a new dimension in psychotherapeutic intervention. 1974, 119, 325-330.

ALTSHULER, Kenneth Z. The social and psychological development of the deaf child: problems, their treatment and prevention. 1974, 119, 365-376.

ROBINSON, Luther D., and DAWSON, Susan D. EEG and REM sleep studies in deaf people. 1975, 120, 387-390.

Psychology (Contd.)

ANNALS OF THE DEAF (Contd.)

FREEMAN, Roger D., MALKIN, Susan F., and HASTINGS, Jane O. Psychosocial problems of deaf children and their families: a comparative study. 1975, 120, 391-405.

SCHWARTZ, Jane Lake, ROSS, Linda F., and HOUCHINS, Rollie R. An investigation of the self concept of expressive language of thirty adolescent hearing impaired students using the Q-Sort technique. 1975, 120, 572-577.

SINGER, Dorothy G., and LENAHAN, Mary Louise. Imagination content in dreams of deaf children. 1976, 121, 44-48.

ALTSHULER, Kenneth Z., DEMING, W. Edwards, VOLLENWEIDER, John, RAINER, John D., and TENDLER, Ruth. Impulsivity and profound early deafness: a cross cultural inquiry. 1976, 121, 331-345.

ZWIRECKI, Robert J., STANSBERRY, David A., PORTER, Gerald G., and HAYES, Patrick. The incidence of neurological problems in a deaf school age population. 1976, 121, 405-408.

Religion

THE VOLTA REVIEW

PECK, Annetta W. Sunday evening in an office building. 1917, 19, 570-571.

ANDERSON, Marian J. An appeal to the ministers of Los Angeles. 1921, 23, 232-234.

MOORE, Lucile M. A deaf child's religion. 1927, 29, 88-90.

FITZGERALD, E. The daily devotional period in schools for the deaf. 1927, 29, 245-248.

MOSELEY, Nancy B. The chapel service. 1927, 29, 248-249.

STOVEL, Laura. A new avenue of approach to the general public. 1929, 31, 55-57.

Religion (Contd.)

THE VOLTA REVIEW (Contd.)

GLENN, Frances L. Chapel exercises for the primary department. 1929, <u>31</u>, 245-247.

MAYS, Lenable. A Sunday school suggestion. 1931, <u>33</u>, 392-393.

HANNA, Elizabeth. Religious education for the deaf. 1932, <u>34</u>, 393-394; 625; 649.

HUNTER, Annie R. The church and the hard of hearing. 1936, <u>38</u>, 470; 490.

TREIBERT, Marjorie. Religion in the home. 1940, <u>42</u>, 710-714.

ROBINSON, Ruth. What can the hard of hearing do for the church? 1940, <u>42</u>, 863-864.

MULHOLLAND, Ann N. A unit on the Bible. 1944, <u>46</u>, 81.

YEAKLE, Hannah E. A church for the hard of hearing. 1944, <u>46</u>, 95-96; 124-126.

CROWTHER, A. E. Religious training for the deaf child. 1948, <u>50</u>, 212; 232-236.

RICHARDSON, Mrs. O. T. Religion for the deaf child. 1954, <u>56</u>, 397-399.

GLASSER, Mrs. Mac. A deaf boy's bar mitzvah. 1963, <u>65</u>, 602-605.

_____. The deaf child and his faith. 1965, <u>67</u>, 627-631; 651.

KOHLER, Clarence N. Religious education of the deaf in state residential schools. 1966, <u>68</u>, 743-748.

ANNALS OF THE DEAF

HASENSTAB, Philip J. The religious training of the deaf child. 1892, <u>37</u>, 15-23.

MANNING, Arthur C. Religious education of the deaf. 1921, <u>66</u>, 354-361.

WILD, Laura H. The religious education of the deaf. 1922, <u>67</u>, 213; 231.

Religion (Contd.)

ANNALS OF THE DEAF (Contd.)

ANDERSON, Tom L. Religious education in schools for the deaf. 1937, 82, 433-439.

HENDERSON, S., and STEIN, S. P. Workshop for Catholic personnel for the deaf. 1961, 106, 294-341.

HENDERSON, S., and FRANCIS, D. H. Workshop for Episcopal workers for the deaf. 1962, 107, 232-291.

LEVINE, Edna S., and JILLETTE, A. G. Interfaith Institute of Denominational Workers with Deaf (Nov. 14-15, 1967). 1968, 113, 878-983.

Schools

THE VOLTA REVIEW

Day

ROBINSON, Anna E. Day schools in large cities. 1900, 2, 150-158; 248-253.

SPENCER, Robert C. The day-schools of Wisconsin. 1900, 2, 254-256.

WESSELIUS, Sybrant. The law and the day school for the deaf. 1901, 3, 311-319.

WETTSTEIN, Frances. The efficiency of the day school. 1906, 8, 136-142.

ADAMS, Mabel E. Day-schools and institutional. 1910, 12, 354-357.

ADAMS, Mabel E. Relative advantages of day-schools. 1911, 13, 292-297.

ARNOLD, Mercer. Advantages of oral day schools. 1914, 16, 354-357.

Schools (Contd.)

THE VOLTA REVIEW (Contd.)

Day

WETTSTEIN, Frances. The education of the deaf in day schools. 1914, 16, 559-564.

DUFF, Jessie. Advantages of an oral day school for the deaf. 1915, 17, 138-140.

_____. Why parents of deaf children move to cities having oral day schools. 1917, 19, 183-185.

_____. Course of study in public school no. 47, the day school for the deaf in New York City. 1917, 19, 353-357.

_____. Day schools for the deaf. 1919, 21, 593-595; 682-684.

TAYLOR, Harris. Public day schools for the deaf in the U.S. 1937, 39, 328-329; 377; 389-390; 428; 555-557; 594-595; 618-619; 660; 690-693; 720-721; 1938, 40, 15-21; 60; 83-87; 114-116; 133-139; 178-179; 215-217; 241-242; 279-281; 312-316.

DRENNEN, Genevieve. Adjustment of the hearing handicapped in a day class. 1958, 60, 482-484.

NEAS, B. Jack. A day class program. 1960, 62, 347-350.

QUILL, Leonora. The teenager in a day class. 1962, 64, 442-443.

ANDERSON, Norman O. Wyoming's unique program for the hearing impaired. 1964, 66, 537-539.

HARPER, Phyllis M. Problems of a small day class program. 1966, 68, 660-664.

GUNDERSON, A. Norman. Quality education near home. 1966, 68, 665-669.

GANTENBEIN, Andrew. A summer program for young deaf children. 1967, 69, 71-74.

SUGRUE, Timothy J. New York City's high school program for the deaf. 1967, 69, 247-252.

TEEL, Paul L. Tacoma's program for intermediate hearing impaired children. 1971, 73, 557-560.

THE VOLTA REVIEW

Histories and Reports on Specific Schools

HANSEN, Anders. A visit to American schools for the deaf. 1908, 10, 48-63.

_____. The Clarke School. 1912, 14, 31-40.

MCFARLANE, J. H. The Alabama School for the Deaf. 1913, 15, 212-218.

_____. The Wright Oral School for the Deaf, New York City. 1914, 16, 273-301.

ROBERTS, Emma. A southern oral school. 1914, 16, 793-797.

_____. An historical pageant produced on the fiftieth anniversary of the founding of Clarke School, Northampton, Mass. 1918, 20, 31-44.

LEONARD, Eleanor C. The fiftieth anniversary of the founding of the Clarke School, Northampton, Mass. 1918, 20, 45-65.

_____. Schools for the deaf in New York State. 1918, 20, 601-603.

BOATNER, Edmund B. A half century of progress in the New England schools--I. The American School for the Deaf. 1939, 41, 485-488.

REITER, Frank H. A half-century of progress in the New England schools--II. The Clarke School for the Deaf. 1939, 41, 562-565; 601.

HENDERSON, Jennie M. A half-century of progress in the New England schools--III. The Horace Mann School for the Deaf. 1939, 41, 627-630; 662.

TUCKER, Walter J. A half-century of progress at the New England schools--IV. The Mystic Oral School. 1939, 41, 682-684.

YOUNG, Louise T. A half-century of progress in the New England schools--V. Maine School for the Deaf. 1940, 42, 19-20.

JENNINGS, Gertrude J. A half-century of progress in the New England schools--VI. The Rhode Island School for the Deaf. 1940, 42, 73-76; 118-119.

Schools (Contd.)

THE VOLTA REVIEW (Contd.)

Histories and Reports on Specific Schools

MCDANIEL, Nettie. A half-century of progress in the New England schools--VII. The Beverly School for the Deaf. 1940, <u>42</u>, 139-143.

SISTER MARY OSWALD. A half-century of progress in the New England schools: The Boston School for the Deaf. 1940, <u>42</u>, 202-205; 252.

SANDERS, K. D. A half-century of progress in the New England schools--IX. The Austine School, Brattleboro, Vt. 1940, <u>42</u>, 263-265.

WALDRON, Grace A., et al. A half-century of progress in the New England schools--X. Three Massachusetts day schools. 1940, <u>42</u>, 334-338; 385-386.

_____. Maxon Oral School. 1953, <u>55</u>, 387-388.

BRILL, Richard G. The California School for the Deaf. 1954, <u>56</u>, 14-16.

O'CONNOR, Clarence D. Lexington School's first century of oral education of the deaf. 1967, <u>69</u>, 128-136.

CONNOLLY, Eileen E. The Horace Mann School yesterday, today and tomorrow. 1967, <u>69</u>, 138-146.

THE VOLTA REVIEW

Residential

FORNARI, P. American institutions for the deaf. 1904, <u>6</u>, 1-8.

Schools (Contd.)

THE VOLTA REVIEW (Contd.)

Residential

FERRERI, Giulio C. The American institutions for the education of the deaf. 1904, 6, 211-221; 288-300; 395-401; 1905, 7, 23-31; 145-152; 201-209; 297-305; 1906, 8, 109-119; 318-328; 397-405; 1907, 9, 297-323; 420-426.

THOMPSON, Emma R. The first year of the child's life in the institution. 1907, 9, 90-98.

HAGENS, E. W. Some facts obtained in a survey of the state schools for the deaf. 1930, 32, 524-529.

ANNALS OF THE DEAF

Day

BOWE, Frank G. Some notes on a little red schoolhouse. 1973, 118, 17-24.
BELLEFLEUR, Philip A. An open letter to my colleagues. 1974, 119, 29-33.
RICHARDSON, Diane, and WINNEY, Betty. Lamar Pilot School survey. 1974, 119, 736-739.

ANNALS OF THE DEAF

Histories and Reports on Specific Schools

PORTER, Sarah H. The individuality of schools for the deaf: The Institute for Improved Instruction, N.Y. (Lexington School). 1917, 62, 426-439.

Schools (Contd.)

ANNALS OF THE DEAF (Contd.)

Histories and Reports on Specific Schools

MCCLURE, George M. The first state school for the deaf. 1923, 68, 97-120.

HALL, Percival. Our debt to the American School for the Deaf. 1923, 68, 217-225.

FUSFELD, Irving S., et al. The survey of schools for the deaf. 1925, 70, 391-421; 1926, 71, 97-135; 284-348; 1927, 72, 2-34; 355-359; 377-414; 1928, 73, 1-36; 184-201; 1-36; 184-201; 273-300.

PINTNER, Rudolf. The survey of institutions for the deaf. 1928, 73, 155-163.

MOSLEY, C. C. Education for life: The Mississippi School for the Negro Deaf rethinks its program. 1956, 101, 251-253.

LAYSEN, Barry. The Rochester School for the Deaf: the second hundred years. 1974, 119, 592-596.

Social Development

THE VOLTA REVIEW

BARNES, F. G. Seaside School and Camp for the Deaf. 1915, 17, 229-235.

HERRICK, Helen. The need and actual functioning of organized activities outside the classroom. 1932, 34, 492-496.

OLANOFF, Rose S. Our house, an activity program. 1932, 34, 618-622.

BALLENGER, Lula, and ZIMMER, Louise. Socializing the deaf and the hearing child. 1935, 37, 397-400; 440-441.

Social Development (Contd.)

THE VOLTA REVIEW (Contd.)

CHARLES, Edna N. Social adjustment of a deaf child. 1937, 39, 271-274.

HEIDER, Grace M. and Fritz. The adjustment of the adult deaf: comments from the deaf about after-school problems. 1943, 45, 325-328; 380-382.

HEIDER, Grace M. and Fritz. The adjustment of the adult deaf: after-school problems as the psychologist sees them. 1943, 45, 389-391; 430.

GRUVER, Elbert A. The adjustment of the deaf to their hearing contemporaries. 1945, 47, 69-71; 112-116.

THOMPSON, Richard. What speech and lipreading mean to me. 1950, 52, 115-118.

MANZ, Fred M., and PRUITT, Elberta E. Social independence: (a secondary school program for its development in the acoustically handicapped). 1950, 52, 445-446; 474-476.

_____. Scouting and the deaf boy. 1953, 55, 343-348.

ROTTER, Paul. Camping for deaf children. 1959, 61, 209-211; 227.

LANE, Helen S. Extracurricular activities for deaf children. 1960, 62, 169-173.

DOMBRO, Robert H. Meeting recreational and social needs. 1960, 62, 328-331.

FLAXMAN, Mrs. G. D. Socialization and the deaf teenager. 1962, 64, 443-445.

NEYHUS, Arthur I. The social and emotional adjustment of deaf adults. 1964, 66, 319-325.

RODDA, M. Social adjustment of hearing impaired adolescents. 1966, 68, 279-283.

ROSENTHAL, Clara. Social adjustment of hearing handicapped children. 1966, 68, 293-297.

BLOOM, Freddy. Deafness termed a social handicap. 1967, 69, 67-70.

MILLER, Anne Small. The "growing up" program at Clarke School. 1969, 71, 472-483.

Social Development (Contd.)

THE VOLTA REVIEW (Contd.)

CONNOR, Leo E. Total development for the total human being. 1971, 73, 404-407.

ANNALS OF THE DEAF

FOX, Thomas F. Character building in deaf mutes. 1912, 57, 453-461.

BRADWAY, Katherine P. The social competence of deaf children. 1937, 82, 122-140.

STRENG, Alice, and KIRK, Samuel A. The social competence of deaf and hard-of-hearing children in a public day-school. 1938, 83, 244-254.

STEWART, Helen L. The social adjustment of the deaf. 1943, 88, 127-130.

FRACKELTON, Berneda P. Adjustments of the deaf. 1944, 89, 173-181.

GOUGH, J. A. Guidance for the deaf child in a residential school. 1945, 90, 206-220.

MYKLEBUST, Helmer R. A study of the usefulness of objective measures of mechanical aptitude in guidance programs for the hypacousic. 1946, 91, 123-150; 205-225.

ULMER, Thomas A. Scouting in the schools for the deaf. 1947, 92, 187-214.

NAIMAN, Davis W. Innovation in dormitory programs: a comprehensive approach. 1974, 119, 398-406.

TOMLINSON-KEASEY, C., and KELLY, Ronald R. The development of thought processes in deaf children. 1974, 119, 693-700.

AUSTIN, Gary F. Knowledge of selected concepts obtained by an adolescent deaf population. 1975, 120, 360-370.

EVANS, A. Donald. Experiential deprivation: unresolved factor in tne impoverished socialization of deaf school children in residence. 1975, 120, 545-552.

Social Development (Contd.)

ANNALS OF THE DEAF (Contd.)

YOUNGS, Joseph P. Experiential deprivation: a response. 1975, 120, 553-554.

STEVENS, Raymond P. Experiential deprivation: another response. 1976, 121, 494-496.

Speech

THE VOLTA REVIEW

_____. Statistics of speech teaching in American schools for the deaf. 1899, 1, 84-106; 1900, 2, 298-315; 1901, 3, 156-160; 280-297; 1902, 4, 134-138; 292-311; 1903, 5, 190-194; 300-316; 1904, 6, 270-281; 1905, 7, 282-293; 1906, 8, 270-283; 1907, 9, 370-383; 1908, 10, 290-302; 1909, 11, 234-246; 1910, 12, 246-258; 1911, 13, 104-116; 1912, 14, 108-121; 681-683; 1913, 15, 92-103; 1914, 16, 79-81; 310-322; 1915, 17, 190-202; 1916, 18, 200-213; 1917, 19, 240-252; 1918, 20, 368-381; 1919, 21, 392-405; 1920, 22, 362-375.

BELL, Alexander G. Historical notes concerning the teaching of speech to the deaf. 1900, 2, 33-68; 113-115; 257-272; 385-409; 489-519; 1901, 3, 131-140; 329-357; 428-452; 1902, 4, 19-41; 139-151; 438-454; 1903, 5, 369-378; 1905, 7, 49-70.

DE L'EPÉE, Abbe. The only method of completely restoring the deaf and dumb to society. 1900, 2, 68-69.

ALLEN, Anna C. Voice culture. 1900, 2, 219-230.

SCOTT, Ella. How to correct defective articulation. 1900, 2, 457-462.

_____. Auricular instruction. 1900, 2, 481-488.

_____. Resolutions relating to speech teaching (1868-1900). 1900, 2, 520-526.

GUTZMANN, Albert. Care of the speech of children in the family and the school. 1902, 4, 107-112.

Speech (Contd.)

THE VOLTA REVIEW (Contd.)

YALE, Caroline A. Formation and development of elementary English sounds. 1902, 4, 240-244; 323-326; 424-427; 1903, 5, 12-15; 140-142; 231-240.

MCKENDRICK, John G. Experimental phonetics. 1902, 4, 327-343.

MONRO, Sarah J. Some "don'ts" and their "whys". 1904, 6, 116-121.

KINSEY, Eveline I. On the management of the voice. 1904, 6, 206-210.

_____. Report on the progress of speech teaching in America. 1904, 6, 264-279; 1906, 8, 270-283; 1907, 9, 370-383.

NITCHIE, Edward B. A study of vowel positions. 1905, 7, 412-415.

GLENN, Frances L. Speech and speech reading in primary classes. 1907, 9, 98-104.

WETTSTEIN, Frances. Articulation in the intermediate grades. 1907, 9, 153-159.

FISH, Kate H. Speech work for older pupils. 1907, 9, 250-255.

MCCOWEN, Mary. How best to secure intelligent speech for deaf children. 1907, 9, 256-261.

GARRETT, Mary S. Helps and hindrances of deaf children in acquiring speech and language at the natural age. 1908, 10, 274-276.

STORY, Arthur J. The speaking mouth. 1909, 11, 13-19.

LUCAS, Frances. Corrective work in speech. 1909, 11, 408-410.

BUTLER, A. Evelyn. Corrective work in speech. 1909, 11, 408-410.

STORY, Arthur J. The importance of consonants in speech and speech-reading. 1909, 11, 479-488.

BELL, Alexander G. French pronunciation in the Melville Bell symbols. 1909, 11, 537-542.

GARDINER, M. The story of "visible speech". 1910, 12, 99-102.

HUDSON-MCKUEN, G. The physiology and psychology of hearing with special reference to the development of speech. 1910, 12, 267-272.

Speech (Contd.)

THE VOLTA REVIEW (Contd.)

CROUTER, A. L. The development of speech in the deaf child. 1910, 12, 288-298.

TAYLOR, Harris. Oralism in oral schools. 1910, 12, 349-353.

GLENN, Frances L. Speech: its place in child culture. 1910, 12, 418-419.

STORY, Arthur J. The development of "natural" speech. 1910, 12, 613-621.

FERRERI, Giulio. Teaching speech to the deaf. 1911, 13, 225-227.

HUDSON-MCKUEN, G. Obstructions to speech-development. 1911, 13, 286-291.

BELL, Mrs. Alexander G. Speech-work in New Zealand. 1911, 12, 677-682.

MONRO, Sarah J. Preliminaries to speech-teaching. 1912, 13, 468-472.

TAYLOR, Harris. Progress of speech-teaching in the United States. 1912, 13, 531-533.

STORY, Arthur J. "Strange voices" in the deaf. 1912, 14, 531-533.

BELL, Alexander G. Reminiscences of early days of speech-teaching. 1912, 14, 579-581.

REED, Mrs. Frank A. The practical correction of impediments of speech. 1913, 15, 11-18.

SCRIPTURE, E. W. The voices of the deaf. 1913, 15, 77-80; 141-145; 269-275; 314-316.

MONRO, Sarah J. The music of speech. 1913, 15, 127-130.

LEONARD, Eleanor C. School-room ethics in speech teaching. 1913, 14, 651-653.

BELL, Alexander M. Principles of speech and dictionary of sounds. 1914, 16, 65-78; 128-142; 217-227; 303-308; 403-408; 486-488; 555-558; 667-670; 731-735; 830-838; 1915, 17, 31-40; 79-80; 116-118; 161-163; 204-206; 248-249; 283-292; 335-336; 405-420; 494-504.

_____. Vocal physiology, the principles of speech, etc. 1914, 16, 66-78.

Speech (Contd.)

THE VOLTA REVIEW (Contd.)

DYER, Helen L. Need a deaf child's speech be expressionless? 1914, 16, 85-87.

JONES, Eleanor P. Details of work in beginning class from February to June, 1913. 1914, 16, 110-114.

_____. Speech diagrams showing positions of vocal organs. 1914, 16, 207-215.

TAYLOR, Harris. Speech diagrams. 1914, 16, 389-399.

THOMASON, Pattie. An experiment in voice culture. 1914, 16, 441-444.

DELAND, Fred. The pioneer pictorial presentation of mouth positions for use in teaching speech and speech-reading to the deaf. 1914, 16, 455-465.

DRIGGS, Frank M. Speech problems in combined-system schools. 1914, 16, 631-635.

WRIGHT, John D. Was the ultimate elimination of oralism foreseen? 1914, 16, 639-641.

ROBERTS, Emma. To speak or not to speak. 1914, 16, 697-698.

REED, Mrs. Frank A. Speech impediments and their correction in the public schools of Detroit. 1915, 17, 7-8.

BINGHAM, Katherine T. Speech is as natural to the deaf as to the hearing child. 1915, 17, 25-26.

TAYLOR, Harris. Speech-teaching in American schools for the deaf. 1915, 17, 56-58.

WORCESTER, Alice E. Pronunciation at sight. 1915, 17, 85-93.

BELL, Alexander M. Phonetic syllabication. 1915, 17, 97-102.

STORY, Arthur J. Some practical points. 1915, 17, 155-158.

FULLER, Sarah. The Melville Bell symbols as an aid in correcting stammering. 1915, 17, 214-216.

MAKUEN, G. Hudson. A study of 1,000 cases of stammering. 1915, 17, 268-273.

CARTER, A. E. Teaching speech to the deaf. 1915, 17, 315-317.

ROE, W. Carey. The "explosive" sounds. 1915, 17, 457-459.

Speech (Contd.)

THE VOLTA REVIEW (Contd.)

DUFF, Jessie. The use of speech and speech-reading. 1916, <u>18</u>, 1-2.

WRIGHT, John D. Fundamentals in teaching the deaf to speak. 1916, <u>18</u>, 132-135.

STORY, Arthur J. Talks to young teachers of speech: errors in the consonantal sounds. 1916, <u>18</u>, 315-317.

BENEDICT, A. L. Notes on the sequence of elementary sounds in English. 1916, <u>18</u>, 393-397.

STORY, Arthur J. Talks to young teachers of speech: the synthetic method. 1916, <u>18</u>, 397-399.

WRIGHT, John D. Natural speech. 1916, <u>18</u>, 401-403.

WRIGHT, John D. Interest: another fundamental in speech teaching. 1916, <u>18</u>, 437-439.

BENEDICT, A. L. Vowel pronunciation in English. 1916, <u>18</u>, 495-498.

SPYKER, Sally. The development of speech in the case of a so-called deaf-mute. 1917, <u>19</u>, 61-63.

STORY, Arthur J. Talks to young teachers of speech: the development of voice for speaking. 1917, <u>19</u>, 68-70.

STEDMAN, Anne B. An outline of the elements and treatment of stammering. 1917, <u>19</u>, 71-72.

BENEDICT, A. L. Vowel incidence in English. 1917, <u>19</u>, 97-101.

WRIGHT, John D. Desk work in speech. 1917, <u>19</u>, 105-106.

SCRIPTURE, E. W. The nature of stuttering. 1917, <u>19</u>, 297-298.

THOMASON, Pattie. Suggestions for improving the quality of the voice. 1917, <u>19</u>, 361-364.

BENEDICT, A. L. Speech with reference to delicacy of auditory sensations. 1917, <u>19</u>, 419-425.

CLAPP, John M. What good speech can do for the business man. 1917, <u>19</u>, 611-613.

HUBBARD, Elbert. Stutterers and stammerers. 1917, <u>19</u>, 627-629.

MONRO, Sarah J. Rhythm in speaking. 1917, <u>19</u>, 641-645.

Speech (Contd.)

THE VOLTA REVIEW (Contd.)

BENEDICT, A. L. Pronunciation of "th" in English. 1917, 19, 696-698.

_____. The development of pitch in the voice of congenitally deaf children. 1918, 20, 258-261.

THOMASON, Pattie. Voice training for deaf children. 1918, 20, 311-314; 387-388.

STORY, Arthur J. Talks to young teachers of speech: the mouth in speech. 1918, 20, 320-322.

DELAND, Fred. Give your child the best educational advantages. 1918, 20, 329-333.

ERSNER, Matthew S. Defective speech and some of its phases. 1918, 20, 392-395.

OSBORNE, Caroline A. Speech defects in the school child. 1918, 20, 517-521.

AVONDINO, Josephine. The babbling method. 1918, 20, 667-671; 767-771; 1919, 21, 67-71; 142-145; 224-228; 273-282.

_____. Editorial comment. De L'Epée, the great advocate of speech. 1918, 20, 801-803.

CONNERY, Julia M. A demonstration in voice training. 1919, 21, 108-109.

WRIGHT, John D. A friendly talk. 1919, 21, 203-209.

MONRO, Sarah J. Phonetics and word study; a plan for pronunciation and speech drill. 1919, 21, 213-216; 286-289; 360-363; 604-606; 669-672; 1920, 22, 15-18; 94-97; 233-235; 383-384.

MARTIN, Frederick. The prevention and correction of speech defects. 1919, 21, 434-438; 1923, 25, 281-284.

DUFF, Jessie. Gaining the speech habit. 1919, 21, 479-483.

THOMASON, Pattie. Voice and speech. 1919, 21, 484-485.

HEDRICK, Jennie. A new nomenclature for nasality. 1919, 21, 538-540.

SWIFT, Walter B. How to begin speech correction in the public schools. 1919, 21, 585-589.

Speech (Contd.)

THE VOLTA REVIEW (Contd.)

KIDDER, Charles W. The serviceability of visible speech. 1919, 21, 589-593.

DELAND, Fred. The Melville Bell symbols for recording speech sounds. 1919, 21, 617-621.

OSWALD, Mabel V. Stammering and voice defects. 1919, 21, 708-711.

KENYON, Elmer L. Stammering as a disorder of speech dependent on conditions of child development. 1920, 22, 39-45.

TOMPKINS, Ernest. Stammering and amnesia. 1920, 22, 85-88.

SWIFT, Walter B. A reasonable objection to unscientific methods in speech correction. 1920, 22, 166-168.

JOINER, Enfield. How we rehabilitated the speech of soldiers. 1920, 22, 245-248.

BENEDICT, A. L. English spelling and pronunciation. 1920, 22, 303-306.

SCRIPTURE, E. W. Inscriptions of speech. 1920, 22, 427-434.

LONG, T. Schuyler. Poetry as an aid to pronunciation. 1920, 22, 448-450.

TOMPKINS, Ernest. Stammering: a reasonable answer to a reasonable objection. 1920, 22, 450-452.

SCRIPTURE, E. W. Tracing from speech records. 1920, 22, 480-485.

SWIFT, Walter B. Discussion of the emotional theory of stuttering. 1920, 22, 510-518.

SCRIPTURE, E. W. The organ of voice. 1920, 22, 571-575.

POWER, Sue B. The difficulties of speech in acquired deafness. 1920, 22, 670-672.

TOMPKINS, Ernest. Is stammering emotional? 1920, 22, 752-754.

SCRIPTURE, E. W. The vowel siren. 1921, 23, 75-76.

THOMASON, Pattie. Voice training in the intermediate grades. 1921, 23, 88-90.

SCRIPTURE, E. W. The analysis of vowel curves. 1921, 23, 99-102.

SCRIPTURE, E. W. The physical nature of a vowel. 1921, 23, 149-150.

Speech (Contd.)

THE VOLTA REVIEW (Contd.)

SCRIPTURE, E. W. The physics of speech. 1921, 23, 366-368.

THOMPSON, Iza. The sensitive flame of the Bunsen burner as an aid to voice production and speech for the congenitally deaf child. 1921, 23, 397-399.

SCRIPTURE, E. W. The mechanism of breathing. 1921, 23, 403-406.

GREENE, James S. National hospital for speech disorders. 1922, 24, 223-227.

LAMB, Helen D. Drill exercises on one hundred difficult words of common speech. 1923, 25, 100-105.

TIMBERLAKE, Josephine B. Voice training for the deafened. 1923, 25, 351-354.

TOMPKINS, Ernest. Stammering and the scientific attitude. 1923, 25, 483-485.

STEVENS, J. E. Stammering. 1923, 25, 532-535.

DUNBAR, Evelina. Articulation, voice and speech. 1925, 27, 5-8.

MARTIN, Frederick. A method of raising a low-pitched voice and lowering a high-pitched voice. 1925, 27, 19-24.

YALE, Caroline A. Phonetic notation (the Northampton Charts). 1925, 27, 49-54.

STEED, Lyman. Visible speech. 1925, 27, 54-57.

TILLY, William. The international phonetic alphabet. 1925, 27, 57-59.

CHRISTMAS, Jeannette J. P, T, and K as breath stops. 1926, 28, 195-197.

WRIGHT, John D. Some homely suggestions in speech teaching. 1926, 28, 614-616.

JOINER, Enfield, and LEWIS, Sarah. Speech correction in the primary grades. 1926, 28, 620-624.

LEWIN, Lucie M. The speech habit. 1927, 29, 242-244.

YALE, Caroline A. Dr. Bell's early experiments in giving speech to the deaf. 1927, 29, 293-295.

HARRIS, G. T. A study in the sound "S". 1927, 29, 298-299.

THOMPSON, Iza. Modernism in forming a basis of intelligible rhythmic speech for the deaf-born child. 1927, 29, 343-349.

Speech (Contd.)

THE VOLTA REVIEW (Contd.)

ELLIOTT, Sarah L. Speech in our advanced department. 1927, <u>29</u>, 457-459.

DAWES, Rachel E. Articulation at the Western Penn. School. 1927, <u>29</u>, 763-780.

HECTOR, Elizabeth R. Speech defects. 1928, <u>30</u>, 173-174.

ECCLESTON, Mary M. How we learn speech in the beginning. 1928, <u>30</u>, 279-280.

RUSSELL, G. Oscar. "Uncanny deaf speech". 1928, <u>30</u>, 566-572.

LAURITSEN, Marné. Methods and results of training with the teletactor. 1928, <u>30</u>, 604-609.

KENYON, Elmer L. Psychophysiologic principles underlying improvement in vocal pitch, tension and quality in the deafened, with the presentation of an effectual physiologic substitute for lost hearing in vocal management. 1929, <u>31</u>, 129-141.

FLEITZ, Mildred, and DACEY, Edward. A game with the vowel sounds. 1929, <u>31</u>, 373-374.

STEINBERG, John C. The teaching of speech. 1929, <u>31</u>, 408-409.

GARNS, John S. Why the deafened should have vocal training. 1929, <u>31</u>, 757-759.

BURKE, Mary M. Making speech more interesting. 1929, <u>31</u>, 789-790.

HENDERSON, Jennie M. Outline of a speech lesson. 1930, <u>32</u>, 134-136.

ALCORN, Sophia. The use of touch. 1930, <u>32</u>, 452-453.

AVONDINO, Josephine. Fluency. 1930, <u>32</u>, 454-455.

HURD, Anna C. The use of speech in all activities. 1930, <u>32</u>, 455-457.

HENDERSON, Jennie M. The teacher's voice. 1930, <u>32</u>, 609-610.

WALKER, Hazel W. Dr. Frederick Martin's speech methods as applied to the deaf and the hard of hearing child. 1931, <u>33</u>, 171-174.

SMITH, Sherman K. Voice and speech problems. 1931, <u>33</u>, 438-439.

ALCORN, Sophia. The Tadoma method. 1932, <u>34</u>, 195-198.

Speech (Contd.)

THE VOLTA REVIEW (Contd.)

BAILEY, Jane D. The value of vibration in teaching speech to the deaf. 1932, 34, 200; 230-231.

GRUSSING, Florence P. Speech as a subject. 1932, 34, 271-272.

SMITH, Sherman K. Can we improve the voice quality of the congenitally deaf? 1932, 34, 528-534.

RIERDON, Beatrice. Speech. 1933, 35, 130; 139-140.

SMITH, Sherman K. Speech patterns. 1933, 35, 160-161; 188.

STOBSCHINSKI, Robert. The Jena method applied to speech. 1933, 35, 325-328.

GAULT, R. H. The use of the sense of touch in developing speech. 1934, 36, 82-83.

HANCOCK, E. Frances. Use of diagnostic speech charts. 1934, 36, 645; 690.

LAMB, Marion H. Some suggestions for corrective speech work. 1935, 37, 133-136.

VOELKER, Charles H. A sound count for the oral curriculum. 1935, 37, 155-156.

CLOUD, Daniel T. Touch and hearing in speech work. 1935, 37, 350; 381.

WEST, Robert. Speech and hearing. 1935, 37, 573-578; 626-629.

_____. Demonstration of how NOT to teach speech. 1935, 37, 585; 617.

HUDGINS, Clarence V. A study of respiration and speech. 1936, 38, 341-343; 373.

LACK, A. Speech problems throughout the school. 1937, 39, 72-75; 123-124.

JOINER, Enfield. Speech contests. 1938, 40, 628-630.

ALCORN, Kate. Speech developed through vibration. 1938, 40, 633-637.

KOPP, George A. The application of recent findings in the field of speech correction. 1938, 40, 638-640.

Speech (Contd.)

THE VOLTA REVIEW (Contd.)

MUYSKENS, John H. The building and maintenance of clear speech for the deaf. 1938, 40, 655-657.

WOLF, Edna L. A questionnaire for the oral teacher. 1939, 41, 328; 376.

TIMBERLAKE, Josephine B. A tool for speech teaching. 1940, 42, 10-12; 56-57.

NITKIN, Nathaniel. Improving your speech. 1940, 42, 35-39.

NEW, Mary C. Speech for the young deaf child. 1940, 42, 592-599.

BOOTH, Iris, et al. The practical use of speech in holding a job. 1940, 42, 600-606.

FROESCHELS, Emil. A new method in the oral education of the deaf child. 1940, 42, 664-666.

HEIDER, Fritz, and SYKES, Jean L. A study of the spontaneous vocalizations of fourteen deaf children. 1941, 43, 10-14.

NEW, Mary C. Color in speech teaching. 1942, 44, 133-138; 199-203.

NUMBERS, Mary E. The place of elements teaching in speech development. 1942, 44, 261-265.

UTLEY, Jean, and WALKER, N.F. Are the Northampton charts outmoded? 1942, 44, 485-490.

HUDGINS, Clarence V. Speech intelligibility tests: a practical program. 1943, 45, 5-6; 52-54.

_____. Speech teaching in schools for the deaf; an association committee report. 1943, 45, 7-11; 50.

SILVERMAN, S. Richard. The speech program of Central Institute. 1943, 45, 12-15; 56-57.

STETSON, R. H. Contributions of teachers of the deaf to the science of phonetics. 1943, 45, 19-20; 54-56.

NELSON, Boyd E. Building a speech vocabulary. 1943, 45, 74-75.

GREGG, F. M. The psychology of speech. 1943, 45, 138-139; 178.

HUDGINS, Clarence V. Concerning the validity of speech tests. 1943, 45, 271-272; 316.

Speech (Contd.)

THE VOLTA REVIEW (Contd.)

PRESTO, Marya. An experiment in voice control. 1943, 45, 490-493.

SILVERMAN, S. Richard. The report on speech teaching. 1943, 45, 622-623; 662.

ROONEY, Alice G. Voice work for the young deaf child. 1944, 46, 558-560; 608.

SIMON, Arthur B. Why take time out for speech teaching? 1945, 47, 326; 378-380.

SISTER ST. ESTHER. Common sense and speech teaching. 1945, 47, 485-486; 542.

NUMBERS, Fred C. Is speech teaching a failure? 1946, 48, 264-266; 316.

PUGH, Bessie. The speech vocabulary of young children. 1946, 48, 267; 312-313.

O'CONNOR, Clarence D. Better speech for better living. 1946, 48, 624-627.

BODYCOMB, Margaret. The speech of the deaf and of the normal speaker. 1946, 48, 637-638.

NUMBERS, Fred C. The versatile consonant. 1946, 48, 638-640.

PETERSON, Gordon E. Influence of voice quality. 1946, 48, 640-641.

HUDGINS, Clarence V. Speech breathing and speech intelligibility. 1946, 48, 642-644.

KOPP, George A., and GREEN, Harriet C. Visible speech. 1948, 50, 60-62; 264-266.

BRECKWOLDT, Gerhart H. The use of the artificial palate for visual control and improvement of articulation. 1948, 50, 301-303.

JOINER, Enfield. Our speech teaching heritage. 1948, 50, 417-422

STOKOE, Agnes. Vibration in speech teaching. 1948, 50, 422-423.

NUMBERS, Mary E., and HUDGINS, Clarence V. Speech perception in present day education for deaf children. 1948, 50, 449-456.

NEW, Mary C. Speech in our schools for the deaf. 1949, 51, 61-64; 98-102.

ALCORN, Sophia. Speech in the Detroit Day School. 1949, 51, 163; 192-194.

Speech (Contd.)

THE VOLTA REVIEW (Contd.)

BRILL, Richard G., and GORDON, Anne. The special speech teacher in a school for the deaf. 1949, 51, 549-550; 588-590.

HUDGINS, Clarence V. A method of appraising the speech of the deaf. 1949, 51, 597-601; 638.

SISTER MARIANNA. How to improve the speech of older deaf children. 1950, 52, 61-62; 100-102.

POULOS, Thomas H. Improving the intelligibility of deaf children's speech. 1952, 54, 265-267; 284.

HUDGINS, Clarence V. The research program in speech at the Clarke School. 1952, 54, 355-362.

O'CONNOR, Clarence D. That the deaf may speak. 1952, 54, 418-420; 466.

HUDGINS, Clarence V. (moderator, panel). Speech and speech perception. 1953, 55, 20-38.

CRUTTENDEN, Mary E. The value of the speechmaster. 1953, 55, 294; 316-318.

NEW, Mary C. The deaf child's speech vocabulary. 1954, 56, 105-108.

FARMAN, J. J. The Farman-Phillips speech intelligibility diagnostic test. 1954, 56, 168-170.

SILVERMAN, S. Richard. Teaching speech to the deaf--the issues. 1954, 56, 385-389; 417.

WRIGHT, John D. On nasality. 1954, 56, 408-409.

PITTINGER, Priscilla. Speech and the deaf adult. 1954, 56, 449-451.

VORCE, Eleanor R. Teaching speech at Lexington School. 1955, 57, 11-13.

STONER, Marguerite. The development of early speech with emphasis on the synthetic method. 1955, 57, 15-17.

GRUVER, Margaret H. The Tadoma method. 1955, 57, 17-19.

CARR, Josephine. The use of spontaneous speech. 1955, 57, 20-21.

QUICK, Marian. A speech program for advanced pupils. 1955, 57, 22-23.

Speech (Contd.)

THE VOLTA REVIEW (Contd.)

ROTTER, Paul. The development of speech in young children. 1955, 57, 53-57; 82.

KOESTER, Diedrich. Visible speech. 1955, 57, 255-256.

KNIGHT, Marian. Making the elements fun to learn. 1955, 57, 360-361.

MCCALMONT, Phyllis. A departure from formal classroom teaching of communication skill. 1956, 58, 61-63.

GARDNER, Mark B. Speech we may see. 1956, 58, 149-155.

LORE, James I. A technique for developing adequate post-plosive aspiration. 1957, 59, 351.

ZALIOUK, A., COHEN, S., and ZALIOUK, D. Intelligible speech through a visual-tactile system of phonetical symbolization. 1957, 59, 426-435; 454.

FRISINA, D. Robert, and BERNERO, R. J. A profile of the hearing and speech of Gallaudet College students. 1958, 60, 316-321.

MONSEES, Edna K. Experiences with children who failed to learn to talk when taught as deaf or hard of hearing. 1958, 60, 328-330.

WOOD, Margaret. Speech in our upper school. 1958, 60, 382-386.

MONAGHAN, Alice. The need for a school to have a philosophy of teaching speech. 1958, 60, 386-391.

MANNEN, Grace. Speech for outside activities. 1958, 60, 391-395.

RICHARDSON, Paul C. Developing fundamental speech patterns. 1959, 61, 276-282.

LARR, Alfred L., and STOCKWELL, Robert P. A test of speech intelligibility. 1959, 61, 403-407; 437.

RAPH, Jane B. Problems and issues in teaching speech. 1960, 62, 302-306.

BLACK, John W. Experimental phonetics. 1960, 62, 313-315.

DICARLO, Louis M. Speech and communication for the deaf. 1960, 62, 317-319.

MANGAN, Kenneth R. Speech teaching for older children. 1960, 62, 319-321

BRUCE, Wallace. Social integration and effectiveness of speech. 1960, 62, 368-372.

LORE, James I. A system of recording American-English speech sounds. 1961, 63, 433-434.

Speech (Contd.)

THE VOLTA REVIEW (Contd.)

PRATT, George T. Oral education for deaf children: why and how. 1961, 63, 480-483.

PETERSON, Gordon E., et al. (panel discussion). Effective speech for the deaf. 1962, 64, 369-374; SISTER MARY LAURENTINE, 374-376; Joseph ROSENSTEIN, 376-377; Cornelius KOUTSTAAL, 377-378.

CALVERT, Donald R. Speech sound duration and the surd-sonant error. 1962, 64, 401-402.

CALVERT, Donald R. Deaf voice quality: a preliminary investigation. 1962, 64, 402-403.

ANGELOCCI, Angelo A. Some observations on the speech of the deaf. 1962, 64, 403-405.

POULOS, Thomas H. A speech improvement program in a large residential school for the deaf. 1962, 64, 405-408.

GOETZINGER, Cornelius P. Effects of small perceptive losses on language and on speech discrimination. 1962, 64, 408-414.

HOUCHINS, Rollie R. Pitch discrimination. 1962, 64, 424-426.

PUGH, Bessie. Clarifying speech problems for the deaf. 1963, 65, 15-21.

DRUMM, Philip R. How speech therapy feels. 1963, 65, 74-75.

SISTER MARY LAURENTINE. The speech program at St. Joseph Institute for the Deaf. 1964, 66, 459-463.

LICHTENBERG, Frances S. A comparison of children's ability to make speech sound discriminations. 1966, 68, 426-434.

BOONE, Daniel R. Modification of the voices of deaf children. 1966, 68, 686-692.

PRONOVOST, Wilbert. Developments in visual displays of speech information. 1967, 69, 365-373.

NUMBERS, Mary E. A plea for better speech. 1967, 69, 576-582.

DENES, Peter B. Speech science and the deaf. 1968, 70, 603-607.

THOMAS, Ian B., and SNELL, Ronald C. Articulation training through visual speech patterns. 1970, 72, 310-318.

Speech (Contd.)

THE VOLTA REVIEW (Contd.)

HARPER, Phyllis. A visible speech aid. 1970, 72, 349-352.

HOLBROOK, Anthony, and CRAWFORD, Gladys H. Modifications of vocal frequency and intensity in the speech of the deaf. 1970, 72, 492-497.

PICKETT, J. M. Some applications of speech analysis to communication aids for the deaf. 1971, 73, 147-156.

BISHOP, Milo E., et al. Orosensory perception in the deaf. 1972, 74, 289-298.

ROWE, Linda. The speech model. 1974, 76, 107-112.

MARIMONT, Rosalind B. How can the deaf learn to speak? 1974, 76, 223-230.

BENNETT, Clint. Speech pathology and the hearing impaired child. 1974, 76, 550-556.

NICKERSON, Raymond S. Characteristics of the speech of deaf persons. 1975, 77, 342-362.

CALVERT, Donald R., and SILVERMAN, S. Richard. Methods for developing speech (the auditory global method). 1975, 77, 501-510.

CLARKE, Bryan R., and LING, Daniel. The effects of using cued speech: a follow-up study. 1976, 78, 23-24.

PICKETT, J. M. Speech-processing aids: some research problems. 1976, 78, 82-87 (monograph).

OLSON, Rosalind Lawson. Screening and teaching irregular verbs. 1976, 78, 341-344.

ANNALS OF THE DEAF

CURTIS, John H. Organs of speech and hearing. 1849, 2, 158-164.

STONE, Collins. Articulation as a medium for the instruction of the deaf and dumb. 1849, 2, 105-112; 232-242.

PEET, Harvey P. Analysis of Bonet's treatise on the art of teaching the dumb to speak. 1851, 3, 200-211.

ELLIOT, Richard. Speech for the deaf. 1869, 14, 129-145.

Speech (Contd.)

ANNALS OF THE DEAF (Contd.)

TRASK, Cornelia. Articulation and lip-reading. 1869, 14, 146-156.

MONTGOMERY, Ida. The practical value of articulation. 1870, 15, 133-136.

HOTCHKISS, J. Burton. Articulation for semi-mutes. 1870, 15, 136-149.

BELL, Alexander G. Visible speech as a means of communicating articulation to deaf-mutes. 1872, 17, 1-21.

PHILLIPS, John. The elements of human speech, as applied to the instruction of deaf-mutes in articulation. 1873, 18, 241-254.

CLARK, A. S. "The elements of human speech" reviewed. 1874, 19, 21-26.

GREENBERGER, D. Visible speech as a means of communicating articulation to the deaf and dumb. 1874, 19, 65-74.

ARNOLD, Thomas. Mr. Thomas Arnold's method of teaching articulation. 1882, 27, 90-98.

STORRS, R. S. Articulation in deaf-mute instruction. 1882, 27, 160-162.

GREENBERGER, D. The organs of speech. 1883, 28, 1-14; 226-234; 1885, 30, 259-270.

GARRETT, Emma. A plea that the deaf "mutes" of America may be taught to use their voices. 1883, 28, 15-20.

WORCESTER, Alice E. How shall our children be taught to pronounce at sight the words of our written language? 1885, 30, 6-25.

ARNOLD, Thomas. The functions of touch in learning to speak. 1886, 31, 120-130.

GRANDGENT, Charles H. Vowel measurements. 1891, 36, 11-38.

FAY, Edward A. The hygenic value of speech. 1892, 37, 80.

PAUL, W. Entrance into school and exercises preliminary to articulation. 1893, 38, 8-14.

PEET, Isaac L. A method of teaching articulation to every pupil. 1893, 38, 281-291.

GREENE, David. Breath and voice. 1901, 46, 477-487.

Speech (Contd.)

ANNALS OF THE DEAF (Contd.)

GILLESPIE, Frances E. The theory and practice of instruction for an oral class of beginners. 1901, 46, 492-507; 1902, 47, 233-242.

STEINKE, Elsie M. Justification of speech teaching and speech reading. 1902, 47, 345-349.

CHRISTMAS, Jeannette J. Articulation work in the primary grades. 1907, 52, 320-330; 1916, 61, 306-315.

NOYES, Marion. Articulation work in intermediate grades. 1907, 52, 330-337; 1916, 61, 315-322.

LUCAS, Frances. Articulation and lip reading in the advanced department. 1907, 52, 344-349.

BUTLER, A. Evelyn. Advanced work in articulation. 1907, 52, 349-354; 1916, 61, 333-338.

DAVIDSON, Emma F. Voice culture for advanced pupils. 1907, 52, 354-372; 1916, 61, 339-360.

TURVEY, T. M. The importance of voice culture in teaching the deaf. 1909, 54, 126-140.

FOWLER, Frances E. Articulation drill. 1909, 54, 416-420.

HUDSON-MAKUEN, G. The physiology and psychology of hearing with special reference to the development of speech. 1910, 55, 325-332.

TAYLOR, Harris. Oralism in oral schools. 1910, 55, 379-385.

WRIGHT, John D. The speech method of educating the deaf. 1910, 55, 439-452.

TAYLOR, Harris. The phonograph as an aid in articulation teaching. 1914, 59, 337-339.

BUELL, Edith M. Easy and natural speech. 1914, 59, 379-386; 443-451; 1915, 60, 129-137.

ADAMS, Mabel E. The intelligibility of the speech of the deaf. 1914, 59, 451-460.

WRIGHT, John D. Why speech teaching fails sometimes. 1915, 60, 322-323.

WRIGHT, John D. The necessity of a speech environment. 1916, 61, 137-141.

Speech (Contd.)

ANNALS OF THE DEAF (Contd.)

THROCKMORTON, Helen. Preparatory work and first steps in articulation. 1916, 61, 289-306.

PYBAS, Adelaide H. Articulation work in the intermediate grades. 1916, 61, 323-329.

STORY, Arthur J. Errors in consonantal sounds. 1916, 61, 443.

STORY, Arthur J. Talks to young teachers of speech. 1916, 61, 443-453.

STORY, Arthur J. The synthetic method. 1916, 61, 449.

STORY, Arthur J. The development of voice for speaking. 1918, 63, 285-292.

YALE, Caroline A. The teaching of elementary English sounds. 1918, 63, 425-435.

STORY, Arthur J. The mouth in speech. 1918, 63, 440-446.

RIO, Armand. The mysteries of speech unveiled. 1919, 64, 402-420.

WRIGHT, John D. The fair chance column. 1921, 66, 5-7.

WRIGHT, John D. Retention of speech. 1921, 66, 462-475.

BREHM, F. Elizabeth. Speech correction. 1922, 67, 361-370.

BLANTON, Smiley. Treatment of stutterers. 1922, 67, 371-385.

JOINER, Enfield. Teaching of speech. 1922, 67, 397-404.

SISTER M. EMMANUEL. Speech work with the deaf child. 1926, 71, 135-141.

THOMPSON, Iza. The use of the sensitive flame for voice production and speech for the congenitally deaf child. 1926, 71, 185-189.

RUSSELL, G. Oscar. Visualizing speech for the deaf. 1927, 72, 329-340.

PINTNER, Rudolf. Speech and speech reading tests for the deaf. 1929, 74, 480-486.

WOLF, E. L. New methods for the development of words in speech. 1931, 76, 442-448.

VINSON, Marietta R. The production of a tone by the human vocal mechanism. 1933, 78, 211-219.

Speech (Contd.)

ANNALS OF THE DEAF (Contd.)

HOUSER, Bessie. Pioneer oral work. 1933, 78, 374-376.

VOELKER, Charles H. The occurrence of homophenous articulations in American usage. 1934, 79, 210-213.

SISTER SYLVANIA. Correlation of comprehension and speech in education of the deaf. 1934, 79, 306-309.

VOELKER, Charles H. The usage of vowel positions. 1935, 80, 5-6.

RAWLINGS, Charles G. A comparative study of the movements of breathing muscles in speech and quiet breathing of deaf and normal subjects. 1935, 80, 147-156; 1936, 81, 136-150.

VOELKER, Charles H. A preliminary strobophotoscopic study of the speech of the deaf. 1935, 80, 243-259.

CARHART, Raymond. A method of using the Gault-teletactor to teach speech rhythms. 1935, 80, 260-263.

SHAW, M. A study in the analysis and correction of the speech of the hard of hearing. 1936, 81, 255-268.

VOELKER, Charles H. The Schwa and other indefinite vowels in deaf oralism. 1937, 82, 253-255.

HUDGINS, Clarence V. Voice production and breath control in the speech of the deaf. 1937, 82, 338-363.

MASON, Marie K., and BRIGHT, Margaret. Tempo in rhythmic speech education. 1937, 82, 385-401.

MEYER, Max F. What retards speech teaching to the deaf parvel? 1938, 83, 153-168.

VOELKER, Charles H. An experimental study of the comparative rate of utterance of deaf and normal hearing speakers. 1938, 83, 274-284.

MASON, Marie K. Individual deviations in the visual reproduction of the speech of two speakers. 1939, 84, 408-424.

VOELKER, Charles H. Demonstration apparatus to teach natural speech to the deaf. 1940, 85, 500-503.

KELLEY, Noble H., and GUILMARTIN, Mary D. The Kelley-Guilmartin speech test for deaf children. 1941, 86, 225-226.

SHAFFER, Chester M. The kinesthetic method of speech development and speech-reading. 1942, 87, 421-442.

Speech (Contd.)

ANNALS OF THE DEAF (Contd.)

POTTER, Ralph K. Visible speech. 1946, 91, 447-452.

COATS, G. Dewey. Characteristics of communication methods. 1950, 95, 486-490.

HEDGECOCK, LeRoy D. Speech and hearing problems of the young deaf child. 1955, 100, 435-445.

FUSFELD, Irving S. How the deaf communicate--speech. 1958, 103, 243-254.

MANGAN, Kenneth R. Speech improvement through articulation testing. 1961, 106, 391-396.

CORNETT, R. Orin. Cued speech. 1967, 112, 3-13.

PICKETT, J. M. Proceedings of the conference on speech analyzing aids for the deaf. 1968, 113, 116-119.

PICKETT, J. M. Sound patterns of speech: an introductory sketch. 1968, 113, 120-126.

LIBERMAN, A. M., et al. Why are speech spectrograms hard to read? 1968, 113, 127-133.

HUNTINGTON, Dorothy A., et al. Some observations on monosyllable production by deaf speakers and dysarthric speakers. 1968, 113, 134-146.

SAKAI, Toshiyuki, et al. Fundamental studies of speech analysis and synthesis. 1968, 113, 156-167.

MARTONY, Janos. On the correction of the voice pitch level for severely hard of hearing subjects. 1968, 113, 195-202.

HOUSE, A. S., et al. Perception of visual transforms of speech stimuli: learning simple syllables. 1968, 113, 215-221.

COHEN, Martin L. The ADL sustained phoneme analyzer. 1968, 113, 247-252.

MOORES, Donald F. Cued speech: some practical and theoretical considerations. 1969, 114, 23-33.

LACH, Rosemary, et al. Early speech development in deaf infants. 1970, 115, 522-526.

ROSS, Mark, DUFFY, Robert J., COOLER, Harry S., and SARGEANT, Russell L. Contribution of the lower audible frequencies in the recognition of emotions. 1973, 118, 37-41.

Speech (Contd.)

ANNALS OF THE DEAF (Contd.)

IRVIN, Bruce E., and WILSON, Linda S. The voiced-unvoiced distinction in deaf speech. 1973, 118, 43-45.

EVESLAGE, Roberta A., and BUCHMANN, Adella V. The effects of consequences delivered contingent upon intelligible speech by deaf children. 1973, 118, 446-453.

LING, Daniel, and CLARKE, Bryan R. Cued speech: an evaluative study. 1975, 120, 480-488.

HERX, Michelle A., and HUNT, Frances E. A framework for speech development within a total communication system. 1976, 121, 537-540.

Speechreading

THE VOLTA REVIEW

FEARON, J. Oral spelling. 1900, 2, 30-32.

VANPRAAGH, William. Lip-reading: what it ought to be. 1902, 4, 45-47.

NITCHIE, Edward B. An educational neglect. 1903, 5, 415-420.

FARRAR, A. The relative value of speech and lipreading. 1903, 5, 429-435.

NITCHIE, Edward B. "Grasping the meaning as a whole." 1904, 6, 198-201.

DEVRIES, J. G. A commandment that should not be obeyed. 1904, 6, 283-287.

KEELER, Sarah W. A method of teaching speech-reading to the adult deaf. 1905, 7, 1-22.

KENNEDY, Mildred. Mirror practice as an aid to lip-reading. 1908, 10, 155-159.

Speechreading (Contd.)

THE VOLTA REVIEW (Contd.)

JONES, Mary D. Some suggestions about lip-reading. 1908, 10, 160-165.

HANSEN, A. A series of tests in lip-reading. 1908, 10, 381-384.

ANDREWS, Harriet U. Of lip-reading adults. 1908, 11, 179-183.

FERRERI, Giulio. Speech-reading. 1910, 12, 161-165.

MCCOWEN, M. The development of speech reading in the deaf child. 1910, 12, 307-312.

NITCHIE, Edward B. The eye as a substitute for deaf ears. 1910, 12, 597-601.

STORY, Arthur J. Speech-reading for the deaf--not dumb. 1910, 12, 671-676.

OLIN, Caroline L. The Müller-Walle method of speech-reading. 1911, 13, 23-26.

GOLDSTEIN, Max A. The practical value of lip-reading. 1911, 13, 220-224.

DUPUIS, L., and LEGRAND, A. Lip-reading for deaf children. 1911, 13, 298-302; 353-357; 412-416.

HAYCOCK, C. Sibley. Lip-reading, the art of Judith Lee. 1912, 14, 9-14.

HULL, Susanne E. Lip-reading as a remedy for deafness. 1912, 14, 129-133.

NITCHIE, Edward B. How to practise lip-reading. 1912, 14, 141-145.

WRIGHT, John D. Where lip-reading reaches its maximum efficiency. 1912, 14, 257-259.

MÜLLER-WALLE, Julius. The Müller-Walle method of speech-reading. 1912, 13, 526-528.

_____. The teaching of speech-reading to the adult deaf. 1912, 14, 540-544.

NITCHIE, Edward B. The physiological basis of the visible movements in lip-reading. 1913, 15, 56-68.

FULLER, Sarah. Speech-reading: a guide for self-instruction where trained teachers are not available. 1913, 15, 253-265; 1918, 20, 428-431; 579-580; 744-749; 1919, 21, 147-149; 209-213.

Speechreading (Contd.)

THE VOLTA REVIEW (Contd.)

NITCHIE, Edward B. Lip-reading, an art. 1913, 15, 276-278.

NITCHIE, Edward B. Synthesis and intuition in lip-reading. 1913, 15, 311-314.

STORY, Arthur J. The development of speech reading. 1914, 16, 13-19.

PIERCE, Jerry A. The psychology of speech-reading. 1914, 16, 56-59; 1923, 25, 522-527.

ROBERTS, Emma. A privilege to enjoy. 1914, 16, 257-259.

TORREY, Gertrude. Lip-reading for the adult deaf. 1914, 16, 535-538.

KITSON, H. D. The role of association in lip-reading. 1914, 16, 619-620.

PIERCE, Jerry A. The experience system of speech-reading. 1914, 16, 739-744.

NITCHIE, Edward B. The "experience system" plus. 1914, 16, 744-746.

BRUHN, Martha E. Methods in lip-reading. 1914, 16, 747-748.

NITCHIE, Edward B. The lip-reading teacher's equipment and opportunities. 1914, 16, 801-803.

CASE, Lucy E. Symposium on conversation-class work in lip-reading. 1915, 17, 2-4.

TORREY, Gertrude. Lip-reading for the slightly deaf. 1915, 17, 51-53.

PIERCE, Jerry A. Theory minus. 1915, 17, 61-65.

NITCHIE, Edward B. Training plus experience. 1915, 17, 66-72.

NITCHIE, Edward B. The detective possibilities of lip-reading. 1915, 17, 81-83.

DYER, Helen Louise. The speech-reading teacher's opportunity. 1915, 17, 175-176.

NITCHIE, Edward B. Why not lip-reading? 1915, 17, 178-179.

STORY, Arthur J. Speech-reading depends more upon use than actual teaching. 1915, 17, 185-188.

Speechreading (Contd.)

THE VOLTA REVIEW (Contd.)

NITCHIE, Edward B. What a deaf adult should do to acquire the art of lip-reading. 1915, 17, 251-254.

MORGENSTERN, Louise I. Teaching lip-reading to the adult hard of hearing in public evening school classes. 1915, 17, 255-257; 297-299; 391-393.

BRUHN, Martha E. The Müller-Walle method of lip-reading. 1915, 17, 293-295.

GORDON, Avondale N. Lip-reading for the adult deaf. 1915, 17, 365-368.

STORY, Arthur J. Lip-reading. 1915, 17, 389-391.

NITCHIE, Edward B. Lip-reading for the hearing. 1915, 17, 435-436.

BRUHN, Martha E. Bruhn lip-reading system (Müller-Walle method). 1916, 18, 65-69.

NITCHIE, Edward B. The use of homophenous words. 1916, 18, 85-93.

MORGENSTERN, Louise I. Lip-reading for class instruction. 1916, 18, 188-190; 1918, 20, 144-146.

NITCHIE, Edward B. Principle and methods of teaching lip-reading. 1916, 18, 269-280.

DELANY, Elizabeth G. Lip-reading hundreds of years old. 1916, 18, 442-445.

HOWELL, Louise. Lip-reading for the hard-of-hearing adult. 1917, 19, 15-16.

BELL, Mabel G. The subtle art of speech-reading. 1917, 19, 109-116.

MORGENSTERN, Louise I. The significance of the study of lip-reading for the hard-of-hearing adult. 1917, 19, 127-129.

NITCHIE, Edward B. Class instruction in lip-reading. 1917, 19, 177-179.

CONKLIN, Edmund S. A method for the determination of relative skill in lip-reading. 1917, 19, 216-219.

BRUHN, Martha E. Relative skill in lip-reading. 1917, 19, 220-222.

BRECKINRIDGE, Mary S. Lip-reading. 1917, 19, 281-287.

Speechreading (Contd.)

THE VOLTA REVIEW (Contd.)

KINZIE, Cora E. The value of speech-reading for the deaf. 1917, 19, 365-367.

BRUHN, Martha E. Learning lip-reading by the Müller-Walle method. 1917, 19, 389-394.

SIMONDS, Elsie H. Achieving success with lip-reading. 1917, 19, 401-403.

THOMASON, Pattie. The Müller-Walle method adapted to children. 1917, 19, 417-419.

WHITAKER, Bessie L. If you want to be a good lip-reader, settle down to business. 1917, 19, 432-439.

BRUHN, Martha E. Manual of lip-reading. 1917, 19, 464-478; 545-553; 595-599; 667-672; 1918, 20, 3-7.

MORGENSTERN, Louise I. Fifty lessons in lip-reading. 1917, 19, 479-488; 501-509; 631-639.

VAN ADESTINE, et al. Presenting the problem to the public. 1917, 19, 511-513.

LINDQUIST, Ida P. Adventures in lip-reading. 1917, 19, 515-517.

HUTMAN, Florence E. The experience of a public-school teacher. 1917, 19, 523-525.

MORGENSTERN, Louise I. Advanced methods of studying and teaching lip-reading. 1917, 19, 529-531.

KIMBALL, Caroline F. What the study of lip-reading means. 1917, 19, 536-538.

DELANY, Elizabeth G. The lip-reader as a beginner. 1917, 19, 541-543.

KENFIELD, Coralie N. What the general public should know concerning lip-reading. 1917, 19, 562-565.

TRASK, Alice N. More about lip-reading and then some. 1917, 19, 567-569.

KENNEDY, Mildred. Lip-reading and the ear-trumpet. 1917, 19, 583-585.

MORGENSTERN, Louise I. Present-day methods of teaching lip-reading. 1917, 19, 599-601.

Speechreading (Contd.)

THE VOLTA REVIEW (Contd.)

TRILL, Ellen M. How to help one who is studying lip-reading. 1917, 19, 705-707.

MORGENSTERN, Louise I. The mental factor in lip-reading. 1918, 20, 14-17.

BRUHN, Martha E. What is the secret of success? 1918, 20, 73-75.

MORGENSTERN, Louise I. None so deaf as those who won't see. A "lipodrama" in one act. 1918, 20, 81-83.

CLARK, Juliet D., and WALKER, Jane B. Lessons in lip-reading for deaf soldiers. 1918, 20, 129-133; 205-212; 282-289; 443-450; 493-498; 655-657; 681-684; 730-732.

KENNEDY, Mildred. How the study of speech-reading may be pursued by one living at a distance from school or teacher. 1918, 20, 135-137.

FERRALL, John A. Let the context twins do your work. 1918, 20, 188-190.

TRASK, Alice N. Correcting misstatements. 1918, 20, 197-198.

KANE, Edith B. Illustrated proverbs. 1918, 20, 229-230.

KINZIE, Cora E. and Rose. The Kinzie method of speech-reading for the deaf. 1918, 20, 249-258; 403-411; 499-509; 593-599; 627-630.

MCKERRAL, Lena and Wilton. The adaptation of practise exercises for lip-readers. 1918, 20, 262-270; 323-328; 390-392; 525-528; 575-577; 708-709; 1919, 21, 60-62; 149-153; 197-200; 291-294; 406-410; 556-559.

MORGENSTERN, Louise I. The conscientious objector. 1918, 20, 270-272.

MONRO, Sarah J. The speech-reader's duty to himself. 1918, 20, 276-278.

_____. Hearing with the eyes. 1918, 20, 278-280.

BRUHN, Martha E. Enseignement pratique de la lecture sur les levres. 1918, 20, 308-309; 357-360; 421-427; 528-534; 651-653; 698-700; 792-796.

KESSLER, Emma B. Lip-reading for the adult hard of hearing. 1918, 20, 355-357.

Speechreading (Contd.)

THE VOLTA REVIEW (Contd.)

BLAKE, Clarence J. Speech-reading for the war deaf. 1918, 20, 361-363; 385-387; 465-470; 557-560.

FERRALL, John A. Lip-reading--"happiness insurance." 1918, 20, 433-437.

WADLEIGH, Grace K. The exercise story. 1918, 20, 470-472.

KANE, Edith B. Questions and answers for practise classes. 1918, 20, 484-486.

MACBETH, Madge. The gateway to the silent world. 1918, 20, 509-511.

LINDQUIST, Ida P. Is it worth while? 1918, 20, 513-516.

TRASK, Alice N. Variety is the spice of practice. 1918, 20, 535-538.

MORGENSTERN, Louise I. Words and their affinities. 1918, 20, 551-553; 642-644; 692-694; 749-753; 1919, 21, 265-271; 323-329; 410-411; 552-554.

BRUHN, Martha E. First report on my lecture courses. 1918, 20, 553-555.

WHITAKER, Bessie L. Speech-reading and its value. 1918, 20, 637-640.

BRAND, Elizabeth. What's the difference? 1918, 20, 701-703.

WADLEIGH, Grace K. Concerning the psychology of the Müller-Walle method. 1918, 20, 705-707.

TRASK, Alice N. Material for practice class. 1918, 20, 721-724; 1921, 23, 21-24.

FERRALL, John A. Speed practise. 1918, 20, 774-777.

STAPLES, Anna L. Suggestions for practise classes. 1919, 21, 5-7.

ANDREWS, Harriet U. First-aid to our relatives. 1919, 21, 15-19.

MORGENSTERN, Louise I. The role of words in the practise of lip-reading. 1919, 21, 52-54.

KANE, Edith B. Variety is the spice of lip-reading. 1919, 21, 194-196.

TRASK, Alice N. Similes. 1919, 21, 248-250.

Speechreading (Contd.)

THE VOLTA REVIEW (Contd.)

POMEROY, Wilmer. Have you trained lips? 1919, 21, 262-265.

ANDERSON, Marian J. Getting the words from the thought and not the thought from the words. 1919, 21, 283-284.

KENNEDY, Mildred. An incident. 1919, 21, 386-389.

POMEROY, Wilmer. Better speech for better speech-reading. 1919, 21, 429-432.

DAVIES, Laura. The practise class. 1919, 21, 432-434.

NOWLIN and KINNIER. Suggestions for practise classes. 1919, 21, 545-549.

POMEROY, Wilmer. God's gift to the speech-reader. 1919, 21, 601-603.

KLINE, Louise T. The value of play in the practise class. 1919, 21, 750-754.

NITCHIE, Elizabeth H. The synthetic method and why I believe in it. 1919, 21, 764-771.

GEBHART, Helen M. The Müller-Walle method. 1919, 21, 771-776.

WOLF, Rena. Speech-reading in the evening high school in Philadelphia. 1920, 22, 92-97.

PORTER, Mrs. Nathan T., Jr. Exercises for teaching of lip-reading. 1920, 22, 208-209; 434-437.

DENMARK, F. L. Speech-reading as a basis for language development. 1920, 22, 278-281.

MCLEAN, Marjorie. The development of speech-reading power. 1920, 22, 485-494.

KINZIE, Cora E. The Kinzie method of instruction in speech-reading. 1920, 22, 609-620; 1923, 25, 66-68.

NITCHIE, Elizabeth H. The Nitchie method of teaching lip-reading. 1920, 22, 621-629.

NITCHIE, Elizabeth H. The hard-of-hearing or deafened teacher of lip-reading. 1921, 23, 97-99.

MCKENNA, Alice. Adventures in lip-reading. 1921, 23, 213-215.

POMEROY, Wilmer. The speech-reader's alphabet. 1921, 23, 236-238.

Speechreading (Contd.)

THE VOLTA REVIEW (Contd.)

SCHUMANN, Dr. Paul. Ninety-nine theses on seeing speech for the deaf, the deafened, and the hard of hearing. 1921, 23, 246-250.

CLARK, Juliet D. Lipreading for the slightly deafened, harmful or beneficial? 1921, 23, 302-304.

SAMUELSON, Estelle E. The lip-reading tournament at the New York League. 1921, 23, 368-370.

BICKLER, Mary H. How a deaf child was taught speech-reading and speech. 1921, 23, 382-388; 424-430; 455-470.

TRASK, Alice N. Riddles for lip-reading practise. 1921, 23, 408-411.

KESSLER, Saul N. Seventeen and more. 1922, 24, 32-35.

KANE, Edith B. Wisps of humor for the practice class. 1922, 24, 94-96.

FERRALL, John A. A sense of humor. 1922, 24, 97-100.

_____. Over 500 war-deafened veterans able to "hear" through lip-reading. 1922, 24, 107-108.

WHITAKER, Bessie L. The possibility of making a complete success of speech-reading, applied in large part to the adult. 1922, 24, 127-141.

ANDERSON, Marian J. Paying my family debts. 1922, 24, 201-204.

BIRGE, Marguerite S. Teaching a child. 1922, 24, 212-214.

DAVIES, Laura A. He that overcometh. 1922, 24, 252-256.

FERRALL, John A. The manifold advantages of soundless speaking. 1922, 24, 262-264.

WESTON, Cora C. Stumbling blocks and pitfalls. 1922, 24, 286-289.

DOWNING, Nora. Elements of success in speech-reading. 1922, 24, 335-339.

FERRALL, John A. Linger longer--do! 1922, 24, 387-391.

KANE, Edith B. Superstitions for the practice class. 1922, 24, 429-430.

LAMB, Helen Davis. Drill exercises. 1923, 25, 29-34.

Speechreading (Contd.)

THE VOLTA REVIEW (Contd.)

LADD, Alice. For the practice class. 1923, 25, 85-90.

ROGERS, Mary. Picking cherries, a lip-reading game. 1923, 25, 135-136.

WALKER, Jane B. Material for the practice class. 1923, 25, 241-245.

KESSLER, Emma B. For the practice class. 1923, 25, 278-281; 1929, 31, 36-38.

KANE, Edith B. Helpful practice material. 1923, 25, 323-325.

ZIEGLER, Clara M. Graded class practice. 1923, 25, 386-389.

DAVIES, Laura A. For the practice class. 1923, 25, 536-539.

KENFIELD, Coralie N. The education or re-education of the deafened adult. 1924, 26, 100-102.

JEWELL, Grace H. Practice class material. 1924, 26, 182-184.

STRICKLAND, Florence I. Practice class material. 1924, 26, 185-187.

VOSE, Persis. Qualities necessary for good lip-reading. 1924, 26, 281.

DELAND, Fred. Ancient and modern methods of teaching lip reading. 1924, 26, 327-328.

MACNUTT, Ena G. Practice material. 1924, 26, 360-363.

KNIGHT, Augustus C. Devices for teachers of lip-reading. 1924, 26, 623-625.

LACROSSE, Edwin L. Corrective speech with older pupils. 1925, 27, 16-19.

BRUHN, Martha E., et al. The conference on lip reading. 1925, 27, 68-73.

STEFFEY, Mary E. Humor in the practice class. 1925, 27, 120-122.

SCRIVER, Helen. The art of lip reading. 1925, 27, 422-424.

WRIGHT, John D. A Swiss pioneer in speech reading for deafened adults. 1925, 27, 465-467.

TRASK, Alice N. Graded practice class: an outstanding feature of the Kinzie method. 1925, 27, 472-475.

Speechreading (Contd.)

THE VOLTA REVIEW (Contd.)

RUFFIN, Henrietta H. "Out of the slough of despond." 1925, 27, 525-526.

IVES, Annie M. Beautiful islands of everywhere. 1925, 27, 695-698.

_____. N.E.A. conference on lipreading. 1926, 28, 64-69.

DURFEE, Marion. Practice class material. 1926, 28, 80-83.

SCRIVER, Helen. Ship ahoy! Practice material for lip-reading class. 1926, 28, 398-402.

HEARTY, Mary G. Practice class material: flower show. 1926, 28, 403-406.

BRUHN, Martha E. Is lip reading a science or an art? 1926, 28, 476-478.

KINZIE, Cora E. Simplified material for school use. 1926, 28, 509-513.

NITCHIE, Elizabeth H. The psychology of teaching unusual pupils. 1926, 28, 516-520.

DRAKE, Margaret L. Practice material for the teacher of hard-of-hearing children. 1927, 29, 76-78.

AMSLER, Fridette. The Jena method of teaching lip-reading. 1927, 29, 107-109.

HOLT, Laura D. The practice class. 1927, 29, 123-126.

MCDONALD, Alice. Practice class material. 1927, 29, 130-132.

LINDQUIST, Ida P. Practice class material. 1927, 29, 229-233.

WHILDIN, Olive. Graded devices for hard of hearing children. 1927, 29, 233-235.

MEREDITH, Anna. Lip-reading practice material. 1927, 29, 339-340.

JEWELL, Grace H. Lip-reading practice material. 1927, 29, 410-412.

STRICKLAND, Florence I. Lipreading practice material. 1927, 29, 412-414.

SMITH, Mathilda W. Lip-reading practice class material, a Bell program. 1927, 29, 414-415.

Speechreading (Contd.)

THE VOLTA REVIEW (Contd.)

LUX, Alta M. Stories for the practice class. 1927, 29, 415-417.

PRATT, Emily A. The importance of determining the need for lip reading among deafened school children. 1927, 29, 558-563.

LINDQUIST, Ida P. Rehabilitation through lip-reading. 1927, 29, 741-744.

BUELL, Edith M. Speech-reading in the classroom. 1928, 30, 94-99.

LEONARD, Bessie N. The general aspects of the teaching of speech and lip-reading to the deaf. 1928, 30, 140-143.

LINDQUIST, Ida P. Practice material for teachers of lip-reading classes. 1928, 30, 342-344.

GAULT, Robert H. Interpretation of spoken language when the feel of speech supplements vision of the speaking face. 1928, 30, 379-386.

HILL, Elsie. Lip-reading practice material, a cat show. 1928, 30, 386-387.

KENFIELD, Coralie N. The practice class, material for teachers of lip-reading. 1928, 30, 432-435.

KENFIELD, Coralie N. The lip-reading practice class. 1928, 30, 486-488.

SCHWARZ, Carrie K. Conversation--intermediate work. 1929, 31, 115-116.

SCRIVER, Helen. The value of play in teaching deafened adults. 1929, 31, 175-177.

VONDERHEIT, Esther C. Lip-reading practice material. 1929, 31, 263-267.

BELL, Martha C. Lip-reading in the first year. 1929, 31, 307-309.

MACNUTT, Ena G. Lip-reading practice material. 1929, 31, 311-333.

ZIEGLER, Clara M. Practice class material. 1929, 31, 377-379.

BUNGER, Anna M. On being converted to the Jena method. 1929, 31, 705-708.

BIGELOW, Jane K. Changing etiquette, adapted for lip-reading practice. 1930, 32, 87-88.

Speechreading (Contd.)

THE VOLTA REVIEW (Contd.)

IVES, Annie M. Practice class material. 1930, 32, 126-129.

LANE, Dorothy H. First year lip-reading. 1930, 32, 142-143.

CORLETT, Juliet C. Lip reading practice material for older deaf pupils. 1932, 34, 411-412; 425-426.

MAXSON, Kathryn P. Story telling. 1933, 35, 289; 314.

BRAUCKMANN, Karl. Speechreading in America, a German view of America's work. 1934, 36, 103-104; 126.

HEIDER, Grace M. Psychological research in lip reading and language. 1934, 36, 517-520; 568.

SCRIVER, Helen. A class menu. 1935, 37, 27-29.

WASHINGTON, Margaret L. Constructive class management. 1935, 37, 30-32.

KENFIELD, Coralie N. The public school class. 1935, 37, 32-34.

CHAMBLESS, Elizabeth. Class lessons and private lessons. 1935, 37, 34-36.

TALLMAN, Mary L. Lip reading in an unusual school. 1935, 37, 36-37.

WHILDIN, Olive A. Is lip reading education or training? 1935, 37, 751-752; 779-780.

WITHERSPOON, Elizabeth. Problems of the lip reading teacher. 1936, 38, 101-103.

DISHER, Dorothy R. Lip reading in Tallahassee. 1936, 38, 352-353; 371-372.

CHANDLER, Flora. Lip reading as a federal project. 1936, 38, 416; 425.

DUNN, Margaret. Lip reading in the elementary grades. 1936, 38, 533-535.

SAMUELSON, Estelle E., and FABREGAS, Minnie B. A treasure chest of games for lip reading teachers. 1936, 38, 592-595; 614; 666-668; 737-740; 1937, 39, 42-44; 56; 106-108; 117; 168-169; 187.

BUNGER, Anna M. Speech reading in college. 1937, 39, 569-572; 601.

MASON, Marie K. Objective scoring in tests of visual hearing. 1937, 39, 576-581; 593.

Speechreading (Contd.)

THE VOLTA REVIEW (Contd.)

PRELUTSKY, Louis. Using cross-word puzzles in the lip reading class. 1937, 39, 586; 602.

MAIGETTER, Elizabeth. An activity program for primary grades. 1938, 40, 23; 54-55.

WALKER, Jane B. With the speech reading class. 1938, 40, 43-44; 55; 108-109; 169-170; 182; 359-361; 412-414; 424-426; 1939, 41, 40-42; 103-105; 1941, 43, 620-621; 1942, 44 39-40; 60.

SCRIVER, Helen. With the lip reading class: a place for homonyms. 1938, 40, 296-298.

CHANDLER, Flora. With the lip reading class. 1938, 40, 582-583; 602.

REITER, Frank H. Profiting by the findings of research workers. 1938, 40, 658-661.

PAXSON, Ruth. Giving lip reading its share of attention in the teaching program. 1938, 40, 663-664.

BRUCE, Lula M. Giving lip reading its fair share of time. 1938, 40, 665-668.

MATLOCK, Gladys D. The improvement of lip-reading through better care of the children's eyes. 1938, 40, 668-675.

MORRIS, Dorothy M. Humor in the speech-reading period. 1939, 41, 5-8; 51.

YOUNG, Leo H. What I get out of lip reading. 1939, 41, 37-39; 53-54.

RANSON, Ethel O. With the lip reading class. 1939, 41, 173; 178.

NUMBERS, Mary E. An experiment in lip reading. 1939, 41, 261-264.

IVES, Annie M. With the lip reading class. 1939, 41, 362-363; 379; 415; 421; 467; 476; 524-525.

HUTCHINSON, Enid. With the lip reading class. 1939, 41, 589-590; 602.

BRAND, Elizabeth. With the lip reading class. 1939, 41, 653-654; 713-714; 722-723.

MORRIS, M. Esther. With the lip reading class. 1940, 42, 44-45; 50; 109-110; 121-123.

Speechreading (Contd.)

THE VOLTA REVIEW (Contd.)

FEILBACH, Rose V. With the lip reading class. 1940, <u>42</u>, 175-176; 188-189.

WRIGHT, Florence F. With the lip reading class. 1940, <u>42</u>, 238-239; 253.

JONES, Carrie L. The development of lip reading as a useful tool. 1940, <u>42</u>, 372-374; 395.

DICARLO, Louis M. With the lip reading class. 1940, <u>42</u>, 375-376.

BELL, Mabel H. Speech reading (1894). 1940, <u>42</u>, 607-610.

HOWES, Esther C. Giving our children speech reading which they can use at home. 1940, <u>42</u>, 610-614.

RUSSELL, Lillian E. Beginning lip reading. 1940, <u>42</u>, 687-693.

FOSS, Bertha M. Advanced lip reading. 1940, <u>42</u>, 694-696.

HEIDER, Fritz and Grace M. An experimental investigation of lip reading. 1940, <u>42</u>, 821-825; 882.

MONTAGUE, Harriet. With the lip reading class. 1940, <u>42</u>, 868-869.

TURLEY, Ethel J. With the lip reading class. 1941, <u>43</u>, 53-55.

COOK, M. Alleyne. With the lip reading class. 1941, <u>43</u>, 139-140; 202-203; 1942, <u>44</u>, 230-231.

YOUNG, Mrs. Arthur J. With the lip reading class. 1941, <u>43</u>, 393; 399.

FRANKENTHAL, Sybil. With the lip reading class. 1941, <u>43</u>, 439-440.

KNOWLES, Elizabeth. With the lip reading class. 1941, <u>43</u>, 680.

EVERS, Louise S. With the lip reading class. 1941, <u>43</u>, 741-742; 758; 1943, <u>45</u>, 231-232; 584.

BRUCE, Lula M. Suggestions for teaching speech reading. 1942, <u>44</u>, 5-9; 93-98; 114.

TRANSUE, Hannah W. A lip reader's views of lip reading. 1942, <u>44</u>, 161-164; 184; 204-206; 252.

TABER, Frank A. With the lip reading class. 1942, <u>44</u>, 360-361; 374.

_____. Speech reading in schools for the deaf. 1942, <u>44</u>, 614-617; 656-658.

Speechreading (Contd.)

THE VOLTA REVIEW (Contd.)

BRUHN, Martha E., et al. Methods of teaching lip reading to adults --a symposium. 1942, 44, 636-641; 658; 701-707; 722; 1943, 45, 30-35; 94-96.

GEER, Alleyne C. With the lip reading class. 1943, 45, 166-168; 188; 1945, 47, 572-574; 599.

KEITH, John. Has lip reading missed the bus?--yes. 1943, 45, 286-288.

ORDMAN, Theodore. Has lip reading missed the bus?--no. 1943, 45, 288-290; 316-318.

NELSON, Boyd E. A lip reading program for a school. 1944, 46, 5-10; 56.

ALBRIGHT, M. Arline. Ear, eye, or both. 1944, 46, 11-13.

MONTAGUE, Harriet. Lip-reading--a continuing necessity. 1944, 46, 91-94; 114-116; 159-162.

BECKER, Margaret R. With the lip reading class. 1944, 46, 360; 366-368.

BENNETT, Josephine. Lip reading for the deaf child. 1944, 46, 489-494; 546.

BERGER, Emma. A speech reading lesson for victory gardeners. 1944, 46, 519-520; 530.

ZIEGLER, Clara M. With the practice class. 1945, 47, 357-358.

STEED, Eleanor L. Speech reading and how it grows. 1946, 48, 69-74; 122-124.

WALKER, Jane B. With the lip reading class. 1946, 48, 226; 240-242; 285; 291-292.

GOLDBERG, Herman R. Lip reading for the baseball fan. 1947, 49, 223; 238-240.

HEIDER, Grace M. The Utley lip reading test. 1947, 49, 457-458; 488-490.

GOLDBERG, Herman R. What do you think of the Marshall Plan? A lipreading practice exercise. 1948, 50, 216.

ELLIS, Vaughn E. Lip-reading at Northwestern. 1950, 52, 26-27.

Speechreading (Contd.)

THE VOLTA REVIEW (Contd.)

YENRICK, D. E. Speechreading materials for the primary public school grades. 1951, 53, 249-251.

NEVILLE, Virginia. Lipreading material for adult beginners. 1952, 54, 71; 76.

HOOD, C. A. Kaleidoscopic English and a lipreader. 1953, 55, 11-14.

CARR, Josephine. A limited or limitless vocabulary through speechreading. 1954, 56, 109-113.

LAMBERT, C. G. A teacher of lipreading. 1954, 56, 212-213.

BRINTNALL, Mrs. Arthur W. Lipreading is fun. 1955, 57, 115-116.

PRALL, Josephine. Lipreading and hearing aids combine for better comprehension. 1957, 59, 64-65.

VAN WYK, Mary K. Beginning speechreading. 1957, 59, 165-168.

COSTELLO, Mary R. Language development through speechreading. 1958, 60, 257-259; 272.

LARR, Alfred. Speechreading through closed circuit television. 1959, 61, 19-21.

MILESKY, Samuel D. Testing lipreading potential. 1960, 62, 372-375.

MISRA, Surya Kant, and PALMER, Martin F. A comparison of speech reading in Hindi and English in a school for the deaf. 1964, 66, 615-617.

HASPIEL, George S. A rationale for lipreading therapy. 1965, 67, 684-687.

STEPP, Robert E. A speechreading laboratory for deaf children. 1966, 68, 408-415.

VIVIAN, Rose M. The Tadoma method: a tactual approach to speech and speechreading. 1966, 68, 733-737.

RICHARDSON, Joan. A review of four methods of lipreading. 1968, 70, 39-41.

BUTT, Dolores S., and CHREIST, Fred M. A speechreading test for young children. 1968, 70, 225-239.

Speechreading (Contd.)

ANNALS OF THE DEAF

BOOTH, Edmund. A genius for lip-reading. 1884, 29, 17-21.

MOFFAT, L. Lipreading for the adult deaf. 1889, 34, 263-271.

REAMY, Olive L. The teaching of speech reading. 1893, 38, 4-8.

BELL, Mabel G. Success in speech reading. 1890, 35, 127-130.

GUTZMANN, Herm. Facial speech-reading. 1899, 44, 272-285; 317-335; 412-419.

STEINKE, Agnes. Lip-reading. 1901, 46, 277-285.

ROBINSON, Warren. Speech-reading--a study. 1905, 50, 169-173.

BELL, Alexander G. Speech reading for the partially deaf. 1907, 52, 28-30.

STONE, Elizabeth A. Story telling. 1909, 54, 1-7.

MCCOWEN, M. The development of speech reading in the deaf child. 1910, 55, 364-370.

MARICHELLE, H. A practical test of lip-reading. 1911, 56, 324-331.

OLIN, Caroline L. The Müller-Walle method of teaching speech-reading. 1911, 56, 335-337.

BOUDIN, Etienne. The conditions of success in speech reading. 1912, 57, 187-197.

WIEDEMER, A. How can speech reading be brought to a higher state of perfection? 1912, 57, 254-278.

DAVIDSON, Emma F. Lip-reading lessons. 1912, 57, 437-453; 1913, 58, 5-15; 239-249; 1914, 59, 181-193; 264-274; 480-505.

FONNER, Mary D. Lip-reading: how to improve it. 1916, 61, 87-91.

BRUHN, Martha E. The Müller-Walle system of lip-reading. 1917, 62, 353-364.

CHAPIN, Alma L. Lip-reading commands. 1920, 65, 499-508.

COBB, Jennie L. Speech reading. 1921, 66, 266-271.

PALEN, Imogen B. Methods used in teaching lip-reading to speaking children. 1926, 71, 190-197.

NEUSCHUTZ, Louise I. The standardization of methods of teaching lip-reading and training teachers. 1926, 71, 219-221.

Speechreading (Contd.)

ANNALS OF THE DEAF (Contd.)

STOBSCHINSKI, Robert. Lip-reading: its psychological aspects and its adaption to the individual needs of the hard of hearing. 1928, 73, 234-242; 355-365.

GORDON, Anne. Lip-reading in the primary department of the California school. 1939, 84, 350-362.

NELSON, Boyd E. Co-ordinating lip-reading and speech with current events. 1944, 89, 132-141.

REID, Gladys. A preliminary investigation in the testing of lip-reading achievement. 1946, 91, 403-413.

FUSFELD, Irving S. Factors in lipreading as determined by the lip-reader. 1958, 103, 229-242.

MILLER, J., ROUSEY, C., and GOETZINGER, C. An exploratory investigation of a method of improving speechreading. 1958, 103, 473-478.

UPTON, Hubert W. Wearable eyeglass speechreading aid. 1968, 113, 222-229.

SANDERS, Jay W., and COSCARELLI, Janet E. The relationship of visual synthesis skill to lipreading. 1970, 115, 23-26.

POPELKA, Gerald R., and BERGER, Kenneth W. Gestures and visual speech reception. 1971, 116, 434-436.

ROMANO, Paul E., and BARLOW, Susan. Vision requirements for lip reading. 1974, 119, 383-386.

FARWELL, Roberta M. Speech reading: a research review. 1976, 121, 19-30.

CLOUSER, Richard A. The effect of vowel consonant ratio and sentence length on lipreading ability. 1976, 121, 513-518.

Teacher Preparation/Certification

THE VOLTA REVIEW

BOOTH, F. W. Normal training for oral teachers of the deaf. 1907, 9, 206-212.

HENDERSON, Jennie M. Voice training and rhythm: their application to the teaching of speech to the deaf. 1914, 16, 435-439.

BRUHN, Martha E. Theory minus versus training plus experience. 1915, 17, 143-145.

WRIGHT, John D. Normal training of teachers. 1918, 20, 727-729.

WINNIE, A. J. Normal training of teachers of deaf children. 1919, 21, 30-31; 153-155.

LEONARD, Eleanor C. The normal course at Northampton. 1919, 21, 72-75.

MOORE, Lucile M. Teacher training. 1923, 25, 356-358.

_____. The normal training of teachers of lip-reading. 1924, 26, 66-73; 107-110; 195-201.

HILLIARD, Ethel M. Modern tendencies in speech teaching. 1926, 28, 616-620.

HALL, Percival. What must be the required training of normal students previous to their special training? 1928, 30, 573-577.

PEARSON, Frank B. Teacher training. 1929, 31, 519-521.

ROWELL, Hugh G. The opportunities which the university offers for the training of teachers of handicapped children. 1929, 31, 613-618.

LANE, Helen S. Preparation of teachers for the handicapped. 1937, 39, 558-561; 592.

CARNEY, Mary V. Qualifications for teachers of lip reading. 1938, 40, 93-96; 124.

NUMBERS, Mary E. What training should be required for the teacher? 1938, 40, 718-721.

YALE, Caroline A. How can we best fit ourselves to teach speech to the deaf. 1940, 42, 589-592.

_____. An examination for teachers of the deaf: the 1943 examination for the diploma issued by the National College of Teachers of the Deaf, England. 1943, 45, 617-619.

Teacher Preparation/Certification (Contd.)

THE VOLTA REVIEW (Contd.)

_____. A bibliography for teachers of the deaf compiled by the association's Committee on the Use of Professional Literature. 1944, 46, 17-20; 85-86; 102.

STONER, Marguerite. What the inexperienced teacher needs in the way of supervision. 1946, 48, 692-694.

KELLY, Elizabeth. The recruiting of teachers. 1946, 48, 698-701.

CRAIG, Sam B. Recruitment of teachers. 1946, 48, 701-704.

LANE, Helen S. (moderator). Teacher recruitment and training. 1952, 54, 491-500; 512-514.

_____. Summer courses in speech and hearing. 1956, 58, 107-116; 1957, 59, 111-124; 1958, 60, 112-119; 1959, 61, 117-128; 1960, 62, 117-136; 1961, 63, 111-130; 1962, 64, 133-148; 1963, 65, 132-145; 1964, 66, 134-148; 1965, 67, 210-225.

PRATT, George T. Planning and organizing a teacher recruitment program. 1957, 59, 9-12; 40.

GROHT, Mildred A. Basic qualifications of a teacher of the deaf. 1957, 59, 13-16.

FLINT, Richard W. Survey shows need for better teacher recruitment program. 1957, 59, 66-71.

CONNOR, Frances P., and Leo E. Future directions in teacher education for teachers of the deaf. 1958, 67-71; 74; 93.

QUIGLEY, Stephen P. Major problems in teacher education and recruitment. 1958, 60, 366-370.

JOHNSON, Evan V., and FRISINA, D. Robert. A study of the need for academic classroom teachers of the deaf. 1960, 62, 500-503.

RUDLOFF, Joseph S. Recruiting teachers for the deaf. 1960, 62, 541-542; 564.

CONNOR, Leo E. Child study in the education of deaf children. 1962, 64, 72-76; 103.

FELLENDORF, George W. Teacher recruitment. 1962, 64, 452-456.

ROTTER, Paul. A study for improving programs for the preparation of teachers of the deaf. 1962, 64, 481-486.

Teacher Preparation/Certification (Contd.)

THE VOLTA REVIEW (Contd.)

COSTELLO, Mary R. The teacher of the deaf--circa 1964--and onward. 1964, 66, 445-449.

BRUCE, Wallace T. Orientation for new teachers. 1964, 66, 456-459.

SIMMONS, Audrey A. Supervision of and experiences for student teaching. 1966, 68, 648-652.

WITHROW, Frank B. Public law 87-276: its effect on the supply of trained teachers of the deaf. 1967, 69, 656-663.

GARBER, Garl E., and FRENCH, Sophie L. Closed circuit television used to train teachers of the deaf. 1969, 71, 362-366.

POWER, D. J. Characteristics of successful student teachers of the deaf. 1971, 73, 529-537.

ROCHE, Adam, Jr., and NEAL, W. R., Jr. State certification policies and services for the hearing impaired. 1972, 74, 150-160.

THIAGARAJAN, Sivasailam. A new role for teachers. 1973, 75, 473-479.

NORTHCOTT, Winifred H. Competencies needed by teachers of hearing impaired infants, birth to three years, and their parents. 1973, 75, 532-544.

_____. Council on Education of the Deaf, Standards for the Certification of Teachers of the Hearing Impaired. 1974, 76, 239-249.

HEHIR, Richard G. Competence based teacher education for teachers of the deaf: the issues from the state level. 1975, 77, 105-116.

HOAG, Ralph L., and STELLE, Roy M. Teacher of the deaf: artisans to professionals. 1976, 78, 47-51 (monograph).

QUICK, Marian A. Licensing of hearing clinicians and teachers of the hearing impaired (editorial). 1976, 78, 178-182.

ANNALS OF THE DEAF

CROUTER, A. L. The training of teachers of the deaf. 1917, 62, 293-304.

Teacher Preparation/Certification (Contd.)

ANNALS OF THE DEAF (Contd.)

MCMANAWAY, Howard M. Proper training of shop teachers. 1925, 70, 424-429.

NUMBERS, Fred C. Advantages and disadvantages in conducting a normal training class in connection with school work. 1927, 72, 341-349.

JONES, John W., et al. The training and certification of teachers. 1929, 74, 244-315.

_____. U.S. Office of Education Study of Training Courses for Teachers of the Deaf. 1938, 83, 428-441.

BRILL, Richard G. The educational preparation of oral teachers of the deaf. 1952, 97, 313-327.

CROSBY, Laura. The classroom teacher. 1953, 98, 362-368.

BRILL, Richard G. A survey of credential requirements for teachers of the deaf in the U.S. 1955, 100, 321-329.

STRENG, Alice H. Educating teachers of the deaf for the schools for tomorrow. 1964, 109, 348-355.

HESTER, Marshall S. In-service education program for teachers of the deaf. 1967, 112, 724-727.

LIVINGSTON, Patricia J. Professional preparation: the deaf college student. 1968, 113, 53-59.

Technology Devices/Sensory Aids

THE VOLTA REVIEW

PETERSON, Gordon E. Technological frontiers in communication. 1962, 64, 369-374.

SMITH, Gale M. Telephone service for the totally deaf. 1963, 65, 579-583.

BENDER, Patricia. The thresholds of hearing of normal, deaf, and hard of hearing children with or without a supplementary tactile vibrator. 1973, 75, 47-53.

Technological Devices/Sensory Aids (Contd.)

THE VOLTA REVIEW (Contd.)

STRATTON, William David. Intonation feedback for the deaf through a tactile display. 1974, 76, 26-35.

ERBER, Norman P., and ZEISEN, M. Lynn. Classroom observation under conditions of simulated profound deafness. 1974, 76, 352-360.

WILSON, Harriet M., and HOLBROOK, Anthony. An instrumental approach to oral-nasal speech balance with a preschool hearing impaired child. 1974, 76, 361-367.

SMITH, Gale M. The telephone adapter and other telephone aids for the hard of hearing. 1974, 76, 474-484.

BOOTHROYD, Arthur. Technology and deafness. 1975, 77, 27-34.

ROMNEY, Frederic C. Deaf students use the telephone for the first time. 1975, 77, 125-128.

BOOTHROYD, Arthur, ARCHAMBAULT, Patricia, ADAMS, Robb E., and STORM, Robert D. Use of a computer-based system of speech training aids for deaf persons. 1975, 77, 178-193.

STRONG, William J. Speech aids for the profoundly/severely hearing impaired: requirements, overview, and projections. 1975, 77, 536-556.

BELLEFLEUR, Philip A. TTY communication: its history and future. 1976, 78, 107-112 (monograph).

ANNALS OF THE DEAF

OFIESH, Gabriel. Educational technology and the necessary revolution in education. 1969, 114, 893-905.

STEIN, Laszlo. A cure for deafness: reality or myth. 1973, 118, 670-671.

Author Index

A

Abernathy, E.B............ 34
Abernathy, E.R. 182
Acker, L. 40
Adametz, J. 92
Adams, B.C. 111
Adams, I.H. 38,133
Adams, M.E. ..19,64,118,119,
    121,134,135,167,187,212
Adams, R.E. 239
Addison, W.H. 92
Adelson, L. 115
Adler, E.P. 35
Adrain, E.D. 173
Agron, G. 90
Albright, A. 6
Albright, M.A. 231
Alcorn, A. 145
Alcorn, K. 204
Alcorn, S. 65,203,206
Allabough, B.R. 59
Allen, A.C. 195
Allison, M.G. 175
Alpiner, J.G. 22
Alsberg, J. 22
Alterman, A.I. 140
Altschuler, D. 148
Altschulor, D. 26
Altshuler, K.Z. 183,184,185
Anato, D. 21
Amcoff, S. 96
Amon, C. 167
Amsler, F. 226
Anderson, D. 152
Anderson, E.W. 46
Anderson, J.S. 8
Anderson, Mrs. J.S. 14,
    113,159
Anderson, M.J....185,223,224
Anderson, N.O. ..148,166,188
Anderson, R.M. 156,158
Anderson, T.L.   24,34,86,
    167,187

Anderson, W.A.............164
Andrews, C.E..............142
Andrews, H.E. 57
Andrews, H.U. ..16,19,51,160,
    161,168,173,217,222
Andrews, J. 62
Angelocci, A.A. 209
Anselmini, A.A. 13
Appel, C.R. 114
Appleman, K. 59
Arbaugh, L.L. 74,76
Archambault, P. 239
Archer, T.V. 38,72,134
Argento, F. 112
Armstrong, L.M. 177
Arnold, A............. 54,176
Arnold, M. 187
Arnold, N.H. 38
Arnold, T. 211
Asals, F.B. 11,12
Asbed, R.A. 71
Ashby, M.T. 124
Ashcroft, S. 155
Ashley, J.B. 133
Askew, L.M. 85
Atwood, M. 121
Aurell, E. 86
Austin, G.F. 194
Avery, C.B. 115,162
Avery, E.B........ 84,122,139
Avondino, J........46,200,203
Ayres, J.A. 82

B

Babcock, E.J. 120
Babcock, J.T. 120
Bailey, J.D. 204
Baker, D. 51
Baldwin, R.L. 82
Balis, S.C. 23,67,84,172
Baldrian, K. 135

242

Ballenger, L. 192
Baller, W.R. 100
Balow, B. 50
Balow, I. 51
Baltzer, S. 129
Bangs, J.L. 155
Bangs, T.E. 11
Banks, M.S. 122
Barlow, S. 234
Barnard, F.A. 132
Barnes, F.G. ...74,120,136,192
Barnes, H.B. 25
Barrett, E.M. 67
Barrett, K. 102
Barron, R. 40
Barrows, A.L. 68
Barrows, C.M. 7
Bartlett, B.L. 160
Bartlett, D.E. 58,132
Basilier, F. 110
Basilier, T. 27
Bates, L.M. 118
Beard, R.O. 113
Beattie, G.M. 53
Beattie, M.B. 55
Beatty, M.M. 122
Becker, M.R. 231
Becker, S. 71,131
Becker, V.A. 22
Beckmeyer, T. 36,49
Beebe, H.H. 4
Behrens, T. 55,57
Bell, A.G. ..14,16,18,28,46,
    59,72,73,74,83,108,133,
    160,195,196,197,198,
    211,233
Bell, Mrs. A.G. 16,197
Bell, D. 117
Bell, J.W. 131
Bell, M.C. 227
Bell, M.G. 219,233
Bell, M.H. 230

Bell, M.M. 70
Bellefleur, P.A. 105,107,
    191,239
Bellows, H.P. 97
Bemis, L. 57
Bender, J.F. 168
Bender, P. 238
Bender, R.E. 11,104,131
Benedict, A.L. ...120,121,199,
    200,201
Bennett, C. 210
Bennett, J. 46,124,126,
    231
Benning, D.B. 60,119
Bensberg, G. 159
Bentley, K. 18
Berenson, B. 89
Berg, L.E. 60
Berger, E. 231
Berger, K.W. 96,106,234
Berglund, J.B. 166
Bergman, E. 35
Bernero, R.J. 208
Bernstein, H.W. 82,166
Berrett, R.D. 166
Berry, A.E. 9
Berry, G. 4,77,97
Berry, H. 124
Berryman, F.S. 38,176
Best, B. 119
Betterly, E.J. 76
Betts, O.A. 24
Bick, M. 35
Bickler, M.H. 160,224
Bickley, C. 75
Bidlake, H. 156
Bigelow, J.K. 227
Biklen, D.P. 144
Bilger, R. 168
Bindon, D. 88
Binet, A. 32
Bingham, C.D. 118

243

Bingham, K.T. 72,198
Birch, J.R. 171,183
Birch, J.W. 35,129,140,
  171,183
Bird, W.L. 56
Birge, M.S. 224
Birkenshaw, L. 43
Bishop, H.M. 168
Bishop, M.E. 105,210
Bitter, G.B. 143,166
Black, J.W. 208
Blackwell, H.R. 89
Bladon, M. 69
Blair, C.L. 120
Blair, F.X. 88
Blair, M. 52,76
Blake, C.J. 2,222
Blake, K.A. 184
Blankenhorn, M.D. 66
Blankenship, O.C. 123
Blanton, S. 213
Blatchford, C.H. 179
Blattner, J.W. 31,85
Blea, W. 68
Blish, I.S. 54,55
Blish, S.C. 44,177
Bliss, S.E. 120
Block, S.A. 69
Bloom, F. 193
Bluett, C.G. 20,21,168
Boatner, E.B..........149,189
Boatner, M.T............26,88
Bodensiek, G. 92
Bodycomb, M........3,77,113,
  206
Bolesta, Mrs. B. 148
Bollbach, B.L. 12,128
Bolton, T.L. 67
Boone, D.R. 130,209
Booth, E. 233
Booth, F.W. .. 39,56,75,120,
  135,142,155,235

Booth, I.................205
Boothroyd, A. 239
Bopst, E.G. 177
Bordman, M.B. 141
Bornstein, H. 35,172
Børrild, K. 107
Bosch, B. 82
Boschler, I.E. 168
Boudin, E. 233
Bourne, J. 154
Bove, C.F. 6
Bowe, F.G. 27,191
Bower, D. 40,150
Bowman, D.L. 66
Bowman, E. 144
Bown, J.C. 128
Box, M.S. 153
Boyd, H. 172,173
Boyd, J. 107,184
Brackett, D. 117
Braddock, M.J. 12
Bradford, C.A. 102
Bradway, K.P. 194
Brady, W.S. 41
Bragg, B. 35
Brainerd, S.H. 32
Braly, K. 10,102
Brand, E. 222,229
Brandon, W.R. 139
Brannon, A.C. 159
Branson, H.K. 21
Brauckmann, K. 228
Breckinridge, M.S.84,155,219
Breckwoldt, G.H. 206
Breese, E. 20
Brehm, F.E. 213
Breitwieser, I.V. 76
Brennan, M. 141
Breunig, H.L. 111,163
Brick, Sr. R.M. 43
Bridgman, O. 182
Bright, M. 214

244

Brill, R.G. 51,61,108,
   144,182,190,207,238
Brill, T. 85,86,122,
   126,181
Brintnall, Mrs. A.W. ...232
Briskey, R.J. 5
Broberg, R.F. 100
Brockman, S.J. 108
Broderick, T.G. 5
Brohman, D. 40
Brown, D.W. 22
Brown, J. 121
Brown, R. 98,177
Bruce, L.M. 47,229,230
Bruce, M.E. 122
Bruce, R.B..............18
Bruce, W.T. 82,208,237
Bruhn, M.E. .19,96,120,218,
   219,220,221,222,225,226,
   231,233,235
Brunschwig, L. 170
Brutten, M. 87
Buchan, Mrs. J. 163
Buchanan, N. 8
Buchli, M.J. 94
Buchman, M. 127
Buchmann, A.V. 216
Buck, L.A. 141
Buckler, Sr. M.S. 130
Budden, S.S. 110
Buell, E.M. 59,76,120,122,
   123,124,125,135,212,227
Bull, J.C. 111
Bunch, C.C. 15
Bunch, G.O. 157
Bunger, A.M. 227,228
Burchard, E.M. 182
Burdge, A.V. 145
Burger, R. 105
Burke, D.J.N. 70,165
Burke, M.M. 203
Burnet, J.R. 67,132

Burnett, A..............116
Burns, M.A. 86
Burroughs, J. 154
Bushnag, S. 111
Butler, A.E. 196,212
Butler, S. 183
Butler, S. 25
Butt, D.S. 232
Butterweck, J.C. 23

C

Cain, E.R. 168
Caldwell, D.C. 153
Caldwell, E.H. 128,129
Caldwell, W.A.... 57,122,133
Calkins, E.E. 174
Callace, C. 152
Calvert, D.R.... 1,7,29,104,
   131,209,210
Cambon, K.G. 110,117
Camp, A.R. 14
Cannon, M. 115
Cardwell, W.A. 180
Carhart, R. 214
Carney, M.V. 235
Caroll, D.H. 59
Carpenter, C.L. 130
Carpenter, L.E. 149
Carr, J...... 89,178,207,232
Carter, A.E. 198
Carter, E. 19
Carter, H.A. 103
Carter, M. 58
Carter, W.H. 63
Carver, V. 111
Case, L.E. 218
Casey, S.L. 48
Castle, D.L. 35
Castle, W. 112
Cavaliere, R.A. 102
Cavanagh, A. 42,146

245

Cayley, S. 160
Chamberlain, N.H. 79,116
Chambers, J.F. 172
Chambless, E. 21,228
Chandler, F. 228,229
Chapin, A.L. 233
Chaplin, J.W. 44
Chapman, J. 100
Chapman, W.C. 66
Charles, E.N. 193
Chasen, B. 37
Cherry, J.D. 100
Chreist, F.M. 232
Christian, H.T. 39
Christmas, J.J. 202,212
Church, L.L. 46,51,52
Clapp, J.M. 199
Clark, A.E. 155
Clark, A.S. 211
Clark, J.D. 221,224
Clarke, B.R. 210,216
Clarke, F.D. 55,62,83
Clarcq, J. 153
Clatterbuck, M.B. 54
Clayton, L. 184
Clayton, N.C. 76
Cleary, E.P. 123
Cloud, D.T. 98,119,204
Clouser, R.A. 89,234
Coakley, E.L. 11
Coats, G.D. 34,215
Cobb, J.L. 38,84,109,
  158,181,233
Coburn, A.T. 135
Cochrane, W.A. 33
Coffey, M.A. 53
Cogswell, E.W. 176
Cogswell, F.H. 19
Cohen, M.L. 215
Cohen, O.P. 90,143
Cohen, S.S. 66,208
Cole, N. 165

Cole, R. 147
Cole, R.H. 163
Coleman, G.D. 181
Colepaugh, G. 115
Collins, H.M. 3
Collins, J.L. 37,90
Collins, M. 54
Collins, V.E. 177
Collins-Ahlgren, M. 141
Commings, J. 141
Conklin, E.S. 219
Conley, J.E. 62
Connally, E.E. 88
Connery, J.M. 200
Connolly, E.E. 190
Connor, F.P. 236
Connor, L.E. 22,79,80,81,
  117,194,236
Constam, A. 151
Cook, M.A. 230
Cook, R.C. 109
Cooler, H.S. 215
Cooper, H.M. 75
Cooper, R.L. 130
Corlett, J.C. 228
Corliss, E.L. 103
Cornell, L.E. 42
Cornett, R.O. 215
Cory, M.W. 71
Cory, P.B. 48,49,50,116,
  147,151
Coscarelli J.E. 234
Costello, M.R. 4,232,237
Costello, P.M. 43,155,157
Cota, A. 126
Cotton, J.C. 3
Cowles, K. 53
Cox, I. 87
Cox, J.R. 12
Cox, M.R. 121,136
Craig, H.B. 90
Craig, S.B. 98,236

Craig, W.H. ...14,23,27,82, 90,112,119,140,144
Cramer, K.D. 141
Crammatte, A.B. 25
Cramp, A.J. 100
Crandell, M.P. 47,126
Crane, N. 147
Crane, N.W. 12
Crawford, G.H. 210
Crawford, M.T. 125,176
Croft, J.C. 144
Croker, G.W. 137
Crosby, L.L......61,138,238
Crouter, A.L. 32,72,84, 197,237
Crouter, A.Y. ..102,126,138
Crouter, J.Y. 114
Crowther, A.E. 186
Crum, C. 79,164,178
Crutchett, R. 102
Cruttenden, M.E. 207
Cuddy, N.M. 9
Culbertson, L.N. 90
Cunningham, D. 148
Curry, L. 162
Curtis, J.H. 210
Curtis, J.J. 91
Curtis, M. 91
Curtiss, L.A. 64
Custer, D. 153
Cutler, E.M. 182
Cutler, S.J. 102
Cypreansen, L. 147
Czily, A. 65

D

Dacey, E. 203
Dahle, A.J. 71
Dale, D.M.C. 81
Dalgarno, G. 82
Dalgleish, B. 141
Dallet, J................44
Dalvi, K. 95
Daly, M.A. 44
Danaher, E.M. 100
Danger, O......72,91,108,173
Daniel, E. 76
Dantona, R. 66
Darling, R.L. 151
D'Audney, W.W. 96
Davenport, V.H. 146
David, E.E. 148
Davidson, E.F...... 212,233
Davidson, H.M. 114
Davidson, S.G.....18,73,119, 120,135,136
Davies, G.B. 3
Davies, L....... 223,224,225
Davies, R.D. 47,125
Davis, J. 55
Davis, M.V. 45
Davis, W.M. 84
Dawes, R.E. 122,203
Dawson, S.D. 184
Day, H.A. 169
Day, H.E. 62,137,138
Dean, K.S. 46
Dean, L.E. 86
Deannard, E. 145
Decondillac, E.B. 95
Deem, H.L. 57
Dehaven, M. 80
Dehearne, D. 33
Deines, R.R. 6
DeLaBat, G. 20,102
Deland, F. 16,17,18,19,65, 72,73,74,75,97,99,108,113, 198,200,201,225
DeLany, E.G...98,173,219,220
DeL'Epée, A. 195
Deming, W.E. 185
Demotte, A. 137,176

Denes, P.B. 209
Denison, J. 56,59
Denmark, F.L. 223
DeSalle, J.M. 145
Devries, J.G. 73,216
Dewalt, P.A. 52
Dewar, D.G. 78
DeYoung, D.P. 20
Diamond, R.M. 150
Dibos, L. 121
DiCarlo, L.M. 1,11,12,28,30, 102,208,230
Dicker, L. 90
Dickey, D.B. 54
Dickinson, M.E. 177
Diedrich, W.M. 148
Dietrich, R.I. 139
DiMichael, S.G. 26
Dinsmore, A.B. 68
Disher, D.R. 228
Divine, L.R. 24,86
Doane, R.C. 26
Doctor, P.V. ...48,87,88,89, 127,158
Dodds, P. 133,134
Doerfler, L.G. 11
Dombro, R.H. 193
Dommisse, E.J. 146
Donald, D. 65
Donald, I.M. 122
Donaldson, E.M. 53
Doneghy, L. 123
Dowling, R.M. 184
Downing, A.V. 38
Downing, N. 224
Downs, M.P. 71,104,165
Doyle, F.W. 10
Doyle, J.B. 5
Dozier, J.D. 87
Drackley, B. 153
Drake, M.L. 226
Draper, A.G. 34

Drennan, G.L. 182
Drennen, G. 98,147,188
Driggs, F.M.....23,63,73,85, 108,121,198
Driscoll, A. 39
Drouot, E. 32
Drumm, P.R. 31,209
Dry, E.B. 131
DuBard, E. 156,178
Dudley, D.C. 36
Duff, J. 20,188,199,200
Duffy, J.K. 81
Duffy, R.J. 215
Dunbar, E. 202
Dunlap, M.M. 76,77
Dunlap, S.C. 123
Dunn, M. 228
Dupuis, L. 217
Duprez, D. 27
Durfee, M.A. 97,226
Dutoit, J.M. 171
Dyer, H.L.   19,41,198,218

E

Eachus, T. 141
Earhart, E.K. 77
Earle, C.W. 149
Easton, H. 184
Eccleston, M.M. 203
Eckstrom, F. 52
Eddy, J.H. 56
Eddy, L. 180
Edgar, L.S. 178
Edge, L.K. 49
Effler, L.R. 175
Egan, A.R. 76
Eickhoff, A.J. 46
Eiseman, M.H. 124
Eisenberg, D. 14
Elias, H. 52
Elkan, D. 1

248

Ellingson, M. 111
Elliot, L.L. 171
Elliot, R. 210
Elliot, S.S. 129
Elliott, A.E. 86
Elliott, C.E. 40
Elliott, H. 69
Elliott, I.D. 86
Elliott, L.L. 171
Elliott, S.L. 3,10,203
Ellis, V.E. 231
Elstad, L.M. 8,9,15,22,
    87,88,111
Ely, G.D. 181
Emerick, L. 5
Empey, M. 4
English, S. 161
Erber, N.P. 14,29,71,
    141,239
Erd, R. 59
Ernst, M. 14
Ersner, M.S. 200
Ervin, A.M. 45,64,121
Espeseth, V.K. 184
Etter, C.L. 21
Eubank, E.E. 97
Euritt, G.D. 24
Evans, A.D. 194
Evans, B. 147
Evans, C.C. 50
Evans, F.L. 97
Evans, M. 77,122,161
Evers, L.S. 230
Eveslage, R.A. 216
Ewing, A.W.G. 96,129
Ewing, E.C. 178
Ewing, I.B. 96,114

F

Fabregas, M.B. 228

Fagan, E. 43
Falberg, R.M. 27,69
Falconer, G.A....88,147,148,
    150
Fallis, J.R. 144
Fant, L. 35
Faris, G. 150
Farman, J.J. 207
Farquhar, G.C. 45,60,61
Farrant, R.H. 171
Farrar, A. 66,76,216
Farrell, G. 68
Farwell, R.M. 234
Fauth, B.L. 87
Fauth, L. 15
Fauth, W.W. 15,87
Favors, A. 43
Fay, E.A. 67,74,109,
    113,132,211
Fay, G.O. 83
Fay, H. 85,161
Fay, O.G. 33
Fearon, J. 65,216
Fechheimer, A. 110
Fehr, J.D. 128
Feilback, R.V. 230
Fellendorf, G.W. 14,18,23,
    28,95,101,104,106,111,163,
    165,236
Fellendorf, Mr. & Mrs....163
Ferdinand, O. 71
Ferguson, D.G. 152
Ferrall, J.A. 19,20,174,
    221,222,224
Ferreri, G.C.   8,32,65,72,
    91,96,101,173,191,197,217
Fessant, J.M. 27,61,150
Fetterly, H.B. 93
Field, L.G. 12,165
Finch, W.J. 125
Finn, B.A. 145
Finney, M.E. 172

Fish, A.G. 68
Fish, K.H. 196
Fishler, T. 27
Fiske, S.A. 58
Fitch, J.L. 153
Fitzgerald, E. 34,52,121,
  122,136,185
Fitzgerald, M.H........12,49,
  60,61,139
Fitzgerald, Sister M.A. ...52
Fitz-Gerald, D. 59
Fitz-Gerald, M. 59
Flanders, G.A. 41
Flange, C.S. 21
Flaxman, Mrs. G.D. 193
Fleitz, M. 203
Fletcher, J.D. 131
Fletcher, H. 2,4
Fletcher, K. 63,134
Flegel, E. 142
Flint, R.W.............50,236
Florence, G. 181
Florian, V.A. 142
Flugarth, J.M. 6
Fogel, H.H. 105
Foley, J.A. 155
Fonner, M.D. 135,233
Fonville, W. 153
Forchhammer, G. 91
Ford, C. 125
Fordyce, C. 45
Fornari, P. 190
Forr, D. 112
Forrester, T.C. 8,15
Forsythe, K.B. 113
Fort, B. 12
Fosmark, L.B. 46
Foss, B.M. 77,230
Fouts, M. 54
Fowler, E.P. 109
Fowler, F.E. 63,212
Fox, T.F. 67,133,194

Foy, R.D. 129
Frackleton, B.P. 194
Francis, D.H. 6,89,187
Frankenthal, S. 230
Franz, S.I. 175
Freck, P. 54
Freeman, R.D. 185
Freeman, S. 56
French, S.L. 165,237
Frick, E. 143
Frick, K.M. 68
Friedman, M. 26
Frisina, D.R. 15,27,71,
  208,236
Fritz, K. 45
Froeschels, E. 205
Frohn, W. 175
Frueh, F. 5,6
Fruewald, E. 98
Fuller, C.W. 167
Fuller, M.B. 58
Fuller, S. 16,67,159,
  169,198,217
Fullington, A.B......54,56,73
Funk, S.C. 165
Furfey, P.H. 36
Furth, H.G. 130,171,184
Fusfeld, I.S........24,27,34,
  78,85,86,111,112,139,192,
  215,234

G

Gaeth, J.H. 14
Gale, E.P. 136
Gallagher, J.J. 90
Gallaudet, E.M. 33,34,
  36,82,83,84,180
Galloway, J.H. 102,106
Gantenbein, A. ...129,130,188
Garber, G.E. 237

Garbett, A.S. 42
Gardiner, M. 196
Gardner, I.B. 181
Gardner, M.B. 208
Gardner, N.M. 3
Gardner, W.H. 3,115
Gare, M.W. 124
Garner, W.L. 152
Garns, J.S. 203
Garretson, M.D. 31
Garrett, E. 211
Garrett, G.W. 22,143
Garrett, M.W. 196
Gates, A.I. 45
Gault, R.H. 85,204,227
Gawith, F.W. 45,53
Gawlick, R. 142
Gay, R.C. 58,149,176,182
Gebhart, H.M. 223
Geddes, K.R. 41
Geer, A.C. 231
Geisperger, F. 94
Gellens, S. 179
Gemmill, W.H. 85
Gentilli, A. 2
George, D.W. 34
Gerber, S.E. 5
Germain, L. 166
Gerwick, S. 179
Gesell, A. 115,116,177
Gesner, E.T. 46
Getz, S.B. 87
Giangreco, C.J. 100,127,
  139,164,171
Giangreco, M. 127
Gibian, R. 175
Gildston, P. 98
Gile, B.C. 2
Gill, P. 9
Gillespie, F.E. 32,212
Gillespie, J.A. 133
Gillet, H.S. 132

Gilmore, M.E. 43
Giolas, T.G. 16
Glasscock, M.E. 101
Glasser, Mrs. M. 186
Glenn, F.L. 186,196,197
Glenn, S. 57
Glowatsky, E. 183
Goda, S. 48,161
Godin (Leonid)............96
Godin (Lev) 96
Godsave, B. 119
Goetzinger, C.B. 6,88,98,
  99,129,169,171,184,209,234
Goetzinger, M.R. 172
Goggin, A.P. 63,64
Goldberg, H.R..........79,231
Goldberg, J.P. 141
Goldberg, L. 154
Goldberg, R.E. 177
Goldfeder, C. 155
Goldfeder, J. 155
Goldin, G.J. 143
Goldstein, H. 89
Goldstein, L. 81
Goldstein, M.A....8,14,15,29,
  32,75,108,217
Goldstein, R. 70,71,104
Gonzales, B.R. 89
Goodenough, F.L. 170
Goodhill, V. 71
Goodspeed, E. 121
Goodwin, E. 121
Gopfert, E. 134
Gordon, A. 207,234
Gordon, A.N. 219
Gordon, M.L. 123
Goss, R.N. 140
Gough, J.A. ...61,148,150,151,
  167,194
Grady, T. 23
Grammatico, L.F. ..29,117,129
Grana, G.M. 166

Grandgent, C.H. 211
Grant, W.D. 63
Gratz, L.A. 175
Graves, F.P. 168
Gray, V.Q. 81
Green, G.G. 44
Green, H.C. 206
Green, R. 21
Green, R.R. 104
Green, S.A. 82
Green, W.B. 141,184
Greenaway, E.S. 115
Greenberg, B.L. 112
Greenberg, S.H. 112
Greenberger, D. 56,62,
  133,211
Greene, D. 211
Greene, J.S. 202
Greenleaf, G. 23
Greenmun, R.M. 20,88
Greenspan, S. 27
Greer, C.W. 29
Gregg, F.M. 205
Grey, H.A. 147
Griffin, B. 49
Griffin, M.E. 24
Griffing, B.L. 81
Griffing, W.T. 86
Griffith, M.J. 46
Griffiths, C. 13,117
Griswold. L.E. 141
Groff, M.L. 138
Groht, M.A. 48,78,116,
  124,125,126,127,128,236
Grosvenor, E.B.(E.M.)......17
Grosvenor, Mrs. G..........17
Grosvenor, M.B. 17
Grussing, F.P. 204
Gruver, E.A. 75,77,120,
  158,193
Gruver, M.H. 78,207
Guedel, A.E. 59

Guertin, R. 69
Guilder, R.P. 3,9
Guilmartin, M.D. 214
Guinness, S. 121
Guldager, L. 95
Gulick, M. 48
Gummarun, M.D. 122
Gunderson, A.N. 187
Gusow, F. 159
Gustafson, M.C.F. 166
Gustason, G. 37
Guthrie, V.S. 78,114
Guttman, N. 7
Gutzman, A. 195
Gutzmann, H. 233

H

Haaby, L.O. 54
Haeseler, C. 9
Hagens, E.W. 191
Hales, G.W. 111
Hall, G.D. 161
Hall, G.S. 67
Hall, I.B. 66
Hall, J. 3
Hall, P. 75,85,192,235
Haller, G.L. 101
Hamel, C.A. 125
Hammer, H.L. 41,46,76
Hammermeister, F.K. 62
Hamilton, R. 27
Hancock, E.F. 204
Haney, M.R. 163
Hanna, E. 186
Hanners, B.A. 106
Hansen, A. 65,93,173,
  189,217
Hansen, M.R. 162
Hanson, E.C. 101
Hanson, O. 23,30,84
Hardy, W.G. 4,12,79,103

252

Hardy-Beck, P. 141
Hargis, C.H. 50,57,131
Harkness, M.M. 126,176
Harlow, J.L..............157
Harman, A. 74,160
Harper, P. 210
Harper, P.M. 188
Harrell, H. 80
Harrington, D.A. 105,130
Harrington, J.D. 38
Harris, G. 10
Harris, G.M. 117,164
Harris, G.T. 202
Harris, J.C. 53
Harris, L. 66
Harris, M. 69
Harris, N. 163,165
Harris, N.P. 88
Harrison, C.E. 107
Harrow, I. 165
Hart, B.O. 51,129
Hartel, H. 94
Harvey, A. 56
Harwood, V. 53
Hasenstab, P.J. 59,186
Haskins, C.N. 34,56
Haskins, H. 103,105
Haspiel, G.S. 232
Hastings, J.O. 185
Haug, O. 104
Haycock, C.S. 217
Haycock, G.S. 73,92
Hayden, J.S. 52
Haynes, C.A. 39
Hayes, P. 185
Hays, D. 55
Hays, H. 19,173
Hearty, M.G. 226
Hector, E.R. 118,203
Hedgecock, D. 144
Hedgecock, L.D. ...15,167,215
Hedges, H.G. 52

Hedley, A. 176
Hedrick, J. 200
Hehir, R.G. 237
Heider, F. 10,114,126,
  145,176,193,205,230
Heider, G.M.   65,66,114,126,
  145,175,176,193,228,
  230,231
Heinich, R. 150
Heinl, S.S. 61
Heinrichs, E.L. 116
Helmle, M.B. 25
Hembrook, M. 39
Henderson, J.M....42,119,189,
  203,235
Henderson, J.M. 62
Henderson, M.L. 161
Henderson, M.W. 137
Henderson, R. 70
Henderson, S.C. 6,89,187
Henniges, M. 117
Henry, V. 66
Herrell, W.E. 100
Herrick, H. 11,95,192
Hersch, L.B. 167,184
Herx, M.A. 216
Hester, M.S.   145,155,238
Heward, Mr. and Mrs. H. ..111
Hicker, H.D. 20,25
Hickernell, W.F. 108
Hickey, M.S. 171
Hicks, D.E. 158
Higgins, E. 37
Higgins, F.C. 87
Higgins, L.F. 120
Hill, A. 44
Hill, A.C. 74
Hill, E. 227
Hill, W. 45
Hilliard, E.M. 74,120,235
Hinckley, R.F. 101
Hines, E.J. 44

Hiney, E. 51,100
Hirsch, D. 36,167
Hirsh, I.J. 13,107
Hiskey, M.S. 168
Hitz, J. 16
Hjorth, E. 24
Hoag, R. 27,237
Hobart, E.L. 123
Hood, C.A. 232
Hodges, M. 90
Hodgson, E.A. 133
Hodgson, W.R. 5,105
Hoemann, H.W. 142
Hoemann, S.A. 142
Hoffman, H. 72,91,92
Hoffman, V. 114
Hofmarksrichter, R. 181
Hogan, L.C. 43
Hogsteater, H.T. 181
Holbrook, A. 210,239
Holley, M.C. 126
Hollister, H.H. 33
Holman, G.L. 90
Holowach, J. 100
Holt, L.D. 226
Hooper, Mrs. J.C. 161
Hopkins, L.A. 3,9
Hopson, A.B. 24
Horowitz, L.S. 79
Horton, K.B. 165
Horvath, R. 27
Hotchkiss, J.B. 211
Houchins, R.R. 172,185, 209
House, A.S. 215
Houser, B. 214
Howard, C.M. 84
Howard, E.S. 114
Howard, J.C. 21,25
Howard, P.F. 22
Howard, W. 27
Howe, A.G. 97

Howe, S.G. 67
Howell, L. 219
Howes, A. 52
Howes, E.C. 45,113,230
Howland, C.R. 35
Howson, J.W. 52,85,136
Hoxter, R. 95
Hubbard, E. 199
Hubbard, G.G. 33
Hudgins, C.V. ..3,11,103,146, 204,205,206,207,214
Hudson, A.F. 118
Hudson-McKuen, G. 196,197,212
Huff, A. 90
Hull, S.E. 134,217
Humason, T.A. 134
Hummel, C.J. 43
Hunt, F.E. 216
Hunt, J.F. 94,181
Hunter, A.R. 186
Hunter, M.R. 110
Huntington, D.A. 215
Hurd, A.C. 76,83,113, 133,134,135,203
Hurst, F.D. ...60,123,137,138
Hurst.....................174
Hutchinson, E. 229
Hutman, F.E. 220
Hutton, C. 13
Hutton, G. 33

I

Iandoli, E.A..............116
Ingle, H.F. 126,137
Ingram, C.P. 77
Ingvarsson, I.M.......124,139
Irion, T.W. 138
Irvin, B.E. 216
Israel, R.H. 106
Issacs, M. 90

Ives, A.M. 226,228,229
Ivey, L.P. 141

J

Jablons, B. 157
Jackson, A.W. 123
Jackson, W.D. 150,152,154
Jacobs, J.A. 33,180
Jacobs, L. 70
Jacoby, B. 163
James, W. 180
Jamroz, A. 107
Jayne, G.G. 42,58
Jeffers, J. 13
Jelks, Mrs. F.W. 160
Jenkins, W.G. 34,56,63,
  64,72,134,172
Jenkins, Wm.G. 133,134,180
Jenks, M.K. 22
Jennings, G.J. 189
Jensema, C. 100,110,142,159
Jesseman, V.C. 15,167
Jewell, G.H. 225,226
Jillette, A.G. 187
Johansen, D. 110
Johansen, E.B. 29
Johnson, C.W. 15
Johnson, D.D. 70,153
Johnson, E.H. 15,87,103,170
Johnson, E.V. 236
Johnson, E.W. 71
Johnson, J.N. 164
Johnson, R.O. 118
Joiner, E. 45,77,122,
  201,202,204,206,213
Jolly, F. 79
Jones, A. 54
Jones, B.L. 6
Jones, C.C. 80
Jones, C.L. 230

Jones, E.P. 198
Jones, E.W. 25
Jones, J.W. 60,67,85,120,
  121,135,136,238
Jones, K.H. 79,128
Jones, L.G. 94
Jones, M.D. 217
Jones, M.K. 121
Jones, O. 8
Jones, P.A. 91,109
Jones, R.S. 119
Jones, U.C. 25
Jordan, S.A. 41
Jordan, S.K. 37
Justman, J. 69

K

Kallman, I.J. 108
Kane, E.B. 221,222,224,225
Kannafell, B. 172
Kapur, Y.P. 95
Kates, S.L. 130
Katsurayama, K. 107
Katz, D.L. 166
Kaufman, M. 50
Kawakami, M. 42
Kawamoto, U. 124
Kearney, J.E. 171
Kearns, C.W. 74
Keaster, J. 4,78,81
Keefer, M.B. 123
Keeler, S.W. 216
Keep, J.R. 33,56,132
Keith, J. 231
Keller, H. 67
Keller, J.F. 90
Keller, L. 127
Kelley, N.H. 214
Kelley, R. 166
Kelly, E. 236

Kelly, E. 136
Kelly, J.B. 2,9
Kelly, J.C. 98
Kelly, R.R. 154,194
Kendall, D.C. 5
Kendall, E.P. 60
Kenfield, C.N. 220,225,
  227,228
Kennard, M.S. 146
Kennedy, E. 57,61
Kennedy, L.B. 145
Kennedy, M......10,11,99,174,
  216,220,221,223
Kennedy, P. 117
Kennedy, W.R. 26
Kenner, M.L. 85
Kent, A. 49,150
Kent, E. 38,56
Kent, M. 42,88
Kent, M.S. 140
Kenwood, J.C. 105
Kenyon, E.L. 201,203
Kerr, A.M. 2
Kerr, M.M. 87
Kessler, E.B.........221,225
Kessler, S.N. 224
Ketcham, M.B. 42
Khan, E. 22
Kharasch, E.N. 43
Kidder, C.W. 201
Kidder, K.B. 45,201
Kiely, A. 132
Kiesel, T.A. 83,118,149
Kilpatrick, W.M. 118
Kimball, C.F. 220
Kimber, W.J. 176
Kindred, E.M. 144
King, G. 180
King, K.L. 53
Kinnier 223
Kinsey, E.I. 196
Kinsley, G. 76

Kinzie, C.E. 220,221,
  223,226
Kinzie, R. 221
Kirk, L. 123
Kirk, S.A. 170,181,194
Kirkhuff, J.D. 31
Kirkley, J. 54,60
Kisor, H. 69
Kitson, H.D. 168,218
Kleffner, F.R. 1
Klienfeld, L. 162
Kline, L.F. 44
Kline, L.T. 223
Kline, T.K. 170
Kling, G.N. 10
Kloepher, W.H. 110
Klopfer, S. 93
Klopping, H.W.E. 141
Knievel, W.R. 26
Knight, A.C. 41,225
Knight, D.L. 63
Knight, M. 208
Knight, M.H. 176
Knowles, E. 230
Knox, A.C. 126
Knudsen, V.O. 101,106
Koch, A. 4
Koester, D. 208
Koh, S.D. 37
Kohler, C.N. 186
Konigsmark, B.W. 109
Kopp, G.A. 204,206
Kopp, H.G. 80,81,150
Koustaal, C. 209
Kraft, D.G. 61,147
Kramer, A. 141
Kramer, M.C. 69
Kranz, F.W. 5
Kraus, M.J. 156
Kretschmer, R.R. 132
Kringlebotn, M. 151
Krippner, S. 184

Krohn, E. 43,66
Krol, S.T. 21

L

Labenz, P.J. 4
Lach, R. 215
Lack, A. 204
Lacrosse, E.L....8,15,156,225
Lacy, M.V. 125
Ladd, A. 225
Lagow, R. 154
Laird, R. 153
Lamb, H.D. 202,224
Lamb, M.H................9,204
Lambert, C.G. 232
Lamm, C.O. 131
Lampard, M.T. 55
Lamprecht, E. 118
Landis, K.S. 83
Lane, D.H. 228
Lane, H.S. 29,51,80,114,146,
    164,170,176,193,235,236
Langdon, M.A. 156
Lange, P. 65
Larr, A. 147,168,208,232
Larson, C.A. 109
Larson, L.L. 11
Larue, M.S. 86,158
Larve, S.J. 145
Lassman, G.H......103,115,162
Latham, W.H. 83
Lauritsen, M. 203
Lauritsen, R. 153
Lauritsen, W. 25,139
Lavos, G.......25,170,171,178
Layman, E. 144
Laysen, B. 192
Layzer, A. 141
Leckie, D.J...........105,143
Lee, J.J. 22,77

Legrand, A. 217
Lehmann, Mrs. F. 163
Leigh, I.W. 100
Leigh, J.W. 176
Leighton, E.V. 96
Leitman, A. 89
Lemley, H.A. 20
Lenahan, M.L. 185
Lennan, R.K. 158
Lenneberg, E.H. 140
Lenox, J. 27
Leonard, B.N. 227
Leonard, E.C......73,113,120,
    189,197,235
Leonard, M.H. 75
Lerman, A. 90
Leshin, G.J........... 80,156
Letourneau, N. 36
Letzter, M.C. 138
Levin, S. 71
Levine, E.S. 69,102,116,162,
    169,176,177,178,179,182,
    183,187
Lewin, L.M. 202
Lewis, B. 59
Lewis, O.N. 104
Lewis, S.E. 39,124
Liberman, A.M. 215
Lictenberg, F.S. 209
Liebman, J. 179
Lindquist, I.P. 21,220,222,
    226,227
Lindsey, D. 172
Lindstrom, T.A. 124
Ling, A.H. 165
Ling, D. 6,7,104,105,
    210,216
Lisensky, R.P. 179
Liveridge, E.B. 166
Livingston, P.J. 238
Lloyd, G.T. 15,23,
    89,140

Lloyd, J.H. 1
Lloyd, L.L. 71
Long, E.F. 39
Long, J.S. 85
Long, T.S. 34,53,118,135, 180,181,201
Longwill, Mrs. J.B. 113
Lore, J.I. 208
Lorene, Sister James......81
Lorge, I. 106
Love, J.K. 73,99,108,112
Lowell, E.L. 6,90,152
Lowell, M.O. 6
Lowry, C.D. 173,180
Lucas, F. 60,196,212
Ludlow, F. 58
Luetke, B. 91
Lundstrom, K. 95
Luterman, D.M. 142,165,166
Lux, A.M. 227
Lyall, J.H. 66
Lybarger, S.F. 101,106
Lynndelle, V. 10
Lyon, V.W. 170

M

MacAuley, D. 100
Macbeth, M. 222
MacDonald, N.V. 48,115
MacFarlan, D.C. 2,101
Mackie, R.P. 87
MacLean, C. 110
Mackin, H. 146
Macklin, F. 145
Macloingsigh, P. 74
MacMillan, B. 124
MacNutt, E.G. 98,225,227
MacPherson, J.R. 158
Madden, A.M. 11
Madison, J.L. 76

Magner, M.E. 50,93,167
Maigetter, E. 229
Makuen, G.H. 198
Malkin, S.F. 185
Mangan, K.R. ...49,80,208,215
Mannen, G. 127,128,164,208
Manning, A.C. 24,186
Manning, C.A. 73
Manz, F.M. 193
Marage, R. 7
Marbur, M. 138
Margolius, E.L. 23
Margulies, Mrs. A.R. 113
Marichelle, H. 233
Marimont, R.B. 210
Markell, A. 43
Marshall, W.A. 140
Martin, E.S. 6
Martin, F. 200,202
Martineau, H. 173
Martony, J. 215
Mashburn, A.G. 64
Masland, R.L. 157
Mason, M.K. 3,146,214,228
Masters, C. 50
Mathas, C. 23
Matkin, N.D. 7,107
Matlock, G.D. 229
Mattick, P. 157
Maxson, K.P. 124,228
Maxwell, M. 62
May, E. 43
Mayberry, R. 37
Mayer, J.H. 177
Mayne, R.E. 17
Mays, L. 186
Mazeas, R. 7
McAleer, M. 142
McAlister, G.W. 42
McAloney, T.S. 118,124,149
McArdle, S.M. 113
McAree, R. 165

McArthur, L. 69
McBride, J. 147
McCabe, B.F. 109
McCain, M. 77
McCalmont, P. 208
McCarr, D. 62
McCarr, J.E. 152
McCauley, R. 117
McClellan, G.A. 161
McClure, G.M. 134,192
McClure, W.J. 26,36,149
McCombs, M.E. 131
McCombs, Z. 131
McConnell, F. 4
McCormick, M. 54
McCowan, M. 38,72
McCowen, M. 196,217,233
McCroskey, R.L. 6
McDaniel, N. 190
McDermott, V.D. 20
McDonald, A. 226
McDowell, E. 75
McElroy, D. 166
McFarlane, J.H. 189
McGee, D.I. 81,100
McGee, T.M. 5,109
McGinnis, M.A. 1
McGrady, H.J. 129
McGroskey, R.L. 70,71
McIntire, W.F. 89
McIntire, W. 142
McIntire, Wm. 152
McKendrick, J.G. 196
McKenna, A. 223
McKenzie, L.B. 8,9
McKerral, L. 221
McKerral, W. 221
McKinney, L.W. 42
McKusick, V.A. 109
McLaughlin, C.L. 39
McLaughlin, H.F. 28,47
McLaughlin, J. 62

McLaughlin, M. 146
McLean, M. 223
McLeod, F. 147
McMahan, M. 150
McManaway, H.M. 2,77, 85,238
McMenamin, S.B. 105
McMillan, K. 39
McNeil, D. 130
McNeil, M.T. 47
McNeil, N. 114
McPherson, J.G. 170
Meadow, K.P. 35,95,96
Meadow, L. 95,96
Mears, E.G. 143
Mecham, M.J. 128
Mecham, S.R. 143
Meierhenry, W.C. 151,153
Meisegeier, R.W. 55
Mendelson, N. 115
Menninger, K.A. 174
Menyuk, P. 132
Meredith, A. 226
Merkl, W. 7
Merklein, R.A. 5
Merrill, E.C. 112
Merry, R.V. 65
Meyer, M.F. 6,138,214
Mikulas, M. 29
Milesky, S.D. 232
Miller, A. 54
Miller, A.L. 5
Miller, A.S. 44,143,193
Miller, B. 48
Miller, E.O. 176
Miller, J. 115
Miller, J.B......28,79,81,87, 98,115,116,164,234
Miller, J.R. 109
Miller, L.K. 181
Miller, L.V. 101
Miller, M. 125,126

Miller, M.K. 118
Miller, R.C. 80
Miller, S.D. 117
Mills, M.M. 58
Minami, K. 107
Mira, M.P. 171
Mirrielees, R. 120
Misra, S.K. 232
Mitchell, D. 123
Mitchell, S.H. 18
Mitra, S.B. 157,158
Moffat, L. 233
Monaghan, A. 156,208
Monro, S.A. 58
Monro, S.J. 41,196,197,
  199,200,221
Monsees, E.K. 1,208
Montague, H.A....9,17,21,65,
  66,77,98,102,103,114,146,
  162,167,230,231
Montgomery, G.W.G. 37
Montgomery, I. 211
Moog, J.S. 132
Moore, C.E. 103
Moore, G. 113
Moore, H.T. 54,122,
  123,181
Moore, L. 147
Moore, L.M. 10,86,175,
  185,235
Moore, M.B. 90
Moore, O.K. 154
Moore, Mrs. S.M. 159
Moorehouse, W. 23
Moores, D.F. 37,140,215
Morgan, L.C. 13
Morgenstern, L.I. ...173,219,
  220,221,222
Morkovin, B.V. 94,178
Morley, D.E. 4
Mormson, J.S. 53
Morris, D. 39,229

Morris, M.E. .84,122,134,229
Morris, M. 67
Morrison, J.S. 20,53
Morrow, E. 46
Morsh, J.E. 86
Moseley, N.B. 185
Moseley, T.F. 133
Moskowitz, S. 69
Mosley, C.C. 192
Moss, M. 46
Mossel, M. 57,138
Motto, J. 142
Muir, P.P. 82
Mulholland, A.M. ... 31,130,
  183,186
Muller-Walle, J. 217
Mullins, J. 110
Mullins, J.B. 1
Munson, H. 27
Murphy, A.T.....17,22,79,178
Murphy, H.J. 153,172
Murphy, K.P. 179
Murphy, M. 9,125
Muyskens, J.H. 205
Myklebust, H.R.....1,87,106,
  158,177,178,182,183,194

N

Nace, J.C. 22,176
Naiman, D. 50,159
Naiman, D.W. 194
Naish, S.J. 6
Nakano, Y. 95
Nall, F. 93
Nance, W.E. 109
Nardine, F.E. 166
Nazzaro, K. 154
Neal, W.R. 237
Neas, B.J. 188
Negley, K. 42

Nelson, B.E. 15,21,78,
    98,205,231,234
Nelson, J.R. 7
Nelson, M. 104
Nelson, M. 156
Nelson, M.S. 139
Nelson, W. 92
Nelson, W.I. 146
Ness, A.D. 102
Neumaur, R. 71
Neuschutz, L.I........68,233
Nevile, B. 75
Neville, V. 232
Nevinson, E. 174
New, M.C. 41,98,115,
    127,205,206,207
Newby, R. 154
Newcombe, F.C. 63
Newell, N. 65
Newhart, H. 8,99
Newlee, C.E. 39,45,60,75,168
Newman, L. 57
Newton, M.G. 47,50
Neyhus, A.I. 183,193
Nicholas, G.C. 162
Nicoll, M.G. 46
Nickerson, R.S. 210
Nielsen, D.V. 42
Niemoller, A.F. 107
Nilson, R.F. 8
Nitchie, E.B.   19,145,173,
    196,216,217,218,219
Nitchie, E.H. 223,226
Nitkin, N. 21,205
Nix, G.W. 31
Nober, E.H. 5,70
Noller, J. 130
Nordin, E.A. 67
Norris, A.C. 95
Norris, Mrs. J.F. 97
Northcott, W.H. (W.N.)...81,
    117,130,143,164,165,237

Northrup, H. 60
Norwood, M.J. 151,153,155
Nowlin 223
Noyes, J.L. 83
Noyes, M. 212
Numbers, F.C.......74,206,238
Numbers, M.E. 10,37,77,126,
    127,205,206,209,229,235
Numbers, L.P. 40

O

O'Connell, A. 53
O'Connor, C.D. 9,10,28,
    78,80,102,144,162,182,
    190,206,207
O'Donnell, E.K. 161
O'Donnell, F. 57
Ofiesh, G. 152,239
O'Halloran, D.M. 115
Olanoff, R.S. 54,192
Oleron, P. 170,183
Olin, C.L. 217,233
Olsen, W.C. 107
Olsen, W.O. 7
Olshin, G.M. 148
Olson, C. 147
Olson, F. 103
Olson, J.R. 141
Olson, L. 154
Olson, R.L. 210
O'Neal, J. 172
O'Neill, V. 40
Ordman, T. 231
Orman, J.N. 137,138,182
Orr, J.P. 25
Orr, M.P. 122,125
Osberger, M.J. 100
Osborn, D. 180
Osborne, C.A. 200
Osborne, J.G. 184

261

Osler, S.F. 179
Ostern, B. 49,146,163
Oswald, M.V. 201
Owrid, H.L. 28,30,166
Owsley, P.J. 22,52,63,
  80,94,143,178
Oyer, H.J. 147
Ozer, M.N. 142

P

Paddleford, L. 137
Pagenstecher, A. 163
Palen, I.B. 76,233
Palmer, E.L. 152
Palmer, M.F. 232
Palva, T. 4
Panara, R.F. 70
Panconcelli-Calzia, G. 75
Parks, R.G. 60
Parrish, O.G. 25
Parsons, J. L. 130
Parsons, M. 95
Parsons, R. 154
Pascoe, D. 93
Paterson, D.   85,136,168,169
Pattan, H.T. 119
Patten, H.T. 60
Patterson, A.W. 20
Patterson, R. 85
Patton, L. 140
Paul, W. 211
Pauls, M. 4,127
Paxson, R. 8,229
Pearson, F.B. 235
Peck, A.W. 97,185
Peck, B.J. 80
Peck, W. 154
Peet, Edwd. 82
Peet, Eliz. 111,137
Peet, H.P. 33,82,210
Peet, I.L. 33,83,211

Pence, H.W. 155
Pendergrass, R.A. 90
Perello, J. 94
Perkins, R. 154
Perrin, D.G. 151,152
Perry, C.S. 72,133
Perry, J. 170
Persselin, L.E. 153
Peters, E.F. 182
Peters, J. 50,51
Peters, N. 50,51
Peterson, E.G. ...124,149,170
Peterson, G.E. ..148,206,209,
  238
Peterson, L.C. 119
Peterson, Peter N. 135
Peterson, P.N. 20,24
Peterson, W. 52
Pettingill, B.D...33,111,118,
  132,133,167
Pettingill, J.H. 132
Pfau, G.S. 140,148,149,
  152,154
Pharis, D.M. 9
Philbrick, W.A. 1
Phillips, F.I. 52
Phillips, J. 211
Phillips, N.D. 151
Phillips, R.M. 26,183
Phillips, W.C. 19
Pickett, J.M. ..6,151,210,215
Pierce, J.A. 19,173,218
Pimonow, L. 16
Pinter, R. 55,75,77,86,
  121,136,168,169,170,180,
  192,213
Pipe, P. 153
Pitchers, B.J. 94
Pitrois, Y. 65,92
Pittinger, P...88,127,128,207
Pless, M.A. 101
Poitras, B. 142

262

Pollack, D.C.   13,14,104,165
Pollard, G. 71
Pollard, N.A. 137
Pollock, B.E. 157
Pomeroy, W. 223
Poore, Mrs. H.T. 114
Pope, A.E. 20,106
Popelka, G.R. 234
Porter, G. 144
Porter, G.G. 185
Porter, G.S. 23
Porter, Mrs. N.T. 223
Porter, S. 132,133
Porter, S.H.....58,67,133,191
Porter, T.A. 7,107
Porter, V.C. 158
Postlethwait, S...150,151,154
Potter, R.K. 215
Poulos, T.H......11,13,40,54,
   87,207,209
Power, D.J. 237
Powers, M.H. 89
Poyntz, L. 118
Prall, J. 103,107,232
Pratt, E.A. 227
Pratt, G.T.   28,177,209,236
Prelutsky, L. 229
Presto, M. 206
Prettyman, E. 94
Pronovost, W. 151,209
Probyn, J.Y. 10
Proctor, D.M. 10
Propp, G. 151,152
Pruitt, E.E. 193
Ptasnik, J. 145
Pugh, B. 49,78,128,
   178,206,209
Pugh, G.S. 47,61
Purdy, M.E. 146
Putnam, G.H. 134,180
Pybas, A.H. 213

Q

Quick, M.A........80,165,178,
   207.237
Quigley, H.M. 87
Quigley, S.P....12,94,131,236
Quill, L. 188
Quinn, J......123,125,139,175

R

Rachlin, C. 11
Radcliffe, E. 42
Rainer, J.D. 183,185
Ralston, F. 164
Ralston, P. 164
Rankin, C.E. 87,115
Ranson, E.O. 229
Raph, J.B. 208
Rapin, I. 157
Rathe, G.H.,Jr. 148,152
Rau, E.F. 93
Raubicheck, L. 175
Rawlings, B.W. 112
Rawlings, C.G. 138,214
Ray, H.W. 90,154
Ray, L. 82,180
Read, E. 46
Read, E.D. 64,181
Read, V. 137
Reamer, J. 169
Reamy, O.L. 233
Reay, E.W. 139
Reed, Mrs. F.A. 197,198
Reed, J.L. 2
Reed, K.F. 56,64,73,
   135,160
Reed, N.D. 78
Rees, N.S. 79
Reeve, J.W. 98
Reeves, J.K. 104
Reich, P.A. 35
Reid, G. 234

Reid, H.W. 22
Reineke, M.E. 164,165
Reinhardt, A.C. 32,70,72,
  76,113
Reiss, Mrs. K. 162
Reiss, M. 48
Reiter, F.H. 106,189,229
Remnitz, A. 142
Renard, E.S. 53
Resnick, L. 13
Reynolds, J.A. 166
Reynolds, L.R. 166
Rhodes, E. 64
Richards, E. 60,126
Richards, G.L. 2
Richardson, B.E. 42
Richardson, C.W. 19
Richardson, D. 191
Richardson, J. 232
Richardson, Mrs. O.T. 186
Richardson, P.C....49,80,116,
  127,129,208
Richardson, P.L. 23
Rider, E.C. 112
Riemann, G. 65
Rierdon, B. 204
Righter, G.J. 102
Rio, A. 213
Risberg, A. 105,151
Rister, A. 144
Rittenhouse, M.F. 73
Roach, R.E. 5,115
Roberts, E. 74,160,189,
  198,218
Roberts, G. 119
Roberts, L. 45,59,108
Roberts, M. 122
Robinson, A.E. 187
Robinson, D.O. 14
Robinson, G.C. 110,116
Robinson, L.D. 184
Robinson, M.W. 138

Robinson, R. 186
Robinson, S. 67
Robinson, W. 63,120,134,
  135,233
Roche, A., Jr. 237
Rocheleau, C. 65
Rodda, M. 119,193
Roe, W.C. 30,74,121,
  122,174,198
Rogers, F.L...............68
Rogers, M. 225
Rogers, W.B. 61
Rollins, J.C. 166
Romano, P.E. 234
Romero, E. 146
Romney, F.C. 239
Rooney, A.G.........1,162,206
Roorda, P. 159
Rose, L. 124
Rose, M.L. 137
Rose, S. 37
Rosen, J. 4
Rosen, R. 37
Rosen, S. 100
Rosentein, J.....22,58,63,81,
  129,130,209
Rosenthal, C. 193
Ross, D.A. 3
Ross, E.B. 174
Ross, L.F. 185
Ross, L. 149
Ross, M. 5,7,14,16,
  29,105,131,215
Rossett, A. 166
Rott, O.M. 108
Rotter, P. 103,116,163,
  164,193,208,236
Rousey, C. 88,234
Rousey, K.L. 171
Rowe, F. 34
Rowe, L. 210
Rowell, H.G. 235

Roy, H. 35
Rubin, M. 7
Rudloff, J.S. 50,236
Ruffin, H.H. 226
Rupley, S. 123
Rupp, R. 29
Rush, M.L. 131,140
Rushford, G. 81
Russell, G.O. 203,213

S

Safian, M.Z. 183
Sakai, T. 215
Salade, R.F. 19
Salem, J.M. 89,143,144
Salzinger, K. 184
Samuelson, E.E. 20,97,224,228
Sanborn, C.J. 35
Sanborn, D.E. 35
Sandberg, I.L. 41
Sandberg, M.W. 43
Sanders, Mrs. G.T. 160
Sanders, J.W. 234
Sanders, K.D. 190
Sanderson, R.G. 70
Sanford, A.B. 62
Sank, D. 108
Santore, F. 14
Sargeant, R.L. 215
Sataloff, J. 108
Saunders, N. 175
Savage, J.W. 53
Sawyer, Mrs. S.E. 159
Scagliotta, E.G. 156
Scheeline, A. 143
Scheeline, Mrs. I. 162
Schein, J.D. 89,111,159
Scherer, P.A. 90
Schick, H. 170
Schick, H.C. 6

Schick, H.F. 168
Schilling, B.W. 38
Schlesinger, H.S. 179
Schmaehl, D. 28
Schmidt, A. 91
Schmitt, P.J. 130
Schmitt, R.J. 150
Schneider, M. 180
Schoenfeld, S.L. 12
Schowe, B.M., Jr. 26,49,
  148,151
Schumann, P. 224
Schunhoff, H.F.....80,89,182
Schwartz, J.L. 185
Schwartz, M.G. 143
Schwartzberg, J.G....131,166
Schwarz, C.K. 227
Schwirian, P. 119
Scott, D.R.C.............103
Scott, E. 195
Scott, E.V.....11,12,128,145
Scott, Mrs. E.W. 1
Scott, W.A. 134
Scouten, E.L. 34,36,140
Scripture, E.W...92,197,199,
  201,202
Scriver, H......225,226,227,
  228,229
Scroggs, C.L. 141
Scyster, M. 114,119
Seal, A.G. 26
Seibert, D.J. 35
Sellin, D.F. 156
Sensenig, A. 9
Sensenig, B. 38,39,56,57,137
Serumgard, I.M. 45
Shaffer, C.M. 214
Shanahan, M. 116
Shaw, J.P. 65
Shaw, M. 214
Shellgrain, E.M. 127
Shepard, C.H. 142

Shepherd, B.D. 166
Shepherd, D.C. 5
Shere, M.D. 156
Sheridan, L.C. 84,181
Sheridan, L.E. 136
Shiels, K. 52
Shiflet, C. 137
Shimota, J. 5
Shimizi, H. 100
Shinpaugh, J.R. 183
Shippy, A. 164
Shirley, M. 170
Shontz, F.C. 179
Shortley, M.J. 25
Shuey, H.E. 155
Siblilio, J.P. 156
Sievers, A.D. 174
Sigelman, C. 159
Siger, L. 35
Sigurdson, H.K. 146,177
Silver, N.H. 27
Silver, R. 38
Silverman, S.R. 17,78,87,89,
   106,107,205,206,207,210
Simmons, A.A. 12,28,129,
   130,131,237
Simmons-Martin, A.A. 29
Simon, A. 161
Simon, A.B. 68,69,78,79,
   164,206
Simon, E. 182
Simon, Mrs. R. 165
Simon, T. 32
Simonds, E.H. 220
Simpson, E.W. 24
Sinclair, M. 49
Singer, D.G. 185
Sister Anna Rose 28,48
Sister Anne Bernadine 49,128
Sister Jeanne d'Arc 127
Sister M. Albert 54
Sister Marianna 12,207

Sister M. Constantia 64
Sister M. DeLaSalle.......46
Sister M. Emmanuel.......213
Sister M. Henriella 79
Sister M. Pauline 156
Sister M. Renee 48
Sister M. Therese 129
Sister M. Walter 79
Sister Mary A. Burke 36
Sister Mary Fanchea 12
Sister Mary Laurentine ..209
Sister Mary Oswald 190
Sister Mary Walter ..128,140
Sister Rose Gertrude 114
Sister Saint Esther......206
Sister Sylvania..........214
Sitton, A.B. 106
Skyberg, V.O. 181
Slankard, H. 177
Smalley, L.D. 3
Smaltz, W.M. 182
Smith, A.H. 89
Smith, A.J. 163
Smith, G.E. 125
Smith, G.M. 105,238,239
Smith, J.L. 34,53,56,57,
   59,84,180,181,120,123,149
Smith, J.M. 60
Smith, M.A. 160
Smith, M.C. 123
Smith, M.E. 64
Smith, M.J. 43
Smith, M.W. 226
Smith, R.A. 173
Smith, S.K. 10,203,204
Smullen, H.S. 131
Snell, R.C. 209
Soissons, M. 103
Solomon, M.A. 184
Sortini, A.J. 4,104,156,163
Sowell, J. 56
Spencer, R.C. 187

Spiegle, J. 153
Spofford, I.P. 97
Springer, N.N. 170,182
Spyker, S. 199
Stack, Sister P.M. 117
Stafford, M.M. 56
Stahlecker, C.V. 80
Stahlecker, L.V. 156
Stahlem, E.M. 79
Stansberry, D.A. 185
Staples, A.L. 222
Stark, B. 62,154
Stark, R.E. 151
Stauffer, C.M. 131
Stedman, A.B. 199
Steed, E.L. 231
Steed, L. 75,202
Steffey, M.E. ...161,174,225
Stein, L. 239
Stein, S.P. 4,11,187
Steinberg, J.C. 203
Steinke, A. 233
Steinke, E.M. 180,212
Stelle, R.M. 26,78,237
Stelling, H. 91
Stephens, A.E. 25
Stepp, R.E. 148,155,232
Steppuhn 34
Stern, R.G. 167
Stern, V.W. 43,117
Sterne, L.C. 50
Stetson, R.H. 205
Stevens, G.D. 158
Stevens, H.C. 180
Stevens, J.E. 92,119,202
Stevens, K.H. 38
Stevens, R.P. 195
Stevenson, E.A. 8,58,99
Stevenson, E.P...........106
Stevenson, M.J. 173
Stevenson, V.M. 37
Stewart, H.L. 139,194

Stewart, J.L. 101
Stewart, L.B. 159
Stewart, L.G. 158
Stewart, P. 177
Stewart, R.B. 32
Stewart, W.J. 136,137
Stillson, S.V. 175
Stix, E.F. 177
Stobschinski, R. 204,234
Stockdell, K.G. 13
Stockwell, R.P. 208
Stokoe, A. 206
Stokoe, W. 35
Stolp, L.E. 80
Stone, A.V. 28
Stone, C. 83,210
Stone, E.A. 59,180,233
Stoner, M........11,116,162,
  207,236
Storey, J.D. 174
Storm, R.D. 239
Storrs, R.S. 31,36,56,83,211
Story, A.J. 73,74,92,93,
  135,173,196,197,198,199,
  200,213,217,218,219
Stovall, E.M. 143
Stovel, L. 185
Stratton, W.D. 239
Strauch, G.B. 124
Streeter, H.M......61,126,139
Streng, A. 79,127,128,
  131,140,194,238
Streshinsky, S.G. 109
Strickland, E.H. 53
Strickland, F.I. 225,226
Strickland, R.G. 49,128
Strizver, G.L. 4
Strong, A. 123
Strong, W.J. 239
Struck, A.N. 136
Stuckless, E.R.....30,35,112,
  129,130,140,183

Stunkel, E. 171
Sturdivant, E. 76
Stutsman, G.T. 24
Suchman, R.G. 157
Suffridge, K.H. 179
Sugrue, T.J. 188
Sullivan, A.M. 67
Sullivan, O.M. 20,24
Summers, H. 40,152
Sung, G.S. 105
Sung, R.J. 105
Sunstrom, F. 42
Suppes, P. 153
Sussman, A.E. 69,70
Sutermeister, E. 30
Sutton, E.V. 63,118
Swaiko, N. 58
Swain, N.G. 44
Swain, W.D. 40
Swainson 92
Swayze, R.H. 122
Sweet, M.E. 1
Swift, W.B. 200,201
Switzer, M.E. 27
Sykes, J.L. 205
Sylvester, E.M. 75,174
Szanton, V.L. 109

T

Taber, F.A. 102,230
Talbot, B. 82
Tallman, M.L. 228
Tatman, Mrs. D. 164,178
Taussig, E. 11,128
Taylor, A.P. 157
Taylor, A.S. 39
Taylor, E.E. 112
Taylor, (Harris).......17,72,
    109,118,136,188,197,198,212
Taylor,(Helen)............112

Taylor, I.W. 94
Taylor, L. 84
Taylor, N.M. 60,136
Taylor, S.D. 88,96
Taylor, W.W. 94
Teel, J.R. 141
Teel, P.L. 188
Templin, M.C. 88,177,182
Tendler, R. 185
Tettemer, C. 152
Tervoort, B.T. 128,140
Thiagarajan, S. 237
Thollon, B......84,85,136,137
Thoma, F.B. 113
Thomas, A. 48
Thomas, D. 99
Thomas, E.S. 139
Thomas, I.B. 209
Thomas, M.L. 34
Thomasia, Sister M. 94
Thomason, P......198,199,200,
    201,220
Thompson, E.M. 122
Thompson, E.R. 191
Thompson, H.N. 24
Thompson, I..........202,213
Thompson, R.E. ...68,157,178,
    179,193
Thompson, W.H. 138
Thorne, B. 98
Thornton, E. 122
Thornton, J. 147
Thornton, M. 58
Throckmorton, H. 213
Tiberio, C.S. 127
Tilden, D. 34
Tillinghast, E.S....28,74,76,
    83,134,135
Tillinghast, H. 86
Tilly, W. 202
Timberlake, J.B.....10,54,93,
    103,110,175,202,205

268

Titsworth, E. 5
Tomb, J.W. 137
Tomlinson-Keasey, C. 194
Tompkins, E.......174,201,202
Tonley, L.S. 174
Torr, D. 153
Torrey, G. 218
Totoki, A. 12
Transue, H.W. 230
Trask, A.N........96,220,221,
  222,224,225
Trask, C. 211
Treibert, M. 186
Trill, E.M. 221
Troll, G.D. 97
Trybus, R.J. 112
Tucker, W.J. 189
Turley, E.J. 230
Turner, W.R. 20
Turner, W.W. 58,82
Turvey, T.M. 212
Tweedie, D.........14,68,157
Tylor, E.B. 33

U

Uden, A. v. ...12,28,42,94,95
Ulmer, T.A. 194
Underhill, O.W. 24
Unholtz, L. 42
Upham, L. 3,121
Upton, H.W. 234
Urban, B. 117
Urbantschitsch, V. 7
Utley, J. 146,205

V

Vaisse, L. 83
Valentine, C. 176

Van Adestine 220
Vandenberg, D.M. 107
Van Der Veer, G. 11
Van Dyke, R.C. 143
Van Ingen, E. 8
Van Nest, M.R. 42,125
Vanpraagh, W. 216
Van Wyk, M.K. ...142,147,163,
  178,232
Varwig, R. 117
Vaughn, G.R. 23
Vegeley, A.B. 171,172
Ventry, I.M. 7,104
Vermillion, F.F.....47,57,149
Vernon, J. 105
Vernon, M........27,30,35,37,
  66,110,157,158
Vetidz, G.W. 181
Vettese, J. 43
Victoreen, J.A. 104
Vinson, M.R. 125,175,213
Vivian, R.M. 232
Vockell, E. 157
Vockell, K. 157
Voelker, C.H. 15,138,204,214
Vollenweider, J. 185
Vonderhaar, W.F. 172
Vonderheit, E.C. 227
Vorce, E.R....116,162,167,207
Vose, P. 225
Voss, D. 151

W

Wade, W. 65,67
Wadleigh, G.K. 222
Wageman, R.M. 184
Wagner, M.A. 118
Wahler, J.J. 69
Wait, S. 56
Waite, H.E. 81

Walcher, H. 163
Waldo, M.S. 118
Waldron, G.A. 190
Walker, C. 104
Walker, E.W. 149,180
Walker, H.D. 133
Walker, H.W. 203
Walker, I. 86
Walker, J.B. 96,120,221,
   225,229,231
Walker, N.F. 205
Walker, R.A. 22
Walker, S.T. 56
Wall, A.P. 77
Wallin, M. 13,115
Walsh, M. 13
Walter, J. 62,94,139,140
Ward, R.H. 123
Warfield, E.B. 182
Warner, L. 80
Warren, N. 115
Warren, S.A. 156
Warren, W. 15,87
Wasell, I.T. 81
Washburne, C. 175
Washington, M.L. 21,228
Watrous, H.D. 124
Watson, C.W. 176
Watson, D. 23
Watson, N.A. 101,102
Watson, R.B. 101
Watson, T.J. 13,94,104
Watts, J.D. 161
Waugh, M. 154
Wawrzaszek, F.J. 142
Way, D.M. 172
Weathers, A.D. 184
Weaver, J.A. 126,136
Weber, L. 117
Webster, L.M. 184
Wecker, K. 58
Wedenberg, E. 13

Weidenmayer, J. 66
Weil, C.S. 174
Weinrich, J.E. 90
Weir, R.C. 156
Weisbord, M.R. 179
Wells, A. 113
Welsh, E.T. 113,122
Welty, H.L. 39,125
Wentling, T.R. 23
Wesselius, S. 187
West, R. 204
Westervelt, Z.F. 31
Weston, C.C. 224
Wetherill, S.J. 121,122
Wettstein, C.T. 92
Wettstein, F. 187,188,196
Whildin, O.A. 77,102,126,
   162,175,226,228
Whitaker, B.L. ...220,222,224
Whitcher, C.M. 64
White, A.H. 37
White, H. 33
White, H.C. 34,59,63
White, S.K. 159
Whitehurst, M.W. 10,11,13,14,
   99,116
Whiteneck, C.I. 150
Whitman, M.P. 46
Whittlesey, A. 137
Whorton, G.P. 99
Wiedemer, A. 233
Wiig, E. 104
Wilbur, R.B. 131
Wilcox, R.M. 9
Wild, L.H. 186
Wilkie, J. 166
Wilkinson, W. 36
Williams, B.R. 25,26,27,
   70,86,164
Williams, H. 93
Williams, J. 67
Williams, K. 84

Williams, M.E. 30
Williams, Mrs. P. 165
Williams, S.M. 117
Williams, T.J. 181
Willoughby, J.E. 121
Wilman, M.C. 47
Wilson, A. 52
Wilson, G.B. 131
Wilson, D.K. 79,178
Wilson, H.M. 239
Wilson, L.S. 216
Wilson, R. 1
Winchester, R.A. 103
Winhey, B. 191
Wing, G. 83,133,134
Winkelman, N.L. 141
Winkler, P.K. 102
Winnie, A.J. 72,235
Winston, M.E. 9,123,161
Winters, L.M........42,47,114
Wirtz, R. 40
Witcher, B. 99
Witherspoon, E. 228
Withrow, F.B.......14,79,129,
 149,154,156,237
Withrow, M.S. 50,129
Wojan, K. 43
Wolach, M. 57
Wolf, E.L. 93,205,213
Wolf, R. 223
Wolfram, B.R. 44
Wood, D.E. 54
Wood, M. 208
Wood, M.W. 61
Wood, N. 128
Woodberg, M.N. 20
Woodby, L.G. 40
Woodruff, L.H. 82
Woods, E.L. 168
Woodward, H.M.E. ...48,49,52,
 55,103,128,131,163
Worcester, A.E. 198,211

Worcester, E.B. 120,160
Work, R. 162
Worthington, A.M. 88,144
Wright, B. 47
Wright, F.F. 230
Wright, J.D. .. 2,8,9,19,30,
 37,73,74,75,85,93,96,99,
 118,161,167,198,199,200,
 202,207,212,213,217,225,235
Wrightstone, J.W. 171
Wyks, H.W. 23
Wyman, R. 148,151,154

Y

Yale, C.A...........17,45,76,
 86,155,196,202,213,235
Yeakle, H.E. 186
Yedland, L.R. 173
Yearsley, M. 2,84,92,113
Yelton, D.C. 138
Yeager, J. 90
Yenrick, D.E. ...4,12,103,232
Yorty, J.B. 164
Young, Mrs. A.J. 230
Young, E. 28
Young, I.B. 114
Young, L.H. 229
Young, L.T. 189
Young, V..................36
Youngs, J.P. 195
Yunghans, M. 94
Ysaeldyke, J.E. 179

Z

Zaliouk, A. 208
Zaliouk, Z. 208
Zander, A. 164

Zebrowski, A. 92
Zeckel, A. 87,170,182
Zeisen, M.L. 239
Zerrup, C.E. 152
Ziegler, C.M......225,227,231
Zimmer, L. 192
Zink, G.D. 105
Zook, G.A. 23
Zuckerman, W. 37
Zwirecki, R.J. 185